BUSHVELD DOCTOR

BUSHVELD DOCTOR

by

C. LOUIS LEIPOLDT

JONATHAN CAPE
THIRTY BEDFORD SQUARE
LONDON

FIRST PUBLISHED, NOVEMBER 1937
SECOND IMPRESSION, MARCH 1938

JONATHAN CAPE LTD.   30 BEDFORD SQUARE, LONDON
AND 91 WELLINGTON STREET WEST, TORONTO

PRINTED IN GREAT BRITAIN IN THE CITY OF OXFORD
AT THE ALDEN PRESS
PAPER BY SPALDING & HODGE LTD.
BOUND BY A. W. BAIN & CO. LTD.

CONTENTS

INTRODUCTION

Twenty-two years ago I was appointed Medical Inspector of Schools in the Transvaal. Union between the four Provinces had then been in existence for already three and a half years. There was a Central Government and four Provincial Administrations, of which the Transvaal was one. In the enthusiasm and almost nervous haste with which the terms of Union were arranged, the functions that I had always looked upon as primarily those of a central government — health, education and communications — had been assigned to the Provincial Administrations. The Africa Act, the instrument of Union, makes curious reading. It reveals that those who were responsible for it held tightly to many illusions. Indeed, so deeply had these illusions been ingrained that they had become fixed, and were even at that time being incorporated into conventional fictions and ideologies that were bound to react unfavourably upon the most stable and homogeneous community. Crime, agriculture, railways, finance, taxation, and even forestry, were held to be of such immense importance that they could not be delegated to the magnified municipalities that the Provincial Administrations represented. But public health, primary education, and roads, all three the main civilizing factors in any community, were trustfully handed over to these secondary administrations, that were given a free hand so far as initiative and experiment were concerned, but with limited taxing powers.

The Transvaal Administration was then in the power of Labour, which had been returned with a good working majority at the last Provincial election, when public feeling was still deeply stirred by the unconstitutional deportation of several Labour leaders. It was Labour that was responsible for introducing, in that conservative Province, free education for both primary and secondary schools. It was Labour, too, that recognized the important fact that school children need to be healthy and nourished if they are to profit by the education for which the taxpayer pays. Some years before, a Government doctor had made a partial examination of several Transvaal schools, and had shown that the condition of the children was in no way different from that of children in other parts of the world where there was no organized medical inspection of schools. The revelations made in the first report stirred public interest, and the Administration was induced to advertise for a medical inspector of schools. I was at the time working in London, one of the Assistant Medical Inspectors of Schools, under Dr. Kerr, and was selected for the post, mainly, I think, because I was South African born, fully bilingual, and had some experience of the work. The last qualification probably counted the least, for when I came to take up my duties I found that no one appeared to have the slightest conception of what these duties involved. The official conception of them seemed to be that the Medical Inspector should visit a certain number of schools and at the end of the term report to the Department on the health conditions he found. Individual examination of the children had not even been considered; the assistance of a trained nurse, versed in the preparation of children for such examination, had not been contemplated. In the estimates, provision had been made for my salary but for nothing else, although a small amount had been allocated for travelling expenses and for what is known as 'subsistence allowance', the additional expense incurred by officials when away from home on official business.

Before I left London I carefully studied the map, and whatever reports I could obtain that gave data about conditions in the Transvaal, a Province with which I was not personally familiar. My knowledge of conditions, especially in the rural areas, in the Cape, Natal, and the Free State, told me, however, that it was quite likely that I would find similar conditions in the rural areas in the Transvaal. True, the only available statistics, those contained in the General Census Report for 1911, led one to believe that, notwithstanding the three years war of 1899-1902, that Province was either blessed with an astounding recuperative capability, or that its juvenile population was extraordinarily sound and vigorous. Taking the age groups from seven to fifteen years, there were only 19 blind, 54 imbecile and feeble-minded, 58 deaf and dumb, 35 epileptic, 40 paralytic, and 162 deformed children! These figures were so astonishing that one could not accept them as reliable indices of the extent of juvenile invalidity in the Province. I may at once say that my first year's experience showed that they were an absurd under-estimation of the extent and severity of juvenile invalidity in the schools. That first year's inspection gave a percentage of 59 defective children for all schools examined.

There were then some 70,000 European children attending government schools, and the number was rapidly growing, while the native and non-European schools held about a third of that number. There were about two thousand schools, scattered all over the Province, some in districts that were difficult to travel in, malarious and wild. So large an area — more than 110,000 square miles — could obviously not be worked by one doctor, and certainly not by one who did not have the help of a well-trained school nurse.

Moreover, at my first interview with the head of my new Department, Dr. (now Sir John) Adamson, the Director of Education, I found that, although I had been officially appointed, my appointment was in the nature of an anticipation, and that no provision had been made, by ordinance or resolution that had the weight of law, for me to carry out even such routine examinations as I had been accustomed to do in the schools of the London County Council. An interview with the Attorney-General of the Province was even less heartening. I found that if I stripped a boy at school I could be convicted of *crimen injuria*, a particularly comprehensive term that may connote anything from exhibitionism to indecent assault. To safeguard myself against that appalling danger, the Attorney-General advised me to get the written permission of every parent before I examined a child at school, and, as a matter of fact, until medical inspection of schools was properly legalized by ordinance, every parent or guardian was sent a printed form of consent, and no child was examined unless that form had been returned, signed, to the headmaster.

My preliminary inspection of the schools in the capital, Pretoria, and on the Reef, showed at once that if ever there were schools that needed such inspection they were here. But a short tour in the rural areas revealed even more deplorable health conditions in the non-urban schools, where the malnutrition of the children was obvious without detailed inspection. My lay colleagues of the Inspectorate Staff, who were enthusiastic about the new appointment, and to whose generous help and useful advice I owe much, told me of schools in the Lowveld, the Bushveld, where conditions were much worse, and pleaded earnestly that I should not confine even my preliminary attentions to the urban areas but should visit the Bushveld.

My Administration, that had no preconceived ideas about the duties for which it paid me fairly handsomely, was enchantingly indulgent. It said, in effect, 'The public has clamoured for the appointment of a Medical Inspector of Schools. You are It. Now get a move on and do something. It does not much matter what you do, so long as you do something, and you may as well visit the Bushveld as motor about on the Reef.'

An attitude that was at least not discouraging.

Let me say at once that my official colleagues were truly helpful, and that at the Head Office, in the Old Government Buildings, where years before President Kruger had presided over the deliberations of the First Volksraad, and where now the Provincial Education Department was housed, I found all the backing and encouragement that I needed. The Director, and Mr. Scott, the Secretary (now Director of Education in Kenya), the late Mr. Johann Rissik, then Administrator, and the late Mr. van Velden, then Provincial Secretary, were all eager to help me, and I gratefully acknowledge my indebtedness to them for valuable advice and direction. Without their encouragement and assistance I would probably have resigned my job after the first month, when I became fully aware of the immensity of the task that I had so lightly undertaken.

The outbreak of the Great War was followed in the Transvaal by the 'Armed Protest' or Rebellion, which for some months interrupted the campaign against the Germans in South West Africa. I had to leave my work as Medical

Inspector of Schools, and was appointed medical officer to General Botha's staff: many months went by before I could get the opportunity to visit the Bushveld. When at last I was able to do so, I found that my colleague Inspectors had not exaggerated in their account of what I should find there.

In this book I shall try to describe some of these conditions, and tell of my experiences in that park-like sub-tropical lowland, where beauty and disease are close neighbours, and where white civilization struggles against factors that seem to make its perpetuation an improbability. For most of what hereafter appears I have drawn upon my diaries, regularly kept during the years when I visited the Bushveld, as well as upon the official reports and memoranda that I handed in at the Head Office. These years of pioneering inspection are not likely to be forgotten by me, for they were years full of interest, blended with some excitement on occasion. I travelled many thousand miles every year, by rail, in a motor car, and on horseback: sometimes alone, sometimes accompanied by a school attendance officer to guide me when the roads were not marked on the map, or by a small native piccaninny to open the gates. I went chiefly in autumn and summer. Summer is the rainy season; autumn the time when malaria is at its worst. Neither season is an ideal time in which to tour the Bushveld. In summer the soil, which is largely turf, is so sodden with rain that motoring, especially in those early days when the average life of an outer tyre cover was 3000 miles, was a constant succession of exasperating mishaps. In autumn, the local conditions were then, and are still, such that it was, and is, almost impossible for the traveller to safeguard himself against malaria. The ideal time to visit the Bushveld is in winter, from May to November. Then its climate is charmingly even: its mornings, when the sun tinges the tops of the bush, are delightfully crisp and cool; its noon is pleasantly but not relaxingly warm; its afternoons and evenings, stained by an all-too-brief afterglow with amazingly vivid colouring, are as mild and as beautiful as a summer's night in Europe. But my duty was to see what children were so defective as not to be able to profit by the instruction given in class. It was obvious that my inspections should take place when health conditions at the schools were at their worst, and for that reason it was necessary to visit the Bushveld during the malaria season.

As Medical Inspector it was my privilege to see these schools under conditions such as the casual visitor can hardly hope to encounter. I came into close contact with all types of Bushveld dwellers, for although my work made me more particularly attentive to the juvenile population it also brought me into intimate touch with their seniors. The inspection work was arduous, but there were ample compensations. It was pioneering work, for never before had a school doctor adventured so far into the wilds. Like all pioneering work it demanded enthusiasm and above all optimism on the part of the worker. First impressions of these Bushveld schools — some of them mud shanties, staffed by uncertificated teachers who (all honour to them!) worked under the most depressing conditions — were invariably discouraging. Nowhere in the whole Union was there so much to do and so little done. In the chapters that follow I shall try and detail some of the difficulties and discouragements that were met. None of them was great enough to weigh against the greater interest presented by humanity struggling against adverse conditions in an environment, that for all its drawbacks, is one of the most beautiful in Africa. Every year that I went to the Bushveld, I became more interested in and more enchanted by it. It presents so many phases, it has such kaleidoscopic as well as kakeidoscopic variations that its interest proves inexhaustible. The years of my wanderings in it have left an enduring impression on me. To recall them to mind needs no effort, not because they were overflowingly episodal, but because they were passed among a community that retained much of that primitive simplicity and wholesomeness that are lacking in cities and towns. If there is truth in Dante's saying,

che suole a riguardar giovare altrui,

the recollection of these years should prove particularly cheering, for I was at least one factor that helped to improve health conditions for the children. The appalling ravages of the two chief Bushveld diseases, malaria and bilharziasis, shocked me when I became aware of their incidence and gravity. When I reported my findings, in curt, official phrases without any desire to excite emotion — for I recognized that no particular person or party was to blame for a state of affairs that had arisen naturally and inevitably as the result of settling ignorant folk in an unsuitable environment — there were many who cried out that my opinions were tainted by political bias. As if one needed to be a Botha-man or a Nationalist — these, at the time, were the opposing political parties in the Union — to detect malnutrition so glaringly apparent, feeble-mindedness so obvious, and physical deterioration so evident! It is unavoidable for me to refer to these matters in the pages that follow, for without a discussion of their significance one cannot understand what life in the Bushveld means. But they are not the theme of this book, which I have written to chronicle my individual experience, and in which I shall try to put down my impressions, not in malice, but in order to picture the Bushveld as I found it at a time when the district was far less well known than it is to-day.

BUSHVELD DOCTOR

B

CHAPTER I

THE BUSHVELD

LIKE ancient Gaul, in Caesar's time, the Transvaal may be divided into three main districts.

There is the Highveld, that elevated plateau of which the crown and industrial hub is Johannesburg, situate on the rim of that wonderfully rich reef whose geological limits have not yet been definitely ascertained. The Highveld lies 4000-6000 feet above sea-level, and although it encroaches upon the tropical line, which runs transversely across the Province some 150 miles north of the reef, it has a climate that is bracingly keen in winter and, with the exception of a minimum number of intensely hot days in midsummer, not unbearably warm in the other seasons. Originally a tract of undulating hills, with long low valleys, thickly grass covered and spotted with herds of game, it is to-day a very busy industrial district, with a landscape that has been grotesquely variegated by mining dumps and headgear. Where it has not been mined, it still holds large farms and little townships. But as a whole it may be classed as the most prosperous, most civilized — in the ordinary, commercial acceptance of that word — and most ugly part of the Transvaal. Its dust and its disorder are significant indications of its feverish activity.

From it one passes, by descending a couple of thousand feet, into the Middleveld, which declines, nowhere by steep gradations but leisurely as if it were proudly conscious of the paltriness of time and space, into the lowlands that are known as the Bushveld. The Middleveld is far less prosperous and important than the Highveld. It is not yet industrialized, although it, too, can point to some dumps, factories, and shaft-heads within its as yet unspoiled areas. Its farms are more humble, and its open spaces still magnificently clear. Here and there its mountains and hillocks are attractive in colour and diversified in outline. Its community is still largely primitive, but its propinquity to the Reef has inevitably influenced its attitude towards life, which is merely a reflection of what the Highveld thinks and feels.

Still lower, with some parts of it but a few hundred feet above sea-level, lies the Bushveld. The Middleveld, too, has bush, for the ubiquitous thorn tree flourishes magnificently in its mild climate. But it does not possess the almost solid scrub, clothing hundreds of square miles, that is characteristic of the Bushveld. The Bushveld, too, is definitely sub-tropical, for it lies north of the tropical line. Bounded on the extreme north by the great Crocodile or Limpopo River, which is by no means grey or greasy as it is said to have been at the time when the Elephant's Child explored its banks, it is an extensive flat, cut up into smaller areas by mountain ranges of varying altitude. On the west it adjoins the waste lands of Bechuanaland; on the east it is cut off from the Indian Ocean by the territory of Mozambique. Its largest magisterial district is the Waterberg, through which run the Blue Mountains, on the western extremity, but all its districts have a kind of family similarity for they are all part of the Bushveld, and their division into administrative districts was not arranged on a geographical basis but merely for convenience of officialdom. Much of it has been only partially surveyed, and at the time when I made my first motor trip into its wilds one had to depend on the inadequate and often misleading military maps that dated from the time of the Anglo-Boer War and were compiled as much on hearsay evidence as on accurate triangulation. To-day most of that has been changed, and one part of the Bushveld, its eastern part, is beginning to be fairly well known. For it holds the National Game Reserve of the Sabi, one of the show places of the Union of which the Transvaal is, deservedly, proud.

The Bushveld is a part of the Province that is as yet undeveloped, but that has been developed in parts. If one were to glance at it from a height sufficient to enable one to get a bird's-eye view of its entire expanse, one would see here and there little towns, some connected by railways, some dependent solely on road communication, each with a population of some hundreds of white folk whose main occupations are to serve the government in some way or to do such private business as can be transacted in a small community. Scattered between these towns, often at long distances apart, are primitive farms, with here and there a larger one, even a ranch. Few of these homesteads are imposing, though many of them are set in an environment that appeals to the eye. The main difference between them and their far away competitors on the High and Middleveld lies in the fact that they represent what remains of the traditional conception of farming, a conception that modern civilization is rapidly blotting out. They are there for man's fundamental work, to gain from the soil a livelihood for himself and his family. The community that subsists on them is largely a primitive community, untouched by the upsetting influences of what Dr. Brock somewhere calls megalopolitan or super-civic arrogance.

On a morning in mid-May I saw the Bushveld for the

first time. My car breasted the last turn of a low mountain pass. The air was startlingly clear; a beryl sky overhead. Miles upon miles of dull brown bush, a flat land edged, far away in the distance, by the Blue Mountains, beyond which lay the Limpopo. Eyots of green and ochre red — straggling mimosa trees in the foreground, multiplied by thousands in the middle distance — sandstone, or more likely dolomite, tors at infrequent intervals to break the monotony of levelness — patches of grass between — the dust raised by a herd of zebra or wildebeest to the right — and the road winding through the scrub to be lost very soon in that impenetrable secondary forest. A shimmer of haze on the horizon where the sky met that long line of dull grey bush.

In early May the Bushveld is probably at its best, and this, my first visit to it, impressed me with its wonderful beauty. Later, when I regularly visited it in summer and autumn, I came to know it better and to realize that its May beauty is merely the placidity of one who is asleep. Winter is its resting phase, when brown and ochre are its dominating colours. When it is awake, in summer, its greens and yellows and reds are much more impressive; they transform it into a park-like scene, with parts of it so voluptuously lovely that no one who has seen it in winter alone can have any idea of its sleek splendour.

I had set out early one morning from Pretoria to reach the schools lying beyond the Palala River in the Waterberg district. On these expeditions I carried all that I needed for inspection and for camping in the car. The equipment included several spare outer tyres and inner tubes, a couple of tins of petrol, a large tin of engine oil, a barrel of water for the radiator, a bottle of distilled water for the battery, abundant material for repairing punctures (for in those days one could not depend on going a hundred miles without a mishap) and a set of chains. The last I was assured could have been left behind, but my experience of travelling in the rural districts had already convinced me that chains were as necessary as the distilled water for the battery. A mosquito net, a spade, ropes, bucksail, blankets, and cooking utensils were included for camping purposes, for it was impossible always to be assured of sleeping accommodation at a house or hotel. The inspection kit comprised a portable weighing machine and measuring scale, the usual official forms, and the necessary instruments for examination. In addition I carried a small case with drugs, syringe, staining reagents, slides and a microscope with the oil-immersion lens required for examination of blood smears for malaria parasites. I never dragged a tent with me, and found the bucksail quite competent to shield me in rainy weather when it was necessary to spend the night on the veld.

When I was a young lad I was privileged by the companionship of three men, all keen botanists, whose enthusiasm for field botany made a lasting impression on me. One was a young German, with whom I spent several weeks in an ox-wagon on a many hundred mile trek through the western part of what was then the Cape Colony. The second was a school principal who had abandoned teaching high school boys to serve as Government Botanist. The third was a rich stock-broker who devoted his leisure to familiarizing himself with plants and became the foremost authority on South African heaths and orchids. I count myself singularly fortunate that I met these men at an age when the appeal of what Herbart called 'apperceptive masses' was still strong enough to influence me, for I can imagine no more 'formative' influence upon the mind of a moderately intelligent boy than the study of natural history. It is a subject not taught at schools, and not usually included in any curriculum, but it is nevertheless the one subject that, if it evokes any response at all in the boy, is likely to yield him, through its inculcation of correct observation and precise attention to detail, the most lasting pleasure and benefit in later years. I do not allude to systematic biology or any other 'ology', but to the practical teaching in the field of botany, of the habits and life-history of birds, insects, and indeed all living things. The instinctive urge of every small boy to be mildly sadistic, whether inspired by mere curiosity or by the wish to prove his own superiority to his own satisfaction — an urge that leads him to kill harmless small birds with his 'catty' or airgun, or wantonly to pick wild flowers by uprooting them — can be turned to good account by interesting him in field work of this nature. In the jargon of the psycho-analysts, it can be sublimated to serve a higher and more cultural purpose. I can only speak for myself, but the influence of my three scientific friends, by precept and example — and most by example — has been lasting, and in responding to it I have found pleasure without stint in observing plant and animal life in my outings on the veld.

I therefore carried with me a wire frame for botanical specimens, field glasses, a geological chisel for digging, and a collector's gun, the last only to be used for obtaining rare or unidentified birds. Later a shot gun was added to procure partridges for the pot, but I never carried a rifle and never shot anything larger than the small buck that were exterminating a school teacher's garden. There was plenty of game in the Bushveld — far more than there is now — and on more than one occasion I slept within sound of the lions and — what was much more exciting — within a few hundred yards of the hippopotamis' feeding patch, but I never felt the need for a more lethal weapon than the 16 bore that was necessary as a precaution against frightened cobras or *mambas*. When I travelled in company with my colleagues, the circuit Inspectors, they carried with them suitable armament for big game shooting, and assured me that it was indispensable. One had met a crocodile ambling jauntily towards his camp bed; another had to scare a pair of lions away before he could sleep with safety. My own adventures were far less exciting, and never occasioned me any alarm, except once when I was peacefully observing, through the field glasses, the antics of a family of squirrels, and heard the growling purr of a lion or lioness that had killed a bush buck twenty yards away from where I was watching. As I had only my shot gun with me, I hastily retreated, and safely reached my car.

On my first Bushveld trip I was alone in the car — a proof of my complete inexperience of the difficulties and dangers such solitariness invited. After that I always took care to be accompanied by some one who could at least assist me to put on a spare tyre or open the gates that at rare intervals spanned the road. Sometimes it was a native policeman, lent for the occasion by a kindly district magistrate, sometimes the school attendance officer. Both of them had local knowledge of the deviations from the main roads by which I could reach the isolated schools. I had no chauffeur, and did all the driving myself. Much later on I provided myself with a native piccaninny, whose services proved very useful, and on some occasions my first school nurse, Miss Hassall, went with me. An extra passenger always, however, added something to the problems of travelling in a district where the distances to be covered were so great. Time schedules had to be carefully arranged, and it was not always possible to adhere to them. The result was that many times the programme was dislocated. When that happened we had to fall back on improvisation. Every Bushveld dweller, when he is faced with something unforeseen, exclaims cheerfully, 'Let's just make a plan', and before very long we found ourselves quite proficient in 'making plans', in other words improvising for contingencies that had not been scheduled. Every trip was in the nature of an adventure. On some of the roads no motor car had ever travelled, and inquiry hardly ever faithfully elicited the conditions that were met with. In the rainy season the weather was a factor that could never be relied upon. The mornings and early afternoons were usually brilliantly clear. After four o'clock the sky suddenly became overcast and a storm, accompanied generally by much thunder and lightning, would sweep over the landscape and blot out all landmarks, while at the same time transforming a passably good road into a quagmire, to be traversed only with great caution so as not to risk a skid or the ignominy of being pulled out by a donkey team. There were stretches of sand, too, sometimes in the most unexpected places, through which the car had to be driven for miles on low gear, with the result that the radiator boiled and its water had to be replenished. There were dry riverbeds to be crossed, with steep descents into and equally steep ascents out of them, that needed much arduous spade-work. On patches of wet turf it was sometimes necessary to lay a track of grass and branches of bush to prevent the wheels from sinking inextricably into the treacherous soil. Compared with the smooth ease of medical inspection in the London County Council area, inspection in the Bushveld was sometimes a nerve-racking job, but its perplexities were made bearable because it was carried out in an environment that was perennially interesting. The spice of excitement incidental to all pioneering work, gave it a pleasant tang, all the better to be appreciated when a day's difficulties had been successfully overcome.

My schools were all 'single session' schools. That is to say, they followed the old fashion (and exceedingly absurd fashion) of starting school work at nine o'clock in the morning and continuing classes, with a short break of from half an hour to an hour, until two o'clock. The single session had been adopted mainly to facilitate administration and to serve the interests of the parents and teachers; the children had been entirely ignored. Nor were the hours of school suitable for the children. Nine to two is a period in which comparatively little good work can be done, in summer especially, under the climatic conditions in a sub-tropical country. How widely different the results of organized school work could be when the time-table was arranged according to definite and rational requirements, I had had ample opportunity of observing in Java and South America. Here, in the Transvaal, the public supported the single session system, and left the best hours of the morning and afternoon out of the time-table in favour of the relaxing midday single session with its maximum of fatigue and its minimum of achievement.

Another important point in these Bushveld — and for the matter of fact in all South African — schools was the antiquated and unreasonable curriculum, with its insistence on subjects that were of no conceivable interest to rural children, or indeed to any moderately intelligent child. The stress laid on the teaching of arithmetic, for example, was evident throughout the standards; in the higher grades, algebra and Euclid were taught in the secondary schools, even in Bushveld areas — the most fatiguing and utterly useless carting of discarded lumber to and fro in human minds. But tradition, that nowhere has such tremendous power for evil as in pedagogy, ruled that the curriculum here should be more or less similar to what it is in European countries where conditions of life and the character of the people are totally different, and it was not my business to deal with matters outside my purview. There are few educationists to-day who will admit that the school doctor has something to say in the arrangement of the school curriculum, and in those days such an assertion would have been greeted with jeers. Nevertheless, the hygienic effects of a badly arranged curriculum are sometimes so great that one wonders that parents do not realize how much their children still suffer from tradition.

Another point that struck me was the lack of physical instruction. There was a little formal drill; in secondary schools there was what was euphemistically called 'gymnastics', so stereotyped and so uncoordinated with the curriculum that only the most inexperienced optimist could anticipate that the children would derive any benefit from the course. Not one school had a shower bath; when one mentioned 'swimming bath' to the school committees, one was rewarded by a stare of amazement. What had water to do with education?

Yet water had a great deal to do with the health of the children who attended the Bushveld schools. Bad water gave them one of their most debilitating diseases; lack of good lavatory accommodation accounted for the dirt one saw, and incidentally for some of the malnutrition that is encouraged by vermin and dirt. Unfortunately here, as throughout South Africa, the parents, and the public at large, held staunchly to the old-fashioned conception of education. They took it to be the process of preparing boys for examinations in order to enable them to enter business or the Government service. The girls benefit by it indirectly, for most people held that a girl should be dependent on the stronger male and that education for girls was being overdone — and I am not sure that they did not have justification for that complaint, for the education given to most girls was not only utterly useless from a practical point of view but was in some cases definitely harmful. Very few Bushveld parents believed that education was something much more catholic in its scope and aim, a preparation for life and citizenship, a portal to mother- and fatherhood rather than an entrance to a Government office. Few people in South Africa think of it in that light to-day, and as a result the curricula for all four Provinces are as vicious and as deplorable now as they were then.

CHAPTER II

FIRST IMPRESSIONS

I CAME upon my first Bushveld school when the sun was just sinking behind the western scrub that seemed so close but was so far away. Much time and energy had been spent on the road, which had proved unusually sandy. The radiator had boiled fiercely; several miles had had to be travelled on low gear, and there was no water near by. Fortunately a collection of native huts loomed on a rise some miles beyond where my bearings had threatened to melt. Thither I trudged and asked for water. The natives brought me beer, which was refreshingly cool although not agreeable in taste. I pointed to a water gourd, and held up three fingers. The women — there were no men at the huts — brought forward bigger gourds — calabashes they are called — and we set off. For the sake of precaution I filled up my long-exhausted little water-barrel, a wise measure, for twenty miles ahead was another slough of sand, and no Kafir hut in sight. Instead of reaching my destination by two o'clock in the afternoon, as I had planned in order to find the children still in class, I arrived late enough to witness my first Bushveld sunset.

In the east, above the scrub, there lay linear bands of cloud, like long-drawn-out, misty, translucent films that shrouded but could not hide the rays streaming through, over and above them. Immediately below, the veld was dark: a violet blue, with brown reflections where the bush grew sparsely. Over the horizon were splashes of sinople green,

merging harmoniously into a succession of rapidly alter-
nating colours that culminated in a rich deep ruby. To
right and left of the sinking sun the sky was miniated with
nacarat and red, with green and startlingly blue quadri-
laterals, flanked by carmine triangles and mother-of-pearl
squares. A cubist sunset, if ever there was one, but startlingly, astoundingly beautiful; for the lurid colours blended
into numerous intermediate tints, and where they fell on the
veld they merged into a soft brick red or brown that somehow seemed to reflect all the kaleidoscope of the sky. I had
seen many glorious sunsets — off Tangier, in Java, in the
Bermudas, and in the Dolomites — and they were all
incomparable. This, my first Bushveld sunset, was as incomparable as any, and as beautiful. Its ever-changing
gamut of colour passed quickly — within five minutes
almost — and left the landscape darker in the shadows, with
the sky flushed with red that faded rapidly into the short
grey twilight of the tropics.

My objective, the little school building flanked, a
hundred yards to the right, by the teacher's dwelling, and
enclosed in an austere fence of barbed wire, lay a quarter of a
mile in front, and was easily reached. Its environment was
an open space, close to a low ravine, overgrown with
arborescent aloes and the black, loofah-like stumps of the
curious *Barbacenia retinervis*, a liliaceous plant met with
everywhere on stony soil in the Bushveld. Its ugly stem of
coriaceous fibre is crowned by a few insignificant leaves,
usually blackened by the veld fires that have raged round it.
But at their season these fuliginous relics put forth most
delicately blue blossoms, and the whole hill-side becomes one
blaze of a light sapphire that reminds one of the Tibetan
poppy at its best. Now, however, they were barren of flowers,

31

for it was not yet their season. Away to the right was a copse of large trees — karree and wild plum perhaps — and farther away, where the ravine became more precipitous, were splendid specimens of wild figs, sixty feet and more in height and with a proportionate spread of foliage. As I drove through the open gate in the fence, the teacher came forward to meet me. A care-worn, middle-aged man, bearded, thin and pale.

'We have been expecting you all the morning. You are the government doctor, not so?' he remarked as he shook hands.

I admitted that I was, and apologized for the delay, explaining that through no fault of my own — unless, like Dr. Johnson, I confessed to 'ignorance, Sir, sheer ignorance' — I had been held up by those malignant stretches of sand. He shook his head.

'It is ill travelling in the Bushveld without a guide, Doctor. One can so easily lose one's way. You should have someone with you.'

He helped me to cover the car with the tarpaulin, an unnecessary precaution, except that it prevented the dew from wetting the cushions.

My paraphernalia were stacked in the schoolroom; my personal belongings were taken to a little hut that stood some two hundred yards away from the little house. He apologized for that. 'It is the *rondavel* (round hut with thatched roof) that the government contractor built for himself when he erected the school house. My own quarters are too cramped. I trust Doctor will forgive. . . .'

I hastened to assure him that the *rondavel* was much more than I had expected, and that I was quite prepared to camp out, for I knew how ingrained is the sense of hospitality in the Bushveld. My colleague inspectors had told me of many instances where Bushdwellers had given up their one room, and their only bed, to show hospitality to the stranger. Later on I had personal experience of that self-denying hospitality. A brother inspector and I came to a Bushveld homestead, to seek shelter from an oncoming storm. We were unexpected, but the old farmer and his wife received us with engaging friendliness, and we sat up till late chatting with the old man while the hostess busied herself in the adjoining room, and presently came out to announce that everything was ready. We bid our hosts good-night, and retired. There was a big bed, freshly spread with a clean sheet and a couple of warm blankets, and without thought we shared it. In the middle of the night, my colleague suddenly remembered that he had not switched off the ignition of the car, and tiptoed out of the room to repair the omission. He found the host and hostess bedded on the floor of the dining-room; they had given us their only bed and had been content to make shift on the hard clay without even a mattress, and no amount of persuasion could induce them to re-occupy their own bedroom.

My host on this occasion proved to be an unusually interesting man, a type that is unfortunately all too rare in Bushveld schools. Originally a Hollander, he had qualified as a second-class teacher in his homeland, and had come out to the Transvaal in the republican days to take up a post in the railway administration. After the Anglo-Boer War he had been retained in the railway service, but had applied for and been given this teaching post in a small Bushveld 'one man' school. He had a large family, and with his small salary it was difficult to make both ends meet, but the climatic allowance and the conditions of service under the Education Department had helped him, and he considered himself fortunate. He was a man of culture, interested in natural history, a clever draughtsman who wrote a beautiful, old-fashioned script. We sat on the little stoep of his teacher's cottage — a stone and brick, four-roomed house under an ugly galvanized iron roof — and our talk ranged from the innovation of inspection (medical inspection) of schools, to the international situation, which at that time was so chaotic that no man could see or foretell what the future was likely to be. He thoroughly approved of medical inspection of schools, but he looked upon it, perhaps rightly, as the precursor of a State medical service that would cater for the whole of the Bushveld humanity, and he hoped from it much more than I, in my wildest dreams, had dared to expect.

'I try in my humble way', he explained, 'to teach my children something about hygiene, Doctor. But it is hard. You will find them all miserably underfed. They are unable to concentrate; always listless and tired. It is heartbreaking work to have to teach them, and some of them are so eager. There is such good material here, Doctor. Possibly you will find the parents are suspicious and stand-offish. They were so to me when I came, but I think I have won their confidence now, and I can do something with them. They were all waiting for you this morning, and it was a great disappointment when you did not turn up. But you will see them to-morrow. . . .'

He showed me to the *rondavel*, lighting my way with an old-fashioned ship's lantern that he had made out of a petrol tin. The hut looked very cosy. The walls were eight feet high, circular, and the thatch came down two feet below the top of the wall. Under the eaves slept, in the day-time, many bats; in the thatch a family of tarantulas had

34

made their home, and the grandfather was investigating my suitcase when we entered. My host shooed him away with a swing of the lantern.

'They are a nuisance, but quite harmless, Doctor. They don't bite, and they won't come near you when you sleep. I think one's breathing scares them. More likely the wild dogs may disturb you. They are impudent enough, and they've been known to steal into the pantry. Sleep well, Doctor.'

I cannot say I slept well. It was my first night under such conditions, and the tarantula family did not appeal to me as congenial chambermates. Afterwards I slept comfortably under much more disturbing conditions. On one occasion I camped out under a lovely thorn tree, not far from a spring. On the hard clay soil were holes, about two inches in diameter, to which I paid no great attention. It was a fine moonlight night, and as I lay beneath my mosquito net, big, jerky shadows flitted on the outside of the net. I took them to be moths, but closer investigation showed that they were large *Solpuga* spiders, measuring some four inches from head to tip of abdomen, that came out of the holes and careered by dozens around me. The next morning I dug up one of the holes and found, in the turning chamber at the bottom, a much annoyed, hissing male spider, whose size and aggressiveness were certainly far more intimidating than those of my *rondavel* mates. Yet I was never bitten or discomforted by spiders. These large species, that are insect eating, do not attack anything else but their prey, except when they are frightened and defend themselves by using the weapons Nature has given them. Their bite is very painful, almost like the sting of a hornet, but not more dangerous. The dangerous spider is a small species, the

35

size of a split pea, brilliantly flecked with vermilion on a grey-black body. It is one of the *Lathrodectus* group, known all over the world as one of the most poisonous of the Arachnids, and its bite has on many occasions caused death. It lurks in grass and rubble, attacks suddenly, and jumps away as quickly, so that the human victim generally does not know what has bitten him. He feels a burning pain that is quickly followed by the symptoms of profound shock, and his recovery depends to a large extent on his own power of resistance to the poison. So many cases of 'spider bite' have occurred that attempts are now being made to find a serum that will counteract Lathrodectus poison. In our Bushveld camps we had several children bitten by these 'button spiders', but fortunately no death, as treatment, which could in the circumstances be merely symptomatic, was always prompt. The after effects were sometimes serious enough to demand convalescent treatment for some weeks.

To a new-comer, indeed, the risks of being bitten or stung by poisonous animals in the Bushveld may appear alarming. In reality they are minimal. Venomous animals use their venom for practical purposes, mainly to secure their food. They only employ it for defensive purposes when they are attacked or frightened. Even the deadly *mamba*, whose bite kills within a few minutes, is not the aggressive, pugnacious snake that it is popularly supposed to be. It is much more frightened of a human being than the latter is of it, and will only attack if driven by desperation to defend itself. I met many *mambas*, and never had need to kill one of them, although on one occasion I had ample reason to think that some benignant Providence had guarded me. I had taken a party of boys to a well-known camping spot in the eastern Bushveld. We pitched our tent under a magnificent *mopani*

tree, and slept on the bare ground, with merely a waterproof
sheet beneath. There were many other campers round about,
and among them was an old friend, a member of one of my
School Boards, who always camped in style with a marquee
and a commissariat tent. He visited us and expostulated:
'You should really have floor-boards. I will send you mine
as I am going away.' We accepted the floor-boards, and
arranged them concentrically round the tent pole; they
made a nice even surface, and their hardness could easily
be softened by piling grass on top. On our grass beds we
slept comfortably for ten days. When we struck camp, after
removing the floor-boards, we discovered in a depression
in the ground a nest of thirteen little *mambas*, with whom
we had been sleeping for at least a week. The mother snake
was in the *mopani* tree. It is still a mystery to me how that
adder brood — although *mambas* are not adders — managed
to ensconce itself underneath our floor-boards, but since that
time I have always preferred to sleep on the bare ground.

My night in the *rondavel*, at a time when I knew much
less about the innocuousness of things venomous, was not
exactly comfortable, but it was none the less interesting.
The rustle of the tarantulas in the thatch soon ceased to
disturb me; the creatures were evidently not unfriendly,
and if they wanted to investigate the contents of my suit
case they were welcome to do so. The wild dogs — a
howling pack of them — kept far away. Occasionally came
the short, snappy bark of the zebras, the yelp of a jackal,
and the snorting of what I took to be a troop of wildebeest.
The nightjars and stone owls flew past the door, and hooted
occasionally, but nothing else disturbed me, and about
midnight I had lost all interest in the tarantulas and dropped
asleep.

The next morning, after breakfast, the teacher took me
to the school. It was one of the routine-sized, 'new-plan'
rural schools, a low, stone-walled building, divided into two
rooms, with a stoep in front shaded by a galvanized iron
veranda. The furniture was totally inadequate, and the
desks and forms were old-fashioned relics of some town
school that for the sake of economy had been transferred to
this third-class institution. The teacher had managed to
introduce some interest, even some beauty, into the dull
class-rooms. On the walls hung beautifully drawn maps, his
own workmanship. In a corner stood a rudely made open
cupboard filled with curios, the rudiments of a school
museum. A big ochre-coloured native firkin, filled with
flowering twigs of some wild shrub, stood on the table.
Both class-rooms were scrupulously clean, well swept, and
the few books that the children had were all carefully
wrapped in brown paper. School books are dear; some are
handed on from generation to generation of class.

There were forty-five children, sixteen boys and twenty-
nine girls, whose ages ranged from six (a girl) to seventeen
(a boy). Their educational abilities varied from sub-standard
to standard four, but three, all girls, were waiting to be
promoted to standard five. Their curriculum was the same
deadly dull alternation of scripture, two languages —
English and Afrikaans — elementary arithmetic, geography
and history, that was prescribed for all primary schools.
A more uninteresting group of subjects it would be difficult
to select, but it still remains the curriculum throughout the
Union, although here and there it has been magnanimously
varied by including biology, agriculture and handicraft in
some schools. Here the children were doubly fortunate in
having a teacher who was not only keenly interested in his

work but trained and certificated. One can readily imagine how difficult it must have been for even an expert to deal with four different standards, including the sub-standards, on such an inadequate and limited curriculum.

The children came from neighbouring farms, none less than two miles distant from the school, some from farms six miles or more away. Those who lived near enough to trudge to school came on foot; the others by donkey cart. The carts were outspanned within the enclosure of the school, and the donkeys were turned out to graze within the limits of the barbed-wire fence. That was one reason, the teacher told me, why they could not have a school garden; the donkeys ate everything that was planted or that sprouted up from seed. He believed in the cultural influence of gardening, and had his own patch of vegetables and flowers under the protection of the homestead fence; and he some-times allowed the children to have their own plots adjacent to his. But the parents did not quite like it ... they thought ... and he shrugged his shoulders and did not explain to me what they thought.

The parents arrived in driblets; about half of them were represented when it was time to open school. The teacher introduced me. The government, he said, had thought fit to send a school doctor to examine the children to find out which of them needed treatment. There was no com-pulsion; the government would not dream of forcing a parent to have a child examined. But he was grateful to the government for having sent a doctor, and his own children would be the first to be examined. Now the doctor would speak for himself.

Every school doctor knows how to address parents, and my introductory speech was merely similar to the talks

that I had given in many other schools, both in London
and in the Transvaal. I told them what the routine was;
how necessary it was to see if a child was physically fit to
profit by the instruction given in class; how physical defects
caused fatigue, and how simple defects could be remedied.
The parents, outwardly, were no different from the same
class of parent whom I had already met on the High and
Middleveld. They were big, bearded men, sun-tanned;
and placid-faced, bucolic women — rather weary-looking,
but interested, motherly women, who were much more
attentive than the men. Usually routine inspection is
conducted in the presence of the parent, the nurse, and the
doctor. Here I had no nurse, but the teacher's wife acted
as such, helped considerably by the other mothers; and as it
was a close community, in which everyone knew all that there
was to be known about everyone else, all the parents were
allowed to be present during the examination. That gave
me an opportunity of demonstrating obvious defects, which,
when tactfully done, is not regarded as an impertinent
interference with purely private matters, but as something
for the common benefit.

The first child to be examined was so obviously defective
that it could by itself have served as a lesson in the necessity
for routine physical inspection at school. It was profoundly
fatigued; its skin reflexes were sluggish, its pupils widely
dilated, its spine twisted, its mucous membrane pale
and anaemic. Its milk teeth were decayed; it breathed
badly; it had enlarged neck glands, and a hard, enlarged
spleen. I marked out the enlarged spleen with an indelible
pencil.

'Yes,' said the teacher. 'We know, Doctor. It is the
fever.'

Twenty-two children had such enlarged spleens. Ten of them had never, so the parents told me with some indignation in their voices, had a shivering fit. I took blood smears. None showed any parasites — not a finding to be wondered at, for it is difficult to obtain parasites from the capillaries of a child with chronic malaria. One has to drive the parasites from the spleen into the blood-stream by a provocative injection of strychnine or adrenaline, and there was no time, and indeed no reason, for doing that. These were malarious children, and that school had a 'spleen index' of 48.4 per cent, and a defective percentage of nearly a hundred per cent. In other words, nearly every child suffered from some curable defect that made it difficult for him or her to profit by class teaching, put an extra strain upon him, and engendered speedy fatigue even with the best and subtlest methods of class instruction. Dental defects were the most common; not one child had a perfect set of teeth, judged even by the liberal standard that the medical man, as distinct from the dentist, uses when he examines the dentition. Skin defects, veld sores and impetigo, one could pass as of slight importance. Most of the children came barefooted to school, and thorn scratches and abrasions readily became infected and festered. In this school there was a praise-worthy degree of cleanliness; none of the girls had nits in her hair; all faces and hands had been well washed — a proof of the personal attention paid to the class by the teacher. But the most saddening impression of that first morning's examination was the low state of nutrition of all the scholars. There was not a single child who conformed to the demands of the low scale that we habitually use to place children in the class of 'fair' so far as nutrition is concerned.

Routine examination is made with the child stripped to the waist, and no parent had raised any objection, even when it became necessary to divest the child of more clothing. One of the elder boys, a hulking big fellow of fourteen, however, strenuously objected to taking off his shirt. His parent was not present, and as there was some justification for his refusal to undress in public — even though his older classmates had raised no objection and had, like all the other children, rather enjoyed the novelty of being centred on the stage with an interested audience to watch them — the company was asked to retire to allow the examination to be done in private. But the boy was still obdurate, although the teacher, and one of the parents, who happened to be a member of the school committee, reasoned with him. On many occasions I had found this unwillingness to strip in both youngsters and adult males, an unwillingness that seems especially unreasonable in patients who come for examination, and who have no objection to discussing the most private matters but who obstinately refuse to bare themselves for inspection. When thousands of men and adolescents came up for examination, as the result of the call for recruits immediately before the expedition to South-West Africa in 1914, the medical examiners found many who displayed this inordinate shyness. Among them were men who assured me that they had been passed for life insurance but had never 'been stripped naked for folk to stare at them'. One of the most curious cases was that of a well-known Commandant, whose health was such that he needed medical attention, but who indignantly declared that he had never stripped for examination and was not going to do so in his mature age. Curiously enough, I have never experienced, in all my years of school

42

medical inspection, a similar reluctance in girls, though whether that is to be ascribed to the tact of my school nurses, to a better developed logical sense or a slight under-development of modesty on the part of the girls, I do not attempt to determine. I only note the fact that both small boys and big boys give more trouble at the undressing stage than do girls, and that I have not been able to find a reasonable explanation why they should be so ultra-modest.

In this case I made no attempt to force the boy, although his refusal made the inspection incomplete, and disarranged my statistics. But the assembled parents protested loudly, and some of them offered to compel the recalcitrant to submit. The teacher, who seemed much hurt by the incident, made no comment at the time, and when the examinations were over, dismissed the children for the day. The parents came to the house for a parting cup of coffee, shook hands limply, and went away. We sat on the stoep, chatting, waiting for luncheon which was being prepared, when the teacher drew my attention to a small party converging on the school. In front strode a big woman, driving before her a half-naked youth, whom she belaboured with a leather strap, and behind them followed a few small boys and girls.

'That's Mrs. E——,' said the teacher, all smiles. 'Freddy's mother. I knew the children would tell her how obstinate he was, and I knew she would not let me down. Come along . . .'

'Here, Teacher,' Mrs. E—— cried out when she saw us coming, 'I have brought him without his shirt as you see, and if the Doctor wants his pants off' — a vigorous cut with the strap — 'let him just say so. And you, Tin-dish' — another cut with the strap — 'just you tell Teacher how sorry you are that you disobeyed him. If his father were here, Teacher ... But a poor widow woman has enough to do without being disgraced like that before all the folk.'

I examined a much subdued Freddy while Mrs. E—— was regaled with coffee and biscuits. He too had an enlarged spleen, but he also had bilharzia, and his interest was awakened when I showed him the eggs under the microscope. They both stayed to luncheon, and Freddy came with me to guide me to the next school, and proved himself quite a companionable youth. For his redwater I could do nothing, for those were the days when we still experimented with cassia, thymol and such like uselessness. Three years later we learned that in antimony we have a specific against this parasite, and to-day bilharzia is as easily curable as malaria.

I learned much at my first Bushveld school. I learned to appreciate what a conscientious school teacher, with knowledge of human nature, and with tact and friendliness, could achieve by sheer force of personality. When I visited the school again, a year later, conditions were much better. The teacher had organized regular parents' meetings; most of the children had had an intensive course of quinine treatment; some had profited by a school camp at the seaside, through funds raised by the combined efforts of teacher and parents. Encouragement like that freshens and exhilarates. The future of the children of the Bushveld depends largely on the excellence of the teachers, on their personality and on the manner in which they conceive their responsibilities and carry out their obligations as examples and preceptors in a community that needs and appreciates leadership.

CHAPTER III

SETTLERS' CHILDREN

THE white population of the Bushveld is no longer nomadic. It is to a large extent stationary, although here, as elsewhere in South Africa, one notices a steady drift towards the towns. The rural community lives on scattered farms. It is a fertile community. Its birth-rate is high, and only a relatively high death-rate saves it from over-population. Yet that death-rate is by no means so high as local conditions might lead one to suppose, and nothing near so high as the death-rate among native children.

Much has been written about the wrong that modern civilization does to oncoming generations by its increasingly solicitous efforts, labelled social service, to defeat Nature's well-planned intention to keep an even balance. Lowering the death-rate among babies is not the best way to improve the nation. It may keep the unfit alive, perpetuating existence that is not profitable to the race, and burdening the community with misfits that have to be fed and cared for.

The native knows this. He is (or was, until the law stepped in and forbade him to help Nature in this silly way) accustomed to kill what he deems likely to be a potential burden to his tribe. Experience has taught him much that we ourselves are now beginning to find out.

Twins are notoriously difficult children. Unfortunate indeed was the native woman who brought a pair into the world. . . .

My hostess, a missionary's wife, led me into the garden one morning after breakfast. There stood a row of native pots, large, open-mouthed jars coloured ochre-red. There were eighteen of them, all empty.

'Do you know what these are, Doctor?' she asked.

'I suppose water pots.'

'No. My husband collected them. We had more but gave a few away. They are twin-pots. You know, when a native woman has twins they are put in these jars as soon as they are born and the mother pours boiling water over them. We can't stop them doing it, but we try to. . . .'

The native mind reasons logically, like that of a child with ordinary intelligence. Food and nourishment are scarce in the Bushveld. A child that was born with a defect likely to interfere with its progress later on, was killed. A puny, premature baby was left alone. Nature could deal with it unaided. I have often wondered at the public interest in premature babies. When a child is born weighing less than four pounds, the lay press, if it gets to hear of the matter, makes a fuss and regards it as an event if the zealous doctor succeeds in rearing that baby. It never inquires what happens afterwards, and whether or not the child was worth saving. Doctors now generally accept 1200 grammes as the lowest weight at which an infant can be saved, although children who at birth weighed 750 grammes (d'Outerpont) and 840 grammes (Ylppö) have been reared and have attained school-going age. But no Bushveld child below 2000 grammes birth weight has much chance of survival, and immaturity is regarded by the natives as as much a defect as twinship. The prejudice against twins is probably due to the experience that such children, in later life, are difficult to guide. Where they are allowed to survive they are somewhat privileged and some of them become witch doctors.

The natives had an additional method of weeding out misfits. Faults overlooked in childhood but discovered in adolescence — a-social and anti-social traits, the whole gamut of juvenile delinquencies — were summarily corrected by 'smelling out' for witchcraft. By this means the tribe could unburden itself of many troublesome existences in a manner sanctioned by tradition and custom as entirely legitimate and proper.

Now these impediments to overcrowding and under-feeding are no longer tolerated. It is true, baby clinics and ante-natal welfare centres have not yet been established in the Bushveld, but they will come. Meanwhile the settler's child, like the native's child, presents problems that are not only interesting from an academic point of view but are of real importance to the nation.

The most pressing question that clamours for authoritative answer in Africa, South as well as Central, is whether the white race can maintain itself in that continent as the superior race. It is a question that cannot at present be answered for we do not possess data that enable us to reply to it in anything like an authoritative manner. We can merely speculate on the information we possess.

To some, who overlook the fact that the white man has now been established in some parts of Africa for almost three centuries, the answer seems easy. 'Of course he can maintain his superiority! Why not? He is superior in intellect, in brain development, in natural intelligence. Such investigation as has been done seems to show that the cortical development of the native lags behind that of the Nordic settler and his descendants, by about fifteen points.

Even in physical development, the white settler and his descendants are superior. Look at our magnificent footballers; compare the greater height and weight of our adolescents in secondary schools with similar figures for age groups among native adolescents. Climate ... the sun ... endemic disease ... my dear sir, look at Queensland! In two generations we can clear the country of malaria and redwater. Tropical and sub-tropical influences ... stuff and nonsense! Even the Bushveld is two thousand feet above sea level, and the uplands are far higher. . . .'

So we have politicians, who dabble in science as paraphrased for the people, dazzling our imagination with visions of a future Africa populated by Nordic offspring immeasurably better developed physically and mentally than the effete, dole-dieted millions of the homeland. We have even scientists postulating that such visions are not altogether fanciful but based on solid, substantial foundations of fact.

I have always been sceptical of the truth of this glib answer. Not because I do not wish to see white civilization maintained in Africa, but simply because I can see no grounds for such cheerful and cheering optimism. I willingly admit that the data are too few to warrant the formulation of definite conclusions, but my wandering observations in the Bushveld, and elsewhere in South Africa, have given me much material for reflection on the other aspect of the case.

So far as the sub-tropical areas are concerned, their community dates back to nearly three hundred years ago. The first white settlement was established at the southern end of the continent in 1652. The first South African white baby, destined to become a settler, was born two hundred and fifty years ago. Since that time, allowing

48

twenty-five years as a mean time for a generation, we have had ten generations of Nordic-born settlers. It is reasonable to suggest that the tenth generation should show definite signs of adaptation to environment. It is not unreasonable to argue that by this time we should be able to point to a definite South African type of white man, better fitted than the new immigrant to withstand the strain of environmental factors — climate, sun, heat, drought, isolation and humidity — that affect the vitality of the new-comer and impair his industrial powers.

Unfortunately, there is no evidence that we have produced such a type in Africa. What little investigation worth consideration there has been, tends to throw doubt on the contention that a pure Nordic pair can perpetuate their advantageous Nordic race qualities through ten generations without the help of an infusion of new blood. Out of 1000 Bushveld born children of white parents and grandparents 85 per cent showed degenerative defects, although their stature, and in many cases their weight, were superior to European born children of the same age groups. The increase in body height and weight of first generation white children in South Africa is striking enough. It is probably caused by better nutrition and improved environment, perhaps especially due to the stimulative effects of sunlight. Many factors have to be taken into consideration in assessing a child's fitness in relation to his parents' stamina and his racial peculiarities. I know of no investigation that has taken all these factors into account. The data that we possess about South African children are almost entirely derived from the medical inspection of schools, and so far as the Bushveld schools are concerned, one has, in considering these data, to remember the exceptional conditions under which these children live. Nearly fifty per cent of them suffer from redwater or chronic malaria. Some Bushveld schools have a spleen index of over 70 per cent. Ninety per cent of them are definitely malnourished, a small percentage show developmental defects, a still smaller percentage must be classed as mentally subnormal.

Malnutrition is prevalent because food is scarce in the Bushveld, where fresh fruit and vegetables are difficult to obtain, and because the children exist on an unbalanced diet. Their staple food is mealie meal, which has a low nutritive value. Milk and fresh meat are scarce. Wheaten bread is common enough, and of fair quality when obtainable, but it is not a staple article of diet. Fats are rarely included in the diet, and fresh butter is a comparative rarity.

Near the banks of the Limpopo, in a district picturesquely park-like in summer when the rains have made the veld astonishingly green, is the little settlement of D——. There are thirty white families; the average number of children in a family is five. The largest family has ten children; the smallest two. Some families live eight miles away from school; one is sixteen miles distant. There is a small school hostel which, like the school itself, is well built, according to Government specifications. Its inmates plough wearily to school every morning, and return after five hours' wrestle with that dull curriculum, to a 'home' where the facilities for recreation, physical as well as intellectual, are conspicuous by their absence. The children who are not boarders come to school in their donkey carts. The journey to and from school occupies two hours, which in summer time, when the roads are bad, means two hours' extra work for the juvenile drivers. The non-boarders often come to school without having had any breakfast; their luncheon is a crust of bread, sometimes a hard-baked damper, with a wad of *biltong* (dried game) for relish. The boarders get three meals a day, but the meals are monotonously unvaried, and the main item on the bill of fare is mealie meal in some form or other, with sodden meat stews and hashes, rice, and occasionally potatoes. For drink, tea and coffee are served. Butter is too expensive to be provided, and sugar is doled out sparingly. With a little of that energy that is devoted to the absurd single session, children could have a rich garden at D——, for the soil is not poor and there is no difficulty about water. One has merely to glance at the surrounding veld, where everything grows in such luxuriant abundance, to realize how easy it would be to cultivate vitamin-containing vegetables and to interest the pupils in practical agriculture on a small scale.

Close by runs the river. It teems with fish. Yet fish is hardly ever eaten. The natives shun it. The white man does not reckon it good food in the strict sense of the term. Formerly game abounded, but now even wildebeest meat is scarce.

The children at D—— are pitifully listless, languorous, disinclined to exert themselves, fatigued. They play wearily at football in the school playground without displaying any zest. They plod along the dry path of the simple curriculum — the three Rs, a little bilingualism, a good deal of formal religious instruction — that is what they listlessly try to absorb. Few of them when they leave will be capable of writing a sensible letter in either of the two official languages, of answering questions that the average city child can easily reply to, or of passing successfully the tests of motor ability for their age group. Their physique is poor, their intelligence quotient below that of boys and girls of their age. There are exceptions, of course. I found an emaciated, under-fed chronic malarious child of nine scaling three years above his group in intelligence. But such a child is a rarity, and for that reason more precious to the State than the rest of his debilitated and physically and mentally impoverished fellow-pupils.

At another school, equally depressing, the teacher directed my attention to a small, slight figure that displayed unusual interest in what was going on.

'You'd better take him next, Doctor,' he whispered. 'I should like you to examine him well. He is my best pupil, in standard two, and only nine years old.'

The boy was certainly a bright, intelligent youngster. He was miserably undernourished; when he stood stripped one could count every rib. But he was clear-eyed and quick, and his teeth were passably good. When I was examining him, the teacher standing by, I noticed something that made me incautiously ask, 'Sonnie, do you smoke?' The teacher was highly indignant. 'I told you he was my best boy', he said, in a voice of protest, and before the boy could answer, 'He goes regularly to Sunday School.'

I accepted the correction, and went on with my examination. A few minutes later the teacher left the room, and I asked once more, 'Sonnie, do you smoke?' The boy looked at me smilingly, and shook his head.

'No, Oomie (little uncle), I chew,' he replied.

When he left home in the morning his father gave him an inch of twist tobacco which he put into his mouth and chewed on his way to school. That and a cup of coffee (made from the root of a Bushveld tree) constituted his breakfast.

There were other lads in the school who did the same to stay the pangs of incipient hunger.

One morning I arrived at a little school and was asked to minister forthwith to two little girls who were lying under the one thorn tree that grew on the open playground. They had arrived in their little donkey cart, both lying unconscious on the seat. The Principal suggested that both suffered from 'falling sickness' (epilepsy). The donkeys had travelled that road to school so often that no guiding was needed, and when they came to the playground fence they simply stopped and bent their heads to browse on the grass. The children were taken out and deposited under the thorn tree, and the Principal was promptly told that they were dead. I found that they were merely drunk. The explanation was pathetically simple.

On their way to school they had passed a still, wherein a farmer had been distilling peach brandy. He had left his apparatus unattended, and gone indoors to breakfast. When the donkey cart passed, the still was functioning merrily, and through the long spirally coiled copper pipe, home made and wreathed round with wet rags to hasten condensation, the spirit was dropping into the receiving pot. But some had worked its way out through a loose joint in the piping, and was dripping on to the grass. The children stopped their donkey cart, climbed down and investigated. They lay down with open mouths under the tube and caught and drank the drip; just enough to show them that it was not, after all very pleasant, for newly-distilled peach brandy is fiery and a few drops of it go a long way to satisfy anyone's thirst. Then they had climbed back into the donkey cart, started for school, and presently lost all further interest in their environment.

One of my colleagues on the inspectorate staff asked me to visit a school in his area — a malignantly malarious one.

'It is hopeless, Doctor,' he said plaintively. 'Every child seems to me to be mentally defective. They have no power of attention whatever; they cannot concentrate.'

I examined the class a few months later. There were sixteen children, averaging ten years of age, though one boy was sixteen and one girl a year younger. Twelve of them had walked more than three miles to attend school, under a broiling sun, after a breakfast of mealie meal porridge and coffee made from the roots of the white-bole tree. Three had had no breakfast at all, except for a cup of similar coffee, slightly sugar sweetened. Fourteen had large spleens; all were anaemic, five so much so that they should have been at a convalescent home instead of at school. All were malnourished and showed signs of gross physical and mental fatigue.

With such material, intelligence testing is a farce. An intelligence test, in fairness to all concerned, should only be made when the child is physically fit. Otherwise there is no reasonably fair comparison of achievement possible. In those days I still had great faith in such tests, which were then on trial. In the urban schools my colleague, the late Dr. J. Marius Moll, one of the finest psychiatrists of his day, who had been trained in the school of Winckler, was engaged in standardizing such tests to find a suitably modified scale that we could use in all schools. We had all the then known tests, including the practical one used by the United States Immigration Board, for comparison and trial, and in time we did evolve our own modified scale. The subject was however still so nebulous that one hesitated to draw any definite conclusions from the results, and both

Moll and I agreed that our interpretation of whatever data we obtained would have to be extremely guarded. Since then, after many years of experience, I have come to attach far less importance to these tests. A good principal, who knows his children and their capacities, is generally quite as competent to assess the intelligence of any particular child as the psychiatrist who relies on these tests for his assessment. And, although I am quite aware that some of my colleagues think that physical defectiveness does not invalidate the findings, I have become convinced that any defect that can cause fatigue gravely prejudices a child in such intelligence testing. It is, after all, common experience that when one is physically tired, intelligence does not function so rapidly nor so keenly as when one is alert and responsive. I have seen a party of scientists, whose average intelligence quotient was much above the average, but who had been working hard for hours on an intricate problem, fail to perform a very simple observation test. The test consists in drawing on the table-cloth, with the index finger of one's left hand, a round and some dots and repeating a silly rigmarole to the effect that 'the moon's face is round; it has two eyes, a nose and a mouth'. Normally any alert, actively observant school child can do it, but my party of scientists failed miserably. They repeatedly drew the design with their right index finger, and grew worried and petulant when told that they had failed.

Here all the sixteen children scaled two or three years below their real age. They were potentially on the border-line between subnormals and defectives. My colleague was entirely correct. They could not concentrate. One told them a story containing six simple facts; they could memorize merely two. Their power of mental assimilation was obviously low: in some, so low that they were, theoretically at least, certifiable as mentally defective. But they were physically wholly abnormal, and I refused to stigmatize them as mentally defective. Under adequate treatment, with good food, quinine and iron, and abundant rest, they rapidly improved. Four months later, when I revisited that school, there was a marked improvement in their mentality. The result encouraged one to maintain the hope that the degeneration produced by malaria is not a permanent deterioration. But it is a factor to be taken into consideration when one speculates on the future of the white race in the Bushveld.

One can easily be misled by supposed analogies, but everyone who has studied conditions in sub-tropical Africa must hesitate before he discards the lessons that can be learned from analogy. These conditions differ widely from those in Europe. We do not know what these differences amount to, but that they have an influence upon growth and vitality seems clear. European perennials deteriorate under such conditions; they lose their pristine vigour after the second year and their offspring cannot compare with seedlings or cuttings grown under similar conditions in Europe. Even native plants show the same tendency to deteriorate in the same way. I have strains of *oxalis*, now in the twentieth generation and grown under precisely the same conditions as the parent strain, that show this gradual deterioration very strikingly. Their first and second generations were invariably superior to the parents, the stems and foliage more robust, the flowers larger, their fertility excellent. But in the third generation there is a sudden and surprising degeneration, that is perpetuated into succeeding strains and can easily be measured by controls. It is remarkable that the tendency to hybridization — not very common among *oxalis* — appears to be greater after the third generation, and that such hybrids seem to acquire a new lease of vigour.

What little experience I have gained from the study of third- and fourth-generation white children in South Africa (I have elaborate notes made on examination of some 25,000 of them) has led me to think that there are factors that tend to promote similar decay at work among them. Much more investigation is necessary before one can presume to indicate what these factors are, but the matter is of such vital importance that investigation is urgently necessary. In Kenya there is consensus among medical men that the child of Nordic parents brought up under Kenyan conditions shows deterioration. That is certainly not the case with first- and second-generation white children anywhere in South Africa, no matter whether their lives are passed in the highlands or in the lowlands. Excluding manifestly deteriorating factors like malaria and parasitic disease, there is no evidence that first- and second-generation children are affected by environmental conditions. But there seems to be evidence that later generations are affected, and the crux of the matter is whether or not the race can be perpetuated in Nordic integrity without constantly drawing upon new blood and new stamina for its regeneration.

That is a vital question for the Bushveld, and the Bushveld is only a comparatively small portion of the wide stretches that await exploitation and development in Africa. The doubtful operative factors are possibly humidity and direct action of sunlight, both of which may lead to a too rapid and forcible stimulation of growing tissues — to a condition which we now know as hyper-vitaminosis — that may ultimately prove as deleterious to the race as its converse, a lack of vitamins.

But meanwhile there remain factors that are not in the least doubtful so far as their ability to cause physical and mental deterioration are concerned. Malaria is the most obvious one. Its share in producing racial deterioration, through its deleterious effect on character, has been known from the earliest times. Our modern word 'melancholy' is merely a survival from that ancient knowledge, for long ago our ancestors knew that those chronically ill with malaria, whom the Greeks called *melancholikoi*, were psychically abnormal. MacCulloch, the first English writer to use the word 'malaria', in his description of the malaria sufferers in Europe, employed language which I should never have dared to use in my official reports. 'Their apathy,' he remarks, 'as expressed in their physiognomy, is a character which influences the whole conduct of these degraded and unfortunate beings, often proceeding to such a degree that they are scarcely elevated above the beasts in point of feeling. Seeking solitude, shunning society and amusements alike, without affections, without interest in anything, they make no exertions to better their condition; not even to avoid the sources of danger which surround them, or to take the most common precautions that are pointed out; while attached to the soil, from habit of indolence rather than from regard, they will not be convinced of its nature or dangers; fatalists in practice and even in belief and refusing to admit that there is any other lot in life than that which is their own ... And that this condition is even propagated, seems for ever fully proved, so that an universal degeneracy of mind and body both appear to be the certain lot of those races which a combination of unfortunate circumstances have placed in countries that seem to have been intended rather for the habitation of reptiles and insects than for that of man' (John MacCulloch: *Malaria*. 1827).

That description might apply to the Bushveld of to-day. How pitiably accurate it is I have had abundant opportunity to observe. Yet, stated in the bald language that MacCulloch used, it would probably be taken to be a gross exaggeration of the facts.

These facts, on the dark side, are distressingly simple. Most of the children of Bushveld settlers are defective; they are defective because they have been placed in an environment that is unhealthy, demoralizing, debasing and specifically restrictive; they have to live in that environment because their parents must either give up their traditional outlook upon life and seek sustenance and comfort in the towns — as many of them are doing — or continue to fight a losing battle with forces that unaided they cannot possibly conquer. On the bright side there looms one encouraging fact. Some of these children, mentally and physically, are potentially above normality. If they were taken in hand, given a chance to get rid of their malaria, fed, trained and disciplined properly, and husbanded for the State and for themselves, the results would amply repay whatever treasure of time, energy, or money had been spent in obtaining them.

They are so apathetic, so listless, that ordinarily the question of discipline, school discipline, never worries their teachers. A principal who had gained his experience of boys in a Cardiff waterside school, told me that he had never had the slightest difficulty in keeping order among his Bushveld pupils. 'They never answer back,' he said, 'and as for original sin, I don't believe they possess such a thing. It's uncanny, Doctor.'

It isn't. It is simply unhealthy.

The normal child is an active, super-active organism, whose activity must inevitably impinge against order and convention. Parents and teachers who try to mould his behaviour on models that are a mixture of their own recollections of childhood and the accumulated experience that they have themselves amassed through the years, often forget this simple fact. Rebellion against convention, antagonism to what he does not comprehend, and impetuousness in carrying out what he thinks momentarily beneficial, often lead a child to be actively 'naughty'. Such 'naughtiness' is normal and natural in a healthy child, even when its manifestations appear to be definitely a-social and sometimes almost anti-social. Experience and training teach him to modify his desires, to act less on impulse, and in time to become a unit of his community instead of trying to be a community in himself. But physical or mental defectiveness much retards the bettering effects of experience, because it engenders fatigue that dulls apperception, blunts the developing judgment and etiolates the expanding soul. With healthy, normal children, aberrations of conduct, no matter how grave at first sight they may seem, are easily counteracted, and it is a comparatively simple matter, as every experienced juvenile court judge, probation officer, teacher and parent knows, to lead the erring soul into the straight way and make him realize that it pays to be a unit of the community. But when one has to deal with abnormal children, children who are naughty because they are defective, it is another matter altogether. Fortunately, in the vast majority of cases, such children are not naughty; they lack the stimulus that activates their power of initiative; they are conventional and dull simply because they have no energy to be naughty, and if they overstep convention it is not because they are rebelliously active but because they commit sins of omission rather than of intended and determined opposition to authority.

That was the case with the Bushveld children. There were, of course, exceptions. Exceptions that were all the more interesting because they were evidence of something that my textbooks and my training had never taught me — of the subtle, deteriorating influence of chronic malaria upon the character and mentality of the victim. At that time, when I started my work in the Transvaal, comparatively little was known about what medical men call 'malaria psychoses'. It was admitted that in cases of cerebral malaria, where the smaller brain arteries were supposed to be choked by debris and pigment, leading to an almost instant bloodlessness of certain brain areas, the patient showed strange aberrations of conduct, ranging from violent, semi-delirious anti-social actions to mild antagonism to the ministrations of the doctor or the nurse. But these were supposed to be manifestations of the acute attack, and very little was known about the equally serious, if more insidious, psychoses resulting from chronic malaria. Since that time we know much more about the latter, and Professor Anderson, who studied malarial neuroses during the Great War, has written a book on the subject, while many interesting articles on it have appeared in the journals devoted to nervous and mental diseases.

Then, however, it was still an unknown territory, in which I had to grope my way. My first puzzling case was a boy of ten, the son of a parson, a normally bright, intelligent, and very active little lad, who was brought to me because he had attacked his father with a carving knife in the middle of the night and had succeeded in severely wounding his little sister the following morning. The parents, witnessing the boy's frantic efforts to unloose himself when he had been gripped and the knife taken from him, had come to the conclusion that he was mad, and both were very much concerned, naturally, because a near relative had died in an asylum. I found the boy perfectly calm and to all intents and purposes normal, but he was a sufferer from chronic malaria, with an enlarged spleen, and there was no evidence whatever to lead one to suppose that his lapse was anything else but the result of poisoning caused by the malaria parasite. He made an excellent recovery, was sent to a large secondary boys' boarding school, behaved himself admirably and gave no further trouble.

That first example of what malaria could do in changing the character and giving rise to impulses that could lead to anti-social conduct, was very valuable to me. It enabled me to devote more attention to aberrations of conduct that ordinarily one would have attributed to mere waywardness or indiscipline. Later, when juvenile delinquents came regularly, sent by magistrates to me for an opinion on their mentality, I always bore malaria in mind, and in a fair percentage of cases malaria proved to be the factor that was primarily responsible for the delinquency. The most remarkable case that I came across was an adolescent youth of nineteen charged with illicit liquor selling. He came from a good family; both his parents were respectable, law-abiding people; he himself had an intelligence quotient well above the normal, and there could be no question of mental defectiveness. In person he was clean and tidy; he smoked a pipe and did not drink. But he had on several occasions stolen drink, which he had sold to natives on the farm — sometimes for money, but more often for hemp, which on occasion has a greater value than mere cash, as it is a favourite 'habit-forming' drug. The hemp, however, he had buried; the money he had hidden under a stone. Apparently he derived no benefit from his theft, except the possibility of being regarded, by the natives in whom he confided, as a daring, heroic boy. My first impression was that his was a case of auto-exhibitionism such as one sometimes finds among small boys who pose to themselves as miniature supermen. Examination showed the lad to be suffering from malarial cachexia — under nutrition — with malarial parasites in his blood, although he denied having had an attack. His thefts were periodical, and apparently cyclical, corresponding in time to the malarial cycle. He admitted the anti-social nature of his misdeeds, but explained that he could not help himself; when the impulse came to steal drink and sell it, he gave way to it, but he was sufficiently aware of its criminality to conduct all his operations with a sly secretiveness that for many months succeeded in baffling the police. Apart from this awareness of his guilt was the desire on his part to atone for his lapse by saving the money, and incidentally the hemp, until he had accumulated enough to donate both to an orphanage fund in which his parents were interested. I had no doubt in my own mind that malaria was the fountain and origin of his misconduct, but considerable cajolery was needed to make the authorities consent to any other treatment than that which the law demands in such cases. With quinine and iron, and a temporary sojourn at one of our sea-side camps, this boy recovered, and as he was intelligent enough to realize to what he owed his lapse, he co-operated in the treatment and caused no further trouble.

I have already referred to the fact that among these malarious children one finds material, human material, that is of splendid quality. Children whose constitution and build are excellent, children whose mentality is well above the normal, are found among them. One has to discount the effects of the disease to be aware that such good quality exists, but with a little experience in examining children that is relatively easy. If such children are taken away from their malarious surroundings and given a chance to recover and to develop normally, the results are excellent. That is the one encouraging feature in a picture that is otherwise very drab, unlovely and disheartening to look upon.

At a little school on an outlying farm, I came upon two such children. The farm itself was a most picturesque place, almost as park-like as that valley site where the Voortrekkers had planned their first township. The vegetation was luxuriant; the humidity was correspondingly high. Nearly all who lived in its neighbourhood were malaria patients, and its unhealthiness was known but dismissed with a shrug as something for which none was responsible. In the early days, fifty, sixty years ago, it had been regarded as a place of refuge, an asylum for law-breakers, as it lay outside the acknowledged limits of the old Republic although now incorporated within them. In fact it had then been very much like the old town of Culenborg in the southern part of Holland, the town from which came Governor van Riebeeck and also his first lieutenant. Culenborg had for centuries maintained its independence as a free town, lending asylum to outcasts and pariahs who could find no peace elsewhere but who were allowed to reside in it subject to the proviso that they should respect its local laws. This, too, had been such a place of safety, and the parents of the children attending the school were, some of them at least, descendants of folk who had fled to find refuge in it.

A father brought his two children, twins, a boy and a girl of nine years. I have examined about 150,000 boys and girls, but rarely have I come across more perfect specimens of juvenile humanity than those two children proved to be. They were ideal in proportions, symmetrical with a symmetry such as one rarely sees, beautiful in a way that only a sculptor or an anatomist can adequately appreciate. Such perfectly proportioned children are excessively rare, in Europe or elsewhere, and in that respect both children were strikingly abnormal. So much was I impressed by them that I called my nurse's and the Principal's attention to them and demonstrated their perfections with the enthusiasm of one who has discovered a rarity. I asked the father to allow me to take photographs of them, nude, and he readily agreed. I measured them with callipers, took blood smears, tested their intelligence. They scaled eleven years by the tests, thus two years above their age group. Their teeth were perfect; they had never had an attack of malaria, and indeed had had no serious illness of any kind, and showed, *mirabile dictu*, no defect.

That evening, when the Principal and I sat chatting, there came a knock at the door. The Principal went out to see who it was, and I wondered what had brought a stray visitor in such inclement weather — it was raining and thundering outside in the manner peculiar to the Bushveld — and hoped that it was not someone who wanted the services of the doctor. The Principal came back, and ushered in the father of the twins. I felt a moment's uneasiness. Had I exceeded my privileges as a school doctor in taking photographs of two nude children who were undoubtedly among the most perfect I had ever seen? Had mamma raised objections, and had papa come to demand reparation? My talk with the Attorney-General had impressed upon my mind the necessity to be super-exaltedly discreet, even in scientific investigation, so as to avoid that horrible possibility, a charge of *crimen injuria*. Had I criminally injured society by photographing the twins in their naked perfection?

I need not have been anxious. My films were spoiled, for on the return journey we crossed a flooded river and the water came into the car and swamped Kodak and kit. The measurements were all that remained.

The father came forward and shook hands limply. They all did. There is no grip in the handshake of a chronic malarious settler.

He sat down, and we had coffee. He spoke of many things, not indeed of sealing-wax and cabbages, but of carrots and tobacco and the way the Government was ruining the country. But I could see that he held something back, and I wondered if innate courtesy prevented him from delivering some message of protest that his wife had burdened him with.

At last he came out with it.

'Doctor was much interested in our twins,' he said, haltingly.

'Indeed I was. I told you that they are the most perfectly formed children I have seen in the Transvaal. You ought to be proud of them. One does not often see children like that.'

'I told the wife. She is sorry that she could not attend

the inspection, Doctor, but grateful, Doctor, grateful, for the kind words. She thought Doctor might like to see this . . .

He took from his pocket a double sheet of blue foolscap, the old-fashioned type, ruled, much creased, and handed it to me. There was print upon it and writing, and at the bottom a signature which I made out to be that of an early President of the Orange Free State Republic, one Boshoff. It was a warrant of apprehension, asking all whom it might concern to take into custody the persons of one A—— and one B——, brother and sister, on the charge of 'Blood-shame' (incest).

'They were my great grandfather and my great grand-mother, Doctor,' the father said, simply. 'They were brother and sister, and they married and had to flee from the Free State because of that. And father and mother were cousins, and my wife is my second cousin. She said I should show you this paper, Doctor, and ask you if our children are really as good as you say they are.'

I assured him that they were. I know of no scientific reason why two persons, both physically and mentally sound, should not marry and breed equally sound progeny. But I confess that I have never found progeny of such strict endogamy so perfect as those two twins.

CHAPTER IV

THE PARENTS

THE Bushveld white community comprised the descendants of the old settlers, who had trekked into the Transvaal in the early 'thirties of the last century, and of emigrants from the Cape Colony, Natal, and the Free State who had entered later, together with a much smaller percentage of new-comers, whose residence in the Province was a matter of years rather than of generations. For the most part it was Dutch speaking; in the whole area there were few families whose home language was not Afrikaans. In the little towns alone one found citizens who, although fully naturalized, were as yet alien in outlook and by race to the rest of the community. The rural population could be considered more or less homogeneous, of original South African and largely Dutch stock, who by custom and tradition conformed to their Dutch fellow-citizens throughout the Union, but who had also inherited to a large extent the social, political, and communal likings and prejudices of their Voortrekker forebears.

When I first came in contact with this community, I realized that it was necessary that in order to carry on the work to a successful end, I should sympathetically identify myself with it. There were indeed no inherent difficulties to such a sympathetic approach. I myself come of old Cape stock; my childhood and adolescence had been spent among people with the same language, religion, customs and tradition. The fact that my father had been a pastor of the Dutch

Reformed Church, my uncle a high official in the old Republican Government of the Transvaal before the war, and another uncle a pioneer of the New Republic founded by General Lucas Meyer and now incorporated in the Province of Natal, gave me a sort of unofficial but nevertheless valuable status. A further credential was the fact that I had gained a mild reputation as a writer of verse in Afrikaans, and could be looked upon as one of the younger exponents of the doctrine that Afrikaans possessed a culture of its own, distinct and different from that of English. On my part there was a willing eagerness to make friends, and I had every reason to anticipate that it was reciprocated by the men and women among whom I had to work.

Barely twelve years separated my Bushveld community from what it still had good reason to consider a cataclysm — the Anglo-Boer War. Conan Doyle had called it, perhaps exaggeratedly from the English point of view, 'the *Great* Boer War', for in comparison with what the first four years of my inspectorate were to see, it was a small, almost an insignificant affair. But to these Bushveld burghers it was an event that had overshadowed everything else. It had for three years made them nomads and stragglers. Their families had had to shift for themselves, and the time was yet too short for the bitterness of defeat and failure to have been forgotten. Many of the farmers were still struggling against the economic distress caused by the dislocation of agriculture through the war. As one of them tersely told me: 'I came home and found a burned farm. My sole possessions were a barren cow and a toothless dog. How could I make good with so little?' People still talked with edged emphasis of the concentration camps.

Honest patriotism is not concerned with hatred, that merely breeds enmity and creates nothing but a negative solidarity. Its roots lie in affection for country and in the innate love of the people for tradition, language, culture, custom, belief, everything that is theirs by right of inheritance and birth. Without such love national self-esteem is a hollow show, no matter how firmly it is founded on a pride of achievement or even of failure to accomplish what it desired. Here, among the Bushveld people, there was abundant evidence of such affection. Here dwelt a stolid conservatism that disdained innovation that it did not understand, held rigidly to old custom, and looked upon tradition, with all that it implied, as sacrosanct. There was no hatred. Nowhere did I find, among folk who discussed the past and the future with the confident earnestness that was so characteristic of their talk, any signs of 'racialism' such as one came across in the towns, where the relations between English and Dutch were perhaps less intimate.

Four years before, Union had been achieved, and the Central Government had assumed office with the goodwill and congratulations of practically all white South Africa. It is true, some far-seeing citizens thought that it was not Union based on solid foundations, but a makeshift, a compromise in which the north had gained what it wanted and the south had lost its soul. But that was looked upon as rank heresy by the majority. Equality of language was assured, and lay enshrined in article 147 of the Africa Act as an acknowledgement of the cultural rights of half the white population. Its practical application was a matter of time and administration, but no one doubted that in time all citizens of the Union would be fluently bilingual.

At that time, of course, the second language meant the

Dutch language, the Netherlands used officially in the old Republic and still preached in church and taught in some few schools. But a third language was rapidly gaining an ascendancy over it. Afrikaans, that has now everywhere replaced Netherlands in the Union, was then in its swaddling suit. It is old Dutch as spoken by the first settlers, modified by usage into an inflexionless language that abounds in short syllables and open vowels, and is eminently suited to express the feelings of a simple people who delight in homely, domestic similes and who are by nature emotional and sentimental. Like English it is adaptable; it borrows readily, sometimes picturesquely colouring its loans and savouring them with a refreshing, idiomatic, racily pungent flavour. Then it was not yet recognized as a language that could hold its own with either English or Dutch. Even among the Dutch there were many who scoffed at its pretensions, and denied that it could be classed as a cultural factor. But a few years before Celliers had published his poem *Die Vlakte*, which proved how suitable a vehicle Afrikaans could be for expressing poetic emotion, and Dr. du Toit had followed with his war poems. These first indications of the cultural value of Afrikaans had an almost immediate and lasting effect upon the development of the language, for they showed the people who used it that they talked something that was no longer a mere 'kitchen Dutch' but a vernacular that could hold its own with English as a competitor in the cultural development of the nation.

I could easily understand, and share, that fond feeling for Afrikaans, for I knew how deeply ingrained was the Dutch speaking citizen's love for his own culture and tradition, and how anxious was his desire that it should not be swamped by the culture and tradition of his English-speaking brother citizen. There was reason to believe that if Netherlands was the only opposing factor, English tradition, language and culture would rapidly overwhelm Dutch culture, for Dutch is not only a difficult language, but its great literature and its fine cultural background are little appreciated in a country where the dominant cultural influences, since 1820, have been English. In the Transvaal these influences had not counted for much until the discovery of the gold fields, but since then they have been as potent and as permeative there as in the other Provinces. The love of language is of all national characteristics the one that best exemplifies a solidarity based on cultural aspiration, and it was only natural that the Dutch-speaking citizen should claim for his home language the same rights and privileges that his English brother tacitly assumed for his. Had that premise been accepted from the first, and its direct and indirect implications been honestly and generously acknowledged in practice, South Africa would have been saved much political wrangling and wasteful controversy.

My Bushveld people, then, were simple, primitive folk, living on isolated farms, beyond reach, as yet, of the megalopolitan influences that might ultimately, unless their language proved an effective barrier, wrench from them their homely virtues. There were some English-speaking persons among them — settlers who had bought farms and were trying to make a living under difficulties that most of them had not anticipated when they first came — but these were few. There were families descended from originally English-speaking settlers who now had 'lost all their English' and identified themselves in every respect with their Afrikaans environment. Later on, when political feeling ran high, a member of my Executive Committee, who suspected me of 'anti-Nationalist sympathies', asked why I put only English names on the list of children who were to have free meals at a school. I pointed out that although their surnames happened to be English, none of these children spoke English, and all used Afrikaans habitually as their home language. 'The father of one of them', I added, 'happens to be the secretary of the local branch of your party.' I heard nothing more of my alleged favouritism.

Once a father brought his two children for examination. He was a poor white, a *bywoner* or squatter on a friend's farm, and spoke Afrikaans; he knew no English, and his children knew merely the few words they had learned at the school. His children were physically fine specimens, but both were mentally low in the scale, while he himself could tell me very little, being himself very simple. The Principal sent for the mother who when she appeared proved to be a competent, motherly person, quite different from her slovenly and dull-witted husband. The name on the children's card was unfamiliar to me, so I asked her 'if she came from these parts'.

'No, Doctor,' she said. 'But we have been living here for some years. We come from . . .' and she named the district, and told me her story. She had met her husband, a stray from some patrol during the Boer War. He was not wounded but 'sun-stricken' and had wandered far away from his regiment and camp. For months he had stayed on her father's farm, never, she said, quite right in his head, but ultimately they had married. It had taken him long to learn the Afrikaans he now spoke; he had forgotten his English, and could give no details about his regiment, although — his wife added, naively — they could have found out about it had they wanted to. The fact that he was a deserter had never troubled them, and after twelve years it was nobody's business to investigate these things.

When I told my Administrator about this couple, he capped my story by telling me that when he returned to his farm after the war, his native manager came to him and said, '*Baas*, we have a tame Englishman at the huts. We've hidden him all this time, but he must be a soldier for he was dressed in soldier's clothing.'

'I went to the huts', said the Administrator, 'and talked to him. He could not understand English; his Afrikaans was very broken, but he spoke Shangaan quite well. He couldn't tell me who he was or where he came from, and all we could find out was that he had wandered up from Natal, had been lost in the Bush and found by some natives who had brought him to my farm. He was quite dotty, but he never gave us any trouble. . . .'

Nor can one always go by surnames. A family of the name of Sienand was originally St. John; grandpa had come from England and had trekked north. A former governor of the Cape used to tell a story that on his tours through his gubernatorial domains he once overnighted at a farm owned by a man called Spyker, a typical Dutch name, signifying 'nail'. In after-dinner conversation, his host incidentally mentioned that his grandfather came from the north of Ireland. 'But', said his excellency, who happened to be an Irishman, 'I know of no family of that name in Ireland.' 'Oh, yes,' said his host, 'grandfather was O'Neil, but father thought we might as well change the name into Spyker as we now all talk Dutch.'

My Bushveld community is composed of primitive men and women. It represents the cohesive influence of family life under rural conditions that promote, or should promote, the highest form of satisfaction that a man can obtain from individual effort. The Bushveld is no more an agricultural area than any other part of the Union. South Africa is a land that is highly mineralized, with abundance of precious and base metals. But it is not by any means an ideal agricultural, or even an ideal pastoral, country. Here in the Bushveld, farming is a matter of chance, of luck. In a good season the country is park-like, yielding much pasture, good crops, and perhaps a profit of two per cent on the capital invested in a farm. But the next season may be one of drought, of cattle disease, of locusts or of hail- and wind-storms that sweep everything before them, and what has been gained in the good season of the preceding year is wiped out by the loss on this year's profitless exploitation. Under such conditions, farming for profit is a farce that South Africa has played for generations with sad results to her people. One of these results is the increasing number of poor whites; another is the shift of her rural population from the farms to the urban areas, with a concomitant increase of distress caused by unemployment; a third is the uneconomic distribution of the expenses of staging the farce by the allocation of doles which are euphemistically known as bounties.

These combined results were already being felt in the Bushveld when I started my work there, but their significance was not yet realized. The Bushveld farmer, notwithstanding the set-backs of the war, managed to farm his many *morgen* and to make an existence for himself and his family. Though arduous and exacting, his toil brought him a certain degree of satisfaction, and his experience of the hazards against which he constantly played had inculcated in him qualities of character and temperament that were complementary to those he had inherited or acquired through tradition and custom. His cohesiveness, his clannishness, and his communal solidarity were partly the result of his national — not at all of his racial — characteristics. The Dutch-speaking settler displayed them in no more forcible a manner than did the English-speaking settler. Neither had scope or opportunity for greater cultural development than the circumstances allowed. For culture to progress, leisure and a certain amount of affluence are needed. Here there was neither, and in addition there was privation, with a lack of opportunity for cultural inspiration that reacted upon the community as a whole. Such culture as there was, could be looked upon as the remnant of an older culture that was being threatened by the demoralizing influences of urbanization seeping in from centres that were gradually becoming more densely populated than the surrounding district and creating novel problems that could not be solved by traditional axioms.

Contrary to my expectations, I did not find my Bushveld community rabidly intolerant. They possessed a religious background in the ancestral Protestantism to which the original settlers had subscribed, but it was by no means so formalistic nor so strait-laced as I had been led to believe. Its honest intensity and its dominating influence upon domestic life were plainly apparent, but it did not manifest itself in sombre negation of pleasure that denied to others what they themselves looked askance at. It did inculcate a certain fatalism, a negative attitude towards life, that accepted whatever blows chance dealt without the desire or energy to be actively insubordinate. But at the same time it did not blunt their innate sense of humour, nor dull their response to emotional stimuli that aroused in them what their stricter brethren might have termed Satanic temptations. They could, and did, enjoy hearing stories that verged on the flagitious; they could, and did, laugh heartily at things disparaging to their pastors; they displayed, on occasion, a worldly sagacity that paid more attention to present temporal benefits than to spiritual refreshment in the future. They were shrewd in their domestic affairs, shrewd indeed in most things except in political matters to which they paid far more attention than their knowledge and their interests warranted.

Many years ago an equally shrewd public man told me, 'The two sections of our population that are politically minded are the Dutch-speaking farmers and the natives. Both have more political sense than the urban citizens, for politics is a live thing to them and merely an incident to the town dweller, who has more practical, immediate and material things to think about. That is why you will never have a strong Opposition in a country where politics is primarily a means to secure the interests of the agriculturist.'

This interest is not confined to local politics. It embraces a much wider field and its ambit includes matters about which the disputants have little or no first-hand knowledge. That accounts for the singularly synoptic way in which my Bushveld friends discussed the Great War; they looked at it from the point of view of their local interest, and spoke of it in terms of party phraseology. And they were very earnest and honest about it all, so much so that their honesty and earnestness made them a facile prey for the wily political aspirant who could play on their emotions with the practised skill of an auctioneer selling second-hand goods without a guarantee. At times this earnestness was embarrassing.

I had arrived on Friday at a small school which happened to be on a farm that was more or less central. On the following day there would, I heard, be a preparatory church service, in the open air; on the Sunday the communion service would be held. The pastor, who arrived on the Friday afternoon, called on me when I was examining the last children on the list. He suggested that as practically all the adults from the neighbouring farms would be present at the preparatory service, I should, when it had ended, take the opportunity of speaking to them on health matters. I was very glad to do so, and readily agreed to stay for the Saturday. The service was held under a large fig tree, whose immense spread of branches made a leafy canopy for most of the congregation. Men and women sat on camp stools, home-made with *riempie* or leather-thong plaited seats; children and attendants squatted on the ground in the rear ranks. The simple service — a few hymns, a chapter read out of the Dutch Bible (there not being available at that time an Afrikaans translation) and a straightforward sermon, practical and not too long — ended with the Benediction, after which the pastor held up his hand.

'We have with us to-day', he said, 'the Government school doctor, of whom you have all heard ... The elders and I think that it would be instructive to us all if the doctor were to tell us something about health and how we may keep it. I shall now ask him to address you.' I spoke for twenty minutes, and they listened to me in profound and, so far as I could judge, interested silence. I told them, in the simplest words, about malaria and redwater and dysentery and dirt. Then I suggested that it might be more advantageous to them if they were to ask me questions, which I promised to answer to the best of my ability. No one stirred. The pastor, to help me, intoned the usual formula that follows the conclusion of public speeches. 'The doctor will now answer any questions that may be put.' An old, kindly featured man ose from the second rank. He turned to face the audience, and held up his hand. 'Friends,' he said, impressively, 'it is my duty to propose a vote of no confidence in the speaker.'

My first thought was that I had said or done something woefully amiss, but the general laugh that greeted the old fellow's remark restored my equanimity. Later I heard that 'Uncle Rasmus' moved votes of no confidence at every political meeting he attended; it was a matter of principle with him to oppose, and when his own party's candidate appeared on the platform he had to be forcibly prevented from riding his hobby horse. Here his lapse broke the ice, and for the next twenty minutes I was kept busy in replying to questions that ran the gamut from cancer to the morality of corporal punishment in schools.

At first acquaintance, one who does not look at the background of these lives spent in isolation may conclude that the one blatant blemish of these rural folk is their hypocrisy. It is an accusation often levelled against primitive folk who defend themselves by equivocation and by dissembling. There is some measure of truth in the allegation, as thoughtful and sympathetic critics have more than once pointed out. They have gained no thanks for their criticism, for South Africa bitterly resents anything that seems to cast a reflection upon the accepted super-excellence of the dominant race. The late Mr. W. W. Way, one of the most understanding and charitable of men, wisest of head masters and an influence on the lives of many Dutch-speaking boys to whom he was an exemplar and a friend, was almost ostracized because he dared openly to say what every experienced head master felt to be the truth when he asserted: 'The young South African is also tending to become a hypocrite'; and told the Association for the Advancement of Science, of 'a young rascal, caned several times during the week for lying, cheating and stealing, going to a Christian Endeavour meeting in order to pass a note during the opening prayer to his inamorata for the time being, and then praying fervently that his form-master might be led into the right path'. Because that criticism came from an Outlander, it was perhaps more un-appetizing, but similar comment has not been rare from native-born judges in their caustic remarks from the Bench on occasion. The unpalatable fact is that years of struggle with material forces, through generations that have been always on the defensive and at pains to keep what they had fought for, have engendered a spirit that puts a premium on slyness and cunning when their use appears to be legitimate to gain some material or spiritual advantage. There are words in the Afrikaans language that testify to this. You are *slim* (clever-cunning — cunningly clever — the word has many meanings but to all, except the one where it is used to denote one who has scholarship, there attaches a nuance of unpleasantness that is yet never taken to imply something derogatory) if you get the better of your opponent in business or politics by stratagems that are on the border-line of honourable conduct. You must try to *uit-oorlê* — (an almost untranslatable verb, originally meaning to conquer by premeditation, deliberately to do something, but now with the additional signification of doing that something in a subtle, secretive way) someone to obtain an advantage over him, and you will be thought the more highly of if you succeed in your attempt. It is a defensive hypocrisy, the weapon of one who knows his own weakness and can forgive as venial and excusable the propensity of another to lapse from the straight path of truth and give a false colouring to fact to make life's amble the easier. In some measure it is even the desire to judge fairly and to give full scope to the charity that is fostered by communal cohesiveness and that tries to allow every man his own standard of values, be they moral or ethical.

The late Mr. Samuel Marks, who knew and lamented this trait, told how he had philanthropically given work, a house and board to a poor white on his farm, Swartkoppies, near Pretoria. 'The fellow was unsatisfactory, but I did not care to dismiss him, and I thought I would ask my overseer what he thought about him. So I asked him: "How is So-and-So getting along? Is he making good, do you think?" "Well, Mr. Marks,' he replied, 'I don't want to judge him yet. He is very lazy, he does no scrap of work, he steals, and he is impudent; but on the whole he is quite a sensible, lovable man, and I think we might keep him for a bit."' During the Boer War the republican commandoes invaded the Cape Colony and proclaimed parts of it republican territory. The Dutch-speaking farmers in those 'annexed' divisions were told that they were now republican burghers and had to fight in the commandoes. When the districts were re-occupied, these men, who were British subjects and technically rebels, were arraigned before a special court of three judges and were tried on charges of treason, murder and various offences. It was a circuit court, travelling from district to district, and it tried many rebels, with the majority of whom one could not help sympathizing, since they had gone into rebellion, not always because they rebelled against the Government under which they lived, nor because they so whole-heartedly sympathized with the cause of the republics, but because they had been induced to believe that they were by annexation republican subjects and as such bound to fight in the commandoes. The republican leaders who cajoled

F

them into this belief knew perfectly well that every man they recruited in the Cape Colony ran the risk of being summarily shot as a rebel when captured; they themselves, being republican burghers, could claim the privileges of prisoners of war, but their dupes could not reckon on such immunity. Yet the action of these leaders has never been repudiated by those who write about the war from the Boer side; it is taken for granted that they acted from motives of high patriotism and that their cunning merits praise instead of protest.

I was at the time a correspondent attached to the court, and heard many tales about the intimidation that had forced some of those rebels into rebellion. One evening the solicitor who acted for the defence came and asked me to accompany the lawyer who had been briefed in the case of one of the foremost farmers of the district, and to act as interpreter for his client. We found the accused in the town jail, in a small bare cell, into which he had been brought that afternoon. It was night time when we came, and the jailer lighted us in with a guttering candle that he placed on the form, dropping a few gouts of grease to make it stable on the wood. Huddled in a corner sat the prisoner, an old man with a fine grey beard, a well-to-do, much respected farmer who had been field cornet, elder of the church, and justice of the peace. He was crying when we came in, in the pitiful, restrained way that old men cry when they are affected by their feelings beyond the bounds of control, and when he saw us he started up and spoke agitatedly.

'I have indeed been made to drink the dregs of misery,' he said, wiping his tears away and emphasizing his points with a lean forefinger, 'I am on my farm, Mr. B——, peaceable and quiet, and the brothers from across the river come.

They take away all my sheep, and they nail a paper to the door of my wagonhouse, and they come and tell me that I am now a subject of the Republic and that I must go with them. They put me on a horse, and make me go with them, Mr. B——, to show them the way, and they keep me with them until the English come, and then they leave me behind and the English soldiers catch hold of me and are very rough with me, Mr. B——. They bring me to this prison ... and our family, Mr. B—— have never had a jailbird among them, and I feel the shame of it, Mr. B——. I feel it. And to crown all, I am like Job in his trouble of whom the good Book tells, for when my cup is already full there is this more to make it overflow, since nephew E—— here' — and he pointed to the jailer — 'has just told me that our dearly beloved Alexandrina Victoria is dead. . . .'

To one who is strange to such people, this avowal might have sounded the height of hypocrisy, but both Mr. B—— the lawyer and I knew that it was nothing of the kind. The old man was deeply, sincerely and unashamedly distressed to hear of the Queen's death. He had honoured and respected her, and on her birthday he had put lighted candles in his window and joined in the celebrations. He would never have wept, even over the disgrace of being jailed and the rough treatment he had experienced, but Alexandrina Victoria had been an ideal to him and her death seemed the culmination of distress in which tears alone could bring relief. Among the folk of the Bushveld I found men and women similar in temperament whose appraisement of values differed in no way from that of members of my father's congregation whom I had known in childhood. They showed the same tolerance in some things, the same illiberality in others; they were kind, hospitable and generous to an almost unbelievable extent; emotional for all their stolidity and acquired fatalism; sentimental where one hardly expected them to have feelings, and hard and practical at other times. Together their characteristics made up a mosaic of incongruity, a blend of contrasts that was flecked with curious, elusive harmonies. What jarred in it was the primitive naturalness that, however appreciable in children, seemed extraordinary in grown people. Once one discounted that, as the result of their upbringing and environment, it was easy to admire and respect the positive virtues that outweighed the rest. Basically they were sound as the stock they came from.

There were times when one doubted their virtues and had some justification for thinking worse of them than they really were. Their pride — a pride of race and clan rather than one of culture and accomplishment — made them sometimes intolerant, and they were habitually intolerant towards the native for the simple reason that most of them — not all — did not regard the native as in any sense a human equal. That attitude made them harsh and cruel towards the aboriginal, and accounted for the all-too-frequent disparities between justice as meted out to the white and the same justice extended towards the black. When a hefty young adolescent, convicted of an assault on a native girl, was sentenced to receive a judicial whipping, a whole district rose up, convened a public meeting, and passed a resolution calling upon the Government to remove the magistrate who had ordered such a degrading punishment, and the police sergeant who had inflicted it. Yet a similar punishment of a young native for a like offence would have called for no protest, unless it was one against the lenity of the sentence. Their greatest failing, perhaps, was their laxity. In the Boer

War that disregard of discipline and contempt of authority had burdened them heavily, but the lesson which the war taught them was all too soon forgotten. Parental discipline was either slack or enforced in anger, in a sudden ebullition of temper, when it defeated its own object and was regretted the moment after. That was probably the effect of the apathy that malaria and the climatic environment induced, for I encountered many instances where the parents had cordially co-operated with the teachers in maintaining discipline in the schools.

Their willingness to be exploited by politicians was perhaps the consequence of their want of sophistication, but it was also a result of their greater appreciation of smugness and slyness. Indubitably the finest intellect among the leaders of the northern Dutch party was General Louis Botha. His natural intelligence was far superior to that of his contemporaries; he had broad human sympathies, and was in every sense of the word a leader, an individual with extrovert tendencies that allied him to the great men of his race, but his memory was not phenomenally good. Men are more impressed by feats of memory than by natural intelligence, and even in the Transvaal Botha was not regarded as particularly *slim* and was not credited with many of his great achievements. Of the three Boer generals who gained a reputation during the Boer War, he was the greatest, for he combined the decision and the dash of de la Rey, whose character, mind and genius could be likened to that of the Southern General Johnson, with the tenacity and the caution of a far-seeing strategist — qualities that he prominently displayed in the South-West campaign, which connoisseurs hold to be a model of what such things should be. But he never gained the reputation for cleverness that

General de Wet had, although General de Wet, for all his cleverness, did not possess a tithe of Botha's intellect. Their compatriots were stirred by the spectacular celerity with which the one could evade the enveloping English drives, but were rarely touched by the greater talent of the other that kept together groups of scattered units and planned and carried out strategical moves whose success demanded more than cunning and agility. Among his own people Botha's gifts as a soldier and a leader are not yet appreciated as they should be, for they are overshadowed by the reputation of lesser, but in the public eye more clever, men whose doings appealed to that streak of gamin-like irresponsibility that underlies the stolidity of the Bushveld.

In matters that needed a valuation of ethical soundness, one not infrequently found a disparity between precept and practice. Everyone, in principle, deprecated betting, yet nowhere was, or is, it more frequent than in the Transvaal. Annually that Province spent much money in illicitly financing the lottery at Delagoa Bay, and later on, when the Irish Sweepstake appealed to both the charitable and the thriftless, it sent more money overseas than it donated locally to philanthropy. To-day it vigorously supports the State lottery in Rhodesia, yet a proposal to start lotteries in the Union would be fought tooth and nail in Parliament. Thousands of pounds are spent on dog racing in the Transvaal — the one province that allows this demoralizing sport; in every province horse racing is popular, not because it encourages the breeding of good horses but simply because it gives a chance to the poorer class to win unearned money. For the well-to-do there is always the Johannesburg stock exchange, with its enormous potentialities of acquiring sudden wealth by a shrewd forecasting of the vagaries of mining shares. The hypocrisy of this attitude towards gambling is obvious, but nobody comments on it.

The other side of the picture is much more attractive. Physical bravery — the heroism of the pioneer, the explorer, the hunter — love of country and clan — the love that is capable of sacrifice and self-abnegation — generosity and a loyalty to tradition, these were theirs, and could be counted on. Among them were characters that showed not specks of gold, like the rocks so abundant throughout their country, but solid masses of it, men who through a long life had proved that they possessed the virtues that Plutarch set at the head of his long list. Such were the men who first saw the rainbow glory of the Zambezi Falls and were not too proud to call Mosilekatse, familiarly known as Silkaats, friend and to act as guardians to his adolescent son, Lobengula. One likes to savour their memories, as one savours good wine, a rare and precious vintage, proof that the race from which they came could yield substance as sound as the old stock did in Holland and France when the time called for something more valuable than sounding brass or tinkling cymbals; one likes to think that the breed is not extinct but that what it has produced in the past it may again show in the future.

CHAPTER V

THE CURSE OF THE BUSHVELD

THE curse of the Bushveld is malaria.

The oldest disease of which we have authentic record, malaria, is to-day exactly the same disorder that it was in the time of the Pharaohs, when Egypt was so marshy and mosquito infested that, as Herodotus tells us, men slept under nets to avoid being bitten. It is the disease that depopulated Greece, that reduced that magnificent civilization, of which we are the inheritors, to comparative insignificance. One beautiful gold Greek coin, chiselled by a great sculptor, bears witness to the fact that the ancient Greeks recognized how intimately marshland was associated with malaria. When I was a medical student, the late Sir Herman Weber, one of the greatest numismatists of his day, showed me one of the two extant examples of this gold tetradrachm of Lampsacus struck in memory of some great epidemic, and quoted Theognis and Plato, who both mention the evil effects of the disease upon the health and physique of those exposed to its ravages. From Greece, malaria came to Rome, and there can be no doubt that it was one of the principal factors that sapped the strength and broke the integrity of the empire of the Caesars. Throughout Europe it left its mark, and its history can be traced, not, it is true, in devastating epidemics, but in the steady, persistent degeneration that it caused in localities that were favourable to the breeding of mosquitoes that are the carriers and hosts of the parasite responsible for its effects.

For a detailed account of what it brought about, in de-populating districts and undermining national health, the curious may be referred to Celli's well-known monograph *La Malaria* that contains much interesting information about its malignant achievements in the past.

It is a parasitic disease: that is to say, the signs and symptoms that it causes are the result of the reaction of the body tissues to a circulating poison produced by a small animal that lives in the blood-cells of its human intermediate host. Three such parasites were known to be the cause of human malaria when I started school work in the Transvaal. They were respectively *Plasmodium vivax*, that produced the tertian type of fever: *P. falciparum*, responsible for the tropical or malign tertian form: and *P. malariae* that caused the quartan type. Since then a fourth parasite, *P. ovale*, has been described, but it is a much rarer little brute, and of no great national importance. *P. falciparum* and *P. vivax* are, in the Bushveld, of incomparably greater significance as factors in promoting communal deterioration.

These parasites are protozoal organisms, so small that they cannot be seen by the naked eye and must be measured in fractions of a thousandth part of a millimetre, and must be properly stained before they can be recognized in a blood smear under the high power of a microscope. Their life-history has now been worked out, and although there are still many points upon which we are by no means con-vincingly informed, we know enough to explain how they enter into their human hosts and how they behave when they have obtained lodgement.

Their story is, after all, very simple, but its very sim-plicity adds to the puzzle how they originally came into existence. Like the problem of the hen and the egg, science has not yet solved it. For the malaria parasite exists in two distinct and separate forms. The one is the asexual form, the full-grown organism, that is found in the human blood-cells, where it produces its poison and causes the disease. The second or sexual form, floats free in the blood-stream, and so long as it remains there it does not grow or change, and does not even seem to cause any symptoms. It needs for its further development another host, which is the Anopheline species of mosquito. The mosquito bites a human being in whose blood these sexual forms of the parasite, technically known as gametocytes, swim, and sucks them up into its stomach. They make their way into the insect's spittle glands, where they develop into elongated little forms, the sporozoites, that swarm in the mosquito's saliva. When such an infected mosquito bites a healthy person, some of these sporozoites are introduced into that person's blood and penetrate into the red blood-corpuscles, where they settle and rapidly develop into the mature or asexual form. The bitten person then becomes conscious that he is no longer in sound health. The parasitic poison circulating in his blood, affects his tissues, disorders his metabolism, and gives rise to the complex of symptons that we call malaria. The time needed for the full development of the parasites, after the mosquito has bitten the victim, varies for the different species. It is usually never less than a week, and sometimes prolonged for three weeks or more. Although such an infected person feels out of sorts for several days, the actual attack may come quite suddenly. In my own case my first attack came on when I was playing cards, and was ushered in by an annoying feeling of cold air playing on my back although the room was warm. This is 'the shivers', a stage that is quickly succeeded by intense heat and prostration, headache, and a high temperature, to be followed, some hours later, by the sweating stage, which lasts about six hours. After that the patient feels depressed and weak, but his temperature drops, and he imagines himself recovered. But two days later he has another attack, and if he is not treated these attacks recur, with monotonous regularity, on alternate days for a month or more; then they grow less frequent, and months, even years, may pass without an attack, until some climatic or occupational change calls forth another attack and shows the patient that he 'still has malaria in his system'.

It rarely kills. If it did, the Bushveld folk would be much more interested in it, and would combine in a mass attack against it. But what it does is more insidious, more nationally detrimental. It weakens, it saps the energy and the spirit of its victims, it stunts their growth, it changes their outlook on life itself, it causes widespread physical and mental deterioration. Therein lies its greatest danger.

We are all much more concerned with disease that is dramatic through death. When influenza rages epidemically everyone is up and doing, and even the Government is stirred to tardy and utterly ineffectual action. For death is so obvious, so unarguable. Rheumatic fever, that causes more widespread misery than cancer or tuberculosis, because it acts precisely like malaria, stunting and distorting human life out of all semblance of what it should be, we look upon as of little account, because nowadays no one, or very few, need immediately succumb to it. Its toll is not dramatic enough to impress others than those who study comparative vital statistics and realize that in non-tropical countries rheumatic fever slays its hundreds where tuberculosis and cancer kill their dozens. We grow dithyrambic about plague and yellow fever that kill in concentrated clumps. The sudden realization that there is among us something that within a short time may cut down many of our fellow-beings, is a stimulant to which we all immediately, and sometimes panically, react. It is the insidious, progressive march of disease that makes practically no impression upon us.

We see this attitude towards disease reflected in our eagerness to conquer cancer. If the energy and the millions now annually spent on cancer research, so far with little benefit to the world at large, were devoted to an international, organized attack upon rheumatic fever and its sequelae, the economic results would be such as to satisfy any business-like layman. Cancer is eminently a dramatic disease, and as such occupies a prominent place in the limelight. We are impressed by the mystery that enshrouds it, and by the glaring realities of its presence when it reveals itself in our immediate neighbourhood. But it is a disease of the extreme of life; its economic toll is far below that of pneumonia or rheumatic fever. Yet in the Bushveld it is the most dreaded of all diseases; the community there is much more interested in hearing how one can 'cure' cancer than how one can prevent malaria. In that it is not singular, for every country now has its 'Cancer Associations' that unfortunately insist far too much upon emphasizing the as yet unproved increasing incidence of malignant disease, rather than the fact that such increasing incidence is probably the coincident result of the increasing rise in the expectation of life. In my talks to Bushveld parents, who always wanted to hear something about cancer — a curiosity about which I shall have something to say later on — I always laid stress on the chance of escaping cancer rather than on the risk of getting it, which is, I maintain, the true approach. It is much more encouraging to realize that so many thousands out of every ten thousand of the community die from other diseases than cancer, than to harp on the fact that a comparatively small number of that ten thousand contract cancer when they are well over the average age attained in the community. But even that statement of the case never impressed my Bushveld hearers, to whom cancer stands at the top of the list of all imaginable ills that afflict mankind.

Malaria, unfortunately, has no such dramatic aspect, even though its onset may be with dramatic suddenness. There is no disease so protean in its manifestations, or so insidious in its dangerous possibilities. In times of epidemic, when the mortality from it is slightly greater than in ordinary seasons, a mild flutter of apprehension runs through the Bushveld, but it is never sufficient to stir folk into active, organized attack upon a scourge that is endemic. The Bushveld community has come to accept malaria as an ever-present, almost inevitable accompaniment of life. It is that attitude of almost fatalistic resignation that is so discouraging to those who firmly believe, as I do, that there is no reason whatever why malaria should exist in the Bushveld nor why it should not be exterminated by concerted action on the part of the community. One would have thought that the experience of over a hundred years of the evils wrought by the disease would have spurred the community to such action, but that is not the case. Malaria goes on, year after year, and the position to-day is not much better than it was at the time when I first visited a Bushveld school.

For the propagation of the disease two factors are indispensable — the presence of human beings infected with malaria and of anopheline mosquitoes capable of carrying the disease. The first factor can be eliminated by proper remedial treatment, organized on a large scale, and rigorously enforced, but no measures of treatment can ever succeed if applied only to the white community. Their application must be universal and thorough. The second factor can be eliminated by mosquito destruction, which can, however, only be effective when we know the bionomics of the various anophelines that are carriers. Some of them are swamp- and shade-loving insects; others prefer open reaches of water; some probably breed in collections of water in the sheathing leaves of aloes and agaves. A great deal of investigation is necessary before we can economically apply to the Bushveld malaria, preventive measures that have admirably succeeded elsewhere.

There is a valley in the Bushveld that in summer time, when the rain has brought out the full luxuriance of its semi-tropical foliage, is a park of wonderful beauty. Gently sloping hills, covered with lush grass and topped by tall trees, descend to meet the banks of a rippling stream, over-shadowed by tree ferns and bush wherein troops of blue monkeys chatter. The soil here is deep and fertile. There is an abundance of water, and the maroela (*Selerocarya caffra*) and stem-fruit trees are heavy with fruit. Here and there stands a big peach tree, full of blossom in the spring, but almost fruitless when its time comes to bear, for it has been neglected and unpruned for generations. Among the polls of grass are the ruins of walls, of houses that were erected almost a century ago.

For this is the site of one of the earliest settlements of white folk in the Bushveld. They chose this pretty spot, not knowing that the rippling stream and surrounding boscage were dangerous neighbours. They built and planted and made laws for their community, held service in their little church, and deemed themselves secure and safe from molestation and interference. They were a group of the first 'Trekkers', the pioneers of the Transvaal, who after long and dangerous travel through the wilds had reached this spot and decided to settle there. Within a generation, malaria forced them to abandon their settlement, and the place gained the reputation of being a death-trap. Its many graves, now hidden by the tall grass, testify to the truth of its calamitous fame. The few settlers who escaped found refuge on a slope miles away, and founded a town which they called 'Town of Suffering' (Lydenburg) in memory of what they had endured in the death-trap.

Yet that valley is no more dangerous, no more insidiously fatal to whoever settles in it, than any other Bushveld district. It was an outbreak of epidemic malaria that decimated the settlement, but the settlers were just as much exposed to the risks of endemic malaria at their new settlement. There they died, not by dozens at a time, but occasionally; and their deaths made no great impression, for occasional death is common enough. It is only when death is dealt out in chunks, when large percentages share in it, that the community becomes alarmed and thinks it time to take drastic measures even to the extent of giving up a good site such as this was.

The descendants of those early settlers, like the descendants of all Bushveld dwellers, suffered and suffer from malaria. Every malaria-infected person is a danger to his neighbours in an environment that harbours malaria carrying mosquitoes: and practically all children in certain parts of the Bushveld, white as well as native, are infected. It is quite true that one comes across many persons who allege that they have never had the disease. Immunity is something we know very little about, and about immunity to malaria we know least of all. It is clear that some persons do possess some constitutional peculiarity that makes them more resistant than others to the poison of the parasites. It is also true that children who on examination show all the signs of heavy infection will tell you that they have never had a typical attack of 'the shivers'; and that it is rare to find parasites in their blood. But these apparent contradictions are explainable, and the fact remains that the majority of children are infected children who throughout their childhood and adolescence suffer from the effects of the disease.

When I realized the extent to which malaria was prevalent in the Bushveld, it was clear to me that one could not hope for any improvement in the conditions unless preventive prophylactic and curative treatment was instituted at all schools in malarious districts. Preventive treatment demanded a thorough investigation of the whole malaria problem in the Transvaal, and organized measures such as could only effectively be carried out by a central administration able and willing to spend a considerable amount of money to ensure that these measures were adequate. There was no indication that the Union Government, at that time, had the slightest intention of dealing with malaria as a national problem. Later on, when Dr. D. Malan became Minister of Public Health, he realized the need for an investigation and commissioned Professor Swellengrebel, an international authority on mosquito control, to tour the Bushveld and report on the matter. Professor Swellengrebel's report fully substantiated the 'alarmist' reports about the prevalence and the importance of the disease, and some of the measures which he recommended were adopted. But with the change of government malaria has again become a minor consideration, and while the legislature has trifled with dozens of subjects of ephemeral importance it has done nothing, during the past five years, to cope effectively with the scourge and curse of the Bushveld. Preventive measures, so far, have been confined to regulations, and to research work carried on, with encouraging results, at the Malaria Station at Tzaneen.

There remained prophylactic and curative treatment. Both appeared to be justified because in quinine we possess a drug that is specific in malaria just as arsenic is specific in syphilis and salvarsan in anthrax. The romance of the introduction of quinine does not end with the story of how in 1638, fourteen years before white civilization was introduced in South Africa, the Countess del Chinchon, wife of the Viceroy of Peru, was cured of an intermittent fever by the decoction of the bark of a tree that Linnaeus, a hundred years later, latinized without the initial 'h' in her honour. It embraces the adventures of a number of intrepid explorers, who, when quinine was well established as a remedy for malaria, and cinchona bark was a monopoly, attempted to find the same or similar trees in other parts of America. It ends with the curious and exciting tale of how cinchona seeds were smuggled in a pipe stem to the Jardin des Plantes, and how cuttings from the plants raised there were coaxed by Teysman, the enthusiastic gardener of the Buitenzorg Botanical Garden in Java, to grow until they were large and strong enough to yield other cuttings. From these came the cinchona plantations of Java that are to-day the main source of supply of quinine.

Quinine has always been an expensive drug. During the

Great War its cost more than quadrupled, and supplies were difficult to obtain and not always pure. There was general agreement among medical men that the regular administration of the drug was actively 'prophylactic' against malaria; that is to say that it prevented the person bitten by an infected mosquito from contracting malaria. We were not quite clear why it did so, and some of us doubted if the premise was true, but the consensus, buttressed by the personal experience of many, was that if you took quinine regularly you at any rate very much diminished the risk of getting malaria even if you were constantly exposed to the bites of infected mosquitoes. Now the pendulum has swung the other way, and medical opinion appears to favour the view that quinine is not a preventative, an opinion based on the observation that persons who are taking quinine may be experimentally infected. That view is probably just as unjustifiably extreme as the older opinion, but the question is one for expert discussion and need not be elaborated here.

At that time I felt fully justified in recommending that quinine should be supplied to all Bushveld schools, and that all children should be urged to take it regularly in summer time. The prescribed dose was five grains daily for a child below twelve years of age, and eight for one older, and the teachers were asked to see that the children took their daily doses at school. Quinine was also supplied for free distribution in case of sickness. The cost of this attempt at prophylaxis on a large scale, at a time when quinine was scarce, was so high that the experiment could only be tried at a few selected schools where the spleen index among the children exceeded 50 per cent. As an indication of the efficacy of treatment we took the daily attendance graphs. In malaria schools these attendance graphs looked almost like a

temperature chart of a malaria patient; there were such prodigious ups and downs. In a school of fifty pupils there
might on the Monday be 49, on the Tuesday 15 and on
Wednesday 12, on Thursday 30 and on Friday 22. In
larger schools the graphs did not oscillate so violently, but
during the fever season the attendance always suffered
severely. After a year's trial with quinine prophylaxis, the
graphs, except in a few schools, showed no marked improvement. Investigation proved that in most schools the treatment had not been carried out regularly. One teacher had
used the quinine tablets as punishment; the errant child was
made to crunch them in front of the class! Another had
doled out double supplies once a week — a method that was
utterly useless. Where the teachers had co-operated conscientiously and carefully followed instructions, a marked
improvement in the attendance rate was noticeable. Curative
treatment — giving children with large spleens daily doses
of ten grains for a couple of weeks, followed by iron and
quinine citrate pills as a tonic, and, where possible, supplying
them with extra food — was much more satisfactory, and
the results were encouraging. But in such an environment
it was impossible to prevent relapses and reinfections. No
child ever slept under a net; no Bushveld house was adequately screened. Even the teachers' quarters, which were
supposed to be mosquito proof, contained many mosquitoes,
and I collected many infected anophelines in them. In such
circumstances one knew that one was doing wasteful work,
uneconomic work, and one felt depressed and miserable and
indignant because there was no active co-operation, and
because the community looked upon malaria as something
inevitable and inescapable.

From the first I realized the important part that the

teacher in a malarious area had to play in any organized attack upon the disease. In such a community the teacher should be the leader and guide, especially in health matters. His was the obligation to set a standard of living, the duty to be an example to his neighbours, and to prove, by his own immunity to the disease, that it was possible to prevent malaria by adequate measures and by proper care. But unfortunately the conditions in the rural areas in malarious districts militated greatly against obtaining teachers who possessed the requisite training and cultural development to act as leaders of the community. Few were certificated; none possessed high qualifications or had had university training. Many were young aspirants, who applied for these 'one-man school' posts because they could not obtain appointments in town schools where competition was keen. The small climatic allowance made to teachers in malarious districts attracted the inferior type rather than the superior, and the conditions of life on these isolated farms did not appeal to the better educated teacher. The situation was admittedly difficult, and the Department was fully alive to the drawbacks of the policy then followed. In a special report on the malaria districts, I urged that everything possible should be done to recruit the best type of teacher for the schools in these areas. They should be given, not climatic allowance, which was difficult to assess on an equitable basis, but increased salaries, and an added inducement in the shape of 'extra service' added to their years of service for pension purposes. A year's service in a malarious school should be ranked as equivalent to eighteen months' service in a non-malarious school. An annual bonus was suggested for teachers who kept their schools free from malaria. Teachers' houses to be properly screened; the curriculum for malaria schools to be radically altered; the terms to be modified so that the school term fell in June-July, which were then vacation months, and the holidays in April-May which were the worst malaria months. I also recommended that teachers should have ample leave, and should be forced to take such leave annually instead of accumulating leave to be taken at the end of six years' service. Finally, I strongly urged the closure of many small schools, and the absolute prohibition of starting new schools of this type in malarious areas — a popular policy at the time — with a system of centralization at selected sites, where proper hostels could be established. Political considerations, that are always paramount in South Africa, and local feeling, swung the scale against such centralization at the time, and for years a policy of decentralization has been followed with lamentable results — a waste of effort, money and material that was much to be deplored.

My difficulty in those days was to find anyone who shared my view that malaria was a national problem, a danger that would ultimately lead to widespread degeneration. Those who had had malaria considered it a mild disease, really not worth bothering about. To most of the Bushveld dwellers it was still a miasmatic disease, a real mal-aria. They refused to discuss its transmission by insect carriers. Epidemically it was a visitation, like influenza or typhoid. A member of my executive committee, with whom I discussed the matter to persuade him to vote for an increased grant to malaria schools, told me quite frankly that he had himself been educated in a malaria school and that what was good enough for him was good enough for the children. This apathy was discouraging. Just as discouraging was the failure of local 'malaria societies' that should have been effective propaganda centres. The Highveld was too prosperous and sleek to waste time in discussing the Lowveld. It grabbed what it could in the way of grants to multiply the already superfluous secondary schools, for which money was generously voted while the malaria districts were treated parsimoniously. The real reason for this apathy and want of interest was sheer ignorance of what the disease was daily effecting in the Bushveld districts. Its effects were evident enough to those who had visited the schools during the malaria season — when the incidence of the disease was at its highest — but most people, who raved about the beauty of the Bushveld, went there in the dry winter season, and saw little of the ravages of malaria. These effects can be seen everywhere where malaria is prevalent; they were pointed out more than a hundred years ago in southern Italy and Spain. Here they were saddeningly visible in the stunted physique of the children, the physical and mental decay that my lay colleagues commented upon yearly in their reports, and the widespread malnutrition everywhere to be encountered. Little could be done to improve these matters so long as the policy of decentralization was in force, and conditions remained pretty much what they were when I first visited the schools until some years later it was decided to modify that policy, and a modified system of centralization, with boarding hostels, was introduced.

In the Bushveld, where I took precautions, I never contracted malaria, but I had two attacks of the disease in five years. The first I contracted during a railway journey, for all carriages are unscreened and it is impossible always to safeguard oneself against infection by mosquitoes. The second came upon me on the Highveld, after I had been for more than a month away from a malarious area, and was probably the result of being bitten by an infected mosquito in a native hut where I had examined a woman supposed to be ill with typhus. Both attacks were easily and speedily cured by intensive quinine treatment. I may be quite wrong, but my experience is that one may travel and sojourn in the Bushveld throughout the year — I have been there at all seasons — without contracting malaria provided one takes proper precautions. Camping in the open, as I frequently did, was probably a safeguard, for infected mosquitoes are rarely found away from human habitations. As a matter of fact, wayside hotels and unscreened houses are the danger spots, and the vicinity of a Kafir kraal or a group of Kafir huts is probably the most favourable place for inoculation. I eschewed these as much as possible, sometimes at the risk of appearing ungracious when I was pressed to stay for the night at houses where I could see that the anophelines had a grand time. As these pests come out after sunset and before sunrise, one is reasonably secure against their attacks when the sun is up, and can take precautions when they are about. The car was a source of danger when it was left exposed during the night, but I always flicked it out with a towel, after opening the doors, to rout out any insects that had sought shelter in it.

CHAPTER VI

MY FIRST SCHOOL NURSE

THEY called her *Tannie* (Auntie), a familiarity that she primly resented as repugnant to the dignity of her calling.

'Will you please stop them, Sir,' she complained to me when we drove away from her first morning at a Bushveld school. 'They should say "Sister", or if they like they can call me "Nurse".'

'But they call me *Oomie* (little Uncle),' I replied, conscious of the fact that she had heard them doing so and had equally resented it.

'If you let them do it, Sir,' she said, severely, 'they — they'll go on doing it. But it is not dignified. We are professional people . . .'

'Not in the Bushveld, Sister. Don't imagine yourself back in the atmosphere of the "London". You're six thousand miles away from nursing etiquette.'

'Does that really make a difference, Sir?' Her lips closed in a firm line, and I saw that she was hurt. Then, 'Perhaps if you were to say something, Sir. They should be taught to address us properly.'

'According to their lights, they do, Sister. They can't give you a higher title than Auntie. Or would you prefer to be called "that Government woman"?'

'Please don't make fun of it, Sir. They only said that when they were in a paddy, and anyway the children never called me that. But won't you ask them to call me Nurse?'

I said that I would try to induce them to call her Nurse,

but I knew that endeavour on my part to alter the children's style of address would be perfectly futile. 'Auntie' was as much a honorific as 'little Uncle'. It was really a compliment, a proof that the children regarded her as something, someone with whom they could be on a human footing, someone that deserved to be admitted to communal privileges. For the term Nurse, they had to find a colloquial Afrikaans expression, which was difficult and would take time, for the very conception of Nurse was a novelty to which they were as yet totally unaccustomed. They regarded the school nurse as a somewhat fussy woman, whose obvious kindliness was slightly marred by her insistence that they should have clean hands and faces and hair. They did not really think that clean faces and hands and hair mattered very much, but as Auntie laid so much stress on these points, they tried to please her. I remember when the Secretary of the Education Department, Mr. H. S. Scott, who is now Director of Education in Kenya, accompanied me to interview the half score of selected applicants for the post of first school nurse in the Transvaal. The post was a new one. There had never been a school nurse in South Africa, and the advertisement calling for applications aroused interest not only in nursing circles but in much more exalted quarters. One of my first requests to my Department had been for the appointment of such an official, for without the help of a trained school nurse nothing practically useful could be done. We carefully considered the duties and responsibilities that such a pioneer school nurse would have to undertake. My memorandum on the subject explained the position.

'She must be a doubly certificated nurse, possessing both her general nursing certificate and her maternity nursing certificate, and she must have had experience of organizing nursing work. Her standing must therefore be that of a matron, or at least that of a ward sister, or night sister, in a large general hospital. Ultimately she will have under her control a staff of nurses numbering at least thirty. Not only will she have to undertake school nursing for the first eighteen months single-handed, but thereafter she will have to train whatever assistant nurses we may hereafter appoint. She must be a woman of character, of experience, and of considerable ability and initiative. Such a woman one cannot expect to undertake the work, which will be admittedly arduous and exacting, involving many weeks' absence from her home, much travelling, and constant exposure to hardship and inconvenience, for the relatively small wage offered to nurses in hospital service. As chief of the school nursing service she should have a status at least equivalent to that of a woman teacher, certificated, and I suggest that she be given the status of a third class woman principal with a salary equivalent to that now scheduled for that grade, together with service conditions applicable to teachers, so that she may share in the pension benefits and enjoy the same leave privileges ... It is essential, too, that she should be bilingual, for her work will bring her into constant and intimate contact with parents and children who speak Afrikaans as well as with those whose home language is English. In view of the fact that there are very few nurses in this country who have had any experience of school nursing, it is improbable that among the applicants will be found any who possess the requisite training for this branch of nursing work, but provided the other qualifications can be met, there is no reason to anticipate that a suitable nurse will not be able quickly to learn the routine duties and carry out her work to the satisfaction of the Department. . . .'

My Executive agreed to this appointment, and an advertisement was drafted inviting applications under conditions that were much more favourable than those attached to most nursing posts in the country. The terms, indeed, were considered much too favourable, and one immediate result of the advertisement was a strong letter from the Union Department of the Interior, pointing out that the salary we offered was slightly in excess of that paid to matrons of government hospitals, and hinting, plainly, that the Provincial Administration could hardly expect a mere school nurse to be superior to a hospital matron. The Department asked for a modification of the terms of the advertisement, and suggested that its expert advice should be taken in drafting a new invitation, taking it for granted that our original advertisement would be withdrawn.

Fortunately my own Department vigorously supported me in insisting upon our proposals. We pointed out, politely, that the matter was one which concerned the Provincial Administration alone, in which the Central Government had no business to interfere. The advertisement called for an official of the Department of Provincial Education, and primary and secondary education had been handed over to the Provinces. Secondly, we explained what a school nurse was supposed to be and in what way our first school nurse differed from a matron who merely held one certificate. Thirdly, we drew attention to the fact that a matron had free quarters, and free board and lodging, while the school nurse would only get subsistence allowance when actually away from her domicile. The fact that for the first two years she would be constantly travelling, mostly under conditions that demanded much energy and effort, and that her routine work would be far more severe than that of any ordinary nurse, while she would later on be called upon to organize the whole school nursing for the Province and to build up a system for which there was no precedent in the Province, had also to be taken into consideration.

We heard nothing further from Interior.

Many nurses applied for the job. We sorted out the applications, and selected from among them those that seemed to satisfy the requirements demanded from the candidates. Mr. Scott and I spent a busy, harassing morning, in the swelteringly hot old 'Tin Temple' at Johannesburg, then the headquarters of the Rand Inspectorate, in interviewing the selected candidates and assessing their merits. While we were keen to secure the services of a nurse who spoke both official languages, we recognized that nursing training and experience counted for far more than the ability to converse in both English and Dutch (Afrikaans had at that time not yet attained to the dignity of the third official language) and we knew that a capable, energetic woman, such as our first school nurse had to be, would find no great difficulty in mastering the vernacular of the Bushveld.

Of all the candidates, Miss Frances Hassall impressed us most, although, like all the others, she had no experience of school nursing work. She was a doubly certificated nurse, who had obtained her nursing qualifications at the excellent training school of the London Hospital, where she had held the responsible post of Ward Sister and Night Sister. She was an example of the type of nurse who regards nursing as a vocation rather than as a profession. She gave us the impression that she was fully able to undertake and successfully accomplish the difficult task of organizing our school nursing service, and that she was a woman of outstanding character and ability. She knew no Dutch, but diffidently suggested that 'she could learn it, if that is necessary'. We assured her that it was. 'Then I'll promise to do my best to learn it,' she said.

On that promise she was selected, appointed and approved of. For ten years she served the Province zealously and capably, although she never learned to speak Dutch with ease and fluency. I do not think her inability to talk idiomatically ever militated against her usefulness. Sick children need no interpreter to make them aware of the sympathy that radiates from a good nurse. They want no words to assure them that they are being cared for efficiently and tenderly, for illness and suffering know no barriers of dialect or creed. No doubt Miss Hassall would have been more officially efficient if she had been fluently bilingual, as later on all our school nurses were, but her work could hardly have been more successful or her achievement greater than it ultimately proved to be.

Her success as a school nurse was achieved through her personality. She was a woman of great ability, character and enterprise, exacting from her nurses no more than she exacted from herself and often much less, imbued with a devotion for her work that made her indefatigable in her duties. Trained in a school that appreciated and enforced a rigid professional discipline, she set an example of orderliness and system that was invaluable to the development of our nursing organization.

It was this strenuous endeavour to do her duty that led her to spend her evenings, when she had time to spare, in learning Dutch. Unfortunately, she had no knack of learning languages: some people lack that ability; to others it comes easily. She found the simplicities of Afrikaans, its 'gutturalness' as she complained, too much for her. Now Afrikaans is not, properly speaking, a 'guttural' language. It has some of those curious sounds that are known as 'glottic catches', but in comparison with English it is certainly not a language that presents great difficulty in pronunciation.

'Just say, Holy, holy, holy, Lord God of Hosts, Hallelujah, Sister,' I told her, 'and you'll find out what a guttural really is. It is something you can't repeat without straining your diaphragm, and you don't need much breath to say anything in Afrikaans.'

I advised her to pitch her grammars and textbooks aside — she was paying half a guinea a lesson and her books were not cheap — and to trust entirely to what she could pick up from the children. The result was not quite satisfactory. The youngsters taught her words that a lady should not have used, and Sister Hassall was a lady by nature and upbringing. I do not think they purposely and mischievously led her astray; they merely supplied her with words that were in colloquial use, of some of which they themselves were probably not aware of the exact meaning. She was shy of airing her ignorance to me or a brother inspector, and sometimes asked the playground for translations that were readily and frankly given, without, however, the warning that idiom and usage sometimes give to a perfectly correct literal rendering a meaning quite different from that which it ordinarily has.

Once a Principal came to me in great distress.

'Doctor,' he said, sinking his voice to a confidential whisper, 'Sister calls the girls "bitches". They laugh at it, but,' and he shook his head, 'if the parents get to know of it . . .'

'Good heavens,' I said, 'you surely don't imply that she means it?'

'I must say she talks quite kindly,' he admitted, 'not as if she were in a paddy. I heard her myself just now — that's why I came straight to you, Doctor. She was speaking to little Sannie, and she said, "Bitch, how is your daddy getting on?" '

'She meant', I explained solemnly, for the occasion was too serious for levity, 'to say, "Girlie, how's daddy?" She's got hold of the wrong end of the stick. I'll have a word with her.'

'Please, Doctor. I shall be much relieved if it's a mistake. If the parents were to . . .'

When we drove away, after the inspection, I tactfully turned the conversation to linguistics, and asked how she was getting on.

'Quite well, Sir,' she replied serenely. 'The children are so helpful. I often ask them to explain things to me, and they really do help, you know.'

'I'm sure they do. Have you picked up any new words?'

'Now I'll not let you examine me, Sir,' she said, gaily. 'When I'm proficient, I'll pass the Taalbond and get a certificate.'

'That'll be nice. But tell me some of your new words. Do you know the Afrikaans for "boy" and "girl"?'

'That's easy. Boy is *seen* — I can't pronounce it quite rightly yet, but that's it, isn't it?'

'Fairly. But you must sound the "u" in it. *See-un*, and glide over the "see". You'll get it in time, just as you got *huis* right. You know how that word worried you. . . .'

'It did indeed, Sir, but I can pronounce it now — *haize, haize, haize*. There, isn't that right?'

'It'll do. And what's "girl"?'

'*Teef*. That's easy. If you want to be most particularly pleasant, you add "y" to it, and say *teefie* which means a small girl. . . .'

'No, it doesn't, Sister. *Teef* is the word for a female dog. What you want is *dogter* — daughter. Just get that — *dogter*. Or *meisie* — that should be easy enough. But don't ever use *teef*. It's vulgar.'

Her face was a study in horrified contrition. 'I'll never dare go back to that school, Sir,' she said miserably. 'Do you think they'll fancy I did it on purpose, Sir?'

'Of course not. As a matter of fact they'll . . . Never mind about it now. Write me out some of your new words before you use them and I'll tell you if they are correct.'

She did so that evening, and brought me the script when we sat down to dinner at a little wayside hotel. There were a dozen swear words in the vacabulary, set down as polite phrases, and one horribly vulgar expression that indignant and badly brought up small boys occasionally use in the playground. I eliminated those and wrote down appropriate paraphrases more suitable for conversation.

Yet this ignorance of the vernacular did not interfere with her work in class-room or in the playground. She was popular with the children, and, when they had learned to know her, with the parents. Like every school nurse who starts as a pioneer, she had her initiation into the unpleasant side of medical supervision of schools, when angry parents, misunderstanding the object and intention of the work, assume that the primary intention of the nurse is to insult them. In London, when I started my school work, my nurses more than once had such unpleasant experiences. Some were assaulted; many were actively and aggressively opposed by angry and annoyed parents. Miss Hassall managed these unfortunate situations with so much tact that she converted recalcitrant mothers into good friends who afterwards became willing co-operators in the work.

On one occasion a much-annoyed mother came striding across the playground, flourishing a rhinoceros whip or *sjambok* in her right hand and dragging a reluctant little girl along with her left. The Principal, assisting me at the inspection, recognized her through the window, and exclaimed, 'That's Mrs. Douw. She's a holy terror when she's angry, and I am afraid she is now. We must get Sister away. . . .'

We heard Mrs. Douw proclaiming shrilly her intention of horsewhipping that adjectival 'Government woman' who dared to insult her by saying that her child had nits in her hair. She flourished her *sjambok* and the children trailed after her, eager to see results. *Cet âge*, as we all know, *est sans pitié*, and they had had experience of the lady's energetic reprisals. Once, legend states, she had lambasted an unfortunate Principal who had kept her Freddy in for neglecting his home-work when he was wanted to herd the calves. She had torn out the postmistress's ear-rings — together with a portion of the ear lobe — over an unfortunate difference about an unstamped letter. She looked an earnest and unpleasant female. The Principal was visibly disturbed. 'Sister had better hide somewhere,' he whispered to me. 'It's because of the girl's hair, and she is making straight for the office. . . .' My nurse was engaged in preparing a small boy for the inspection. She went on calmly with her work, and gently propelled the child towards me. Then she turned and walked out of the office to meet Mrs. Douw.

'I'm so glad you brought Hessie back,' she said to the astonished woman, who, face to face with the 'Government interference' in person, almost dropped her whip. 'If you'll come with me, I'll show you how to do her hair.'

Mrs. Douw explained to us afterwards. *'Ek het mos nie geweet dat sy so'n mannetjie vrou was nie'* (Really I didn't know she was such a vigorous woman)', she said. 'Would teacher believe it, I couldn't say hardly a word.'

And usually Mrs. Douw never 'fell on her mouth': which is the idiomatic Afrikaans expression for what elsewhere is described as 'being on the back bench when tongues were dealt out'. Here was an instantaneous and signal triumph of character and moral strength over brute force. Sister Hassall went to have coffee with Mrs. Douw afterwards, and that good lady became, later on, one of the most useful members of the voluntary care committee established at that school.

Her interest in and solicitude for the children were as much personal as professional. She shared her sandwiches with them, and went lunchless on many occasions because she thought some of them had more need of food than she. 'They are so dreadfully hungry, Sir,' she explained to me when I expostulated. This habit of hers led to a mild uprising on one occasion. Miss Hassall had brought with her several boiled penguin eggs. Penguin eggs are a great delicacy; they are priced at five shillings a dozen, and the season for them is short. You boil them for twenty minutes and shell them, when you have before you a beautiful transparent lump of jelly in which is embedded the hard yolk. You eat it, if you are wise, with a dash of pepper, a few drops of melted butter and a sprinkling of good wine vinegar, though in the club restaurants it is invariably served with mayonnaise sauce that masks its delicacy. But penguin eggs are not appreciated by everyone, and some people find them too much for their taste. Miss Hassall had some dozens sent her as a present, and brought half a dozen, properly boiled, along in her luncheon basket. That morning we visited a particularly poor school, where the malnutrition among the children was pitiable. During the midday recess, Sister distributed her eggs and sandwiches and contented herself with a cup of tea and a Marie biscuit. To her came the class that her charity had fed, not with gratitude but with reproaches. 'The eggs are all addled, Auntie. The coolie must have cheated you,' chorused the class, for it could not understand that boiled eggs could be anything but marble white. There was no opportunity to explain, for the recipients had thrown the offending eggs into the river, and for long afterwards there were grave doubts about Auntie's astuteness as a housewife. She was much upset, but the incident effectually cured her of her propensity to think that taste is exactly the same everywhere. She had given her best, she had meant it for a treat, and she had not even reserved one egg for me, although she had given a couple to the Principal. But what hurt her most was not that the children did not like penguin eggs, but the supposition that she, the School Nurse, should have given them bad eggs that were not fit to eat.

When that sorry business, the 1914 rebellion, which the Bushveld still talks of as 'an armed protest' plunged much of the Transvaal into misery, Miss Hassall volunteered for ambulance work, and went with me to search for wounded rebels hiding in the bush. They had no need to hide, for the authorities were not, and could not afford to be, vindictive, and notices had been posted promising amnesty to all who surrendered. But fear of reprisals induced many of the men to flee from home and hide in the bush, for the fact that they were wounded implied that they had been on commando and had taken part in some fight against the Government forces. We hunted systematically and found several. One with a festering gunshot wound of the thigh. We brought him home, where his wife indignantly refused to allow anyone 'connected with this iniquitous Government' to cross her doorstep. First aid had been given when the injured man was picked up, but Sister Hassall wished to see him comfortably in bed, to wash him and make him comfortable. She took the indignant woman by the arm and led her aside. I don't know what she said. Neither, I imagine, could understand the other's speech, so that it did not much matter what was spoken. But again her tact and her moral force conquered. The septic leg was fomented, the man was bedded, and his wife brought coffee and biscuits to us waiting outside in the ambulance, and went back to watch the nurse, at first suspiciously, gradually with more assurance, and finally with frank, volubly expressed gratitude.

A few miles farther on at another farm we deposited a youngster, unwounded but shivering with ague. His home was in a sad state of disorder; three of his brothers and sisters were down with malaria. His mother, a vigorous type, took up the same attitude of angry protest against interference by a this-and-that 'Government woman'. She did not mince her words, for in those days feeling against the Government ran high, and anyone who wore anything that looked in the least like a uniform was violently suspect. When we first appeared on the scene it seemed impossible to do anything. The clinical thermometer was flung out of the window, the tablets of quinine hydrochloride were crushed under the angry mother's feet. Miss Hassall's hair was gripped, but she did not lose her presence of mind, and again her personality conquered. Before a quarter of an hour had passed, she was directing the house and the indignant mother, now very much subdued and tearfully apologetic, was serving as a rather unhandy probationer in the sick room.

Four years later came the influenza epidemic, ravaging both High- and Bush-veld, a visitation such as those parts had never before felt. Sister Hassall, as soon as the general closure of schools that a panicky public demanded made it impossible for us to carry on routine inspections, volunteered for nursing service and offered to accompany me in the outlying districts where the need for immediate assistance was very great. For several weeks she worked indefatigably, at high pressure. She was essentially a nursing nurse, and school nursing, however enthusiastically and conscientiously she carried it out, did not satisfy her urge to nurse people who were really sick. Now she had abundant, overflowing opportunity to show how capable and experienced she was in sick nursing, and she was one of the most efficient and admirable sick-room nurses I have ever met. She had that delicate yet sure touch, that swiftly efficient yet never irritating manner of handling helpless patients, and that calm, comforting assurance of pose and mien that impress those who know anything whatever about nursing technique and the subtle differences that may make or mar good nursing.

For weeks we hurried daily from farm to farm, aiding where human aid was possible, bringing in almost moribund patients to the towns where there were hospital facilities, establishing central farm depots for emergency treatment, and doing what could be done to assuage some of the suffering and misery everywhere apparent. Late one afternoon we drove on to the *werf* of a farm. The *werf*, which properly means a yard, is the open space surrounding the homestead. Here the buildings and the neat garden, the tall, full-blossoming jacaranda trees and the tins of flowering geranium on the stoep, were evidence that the place belonged to someone who knew how to care for it. A well-to-do farmer lived here, and the extent of the native quarters showed that there was plenty of labour. But, like all the farms we had visited that day, there was an air of desolation about the place. No human being was to be seen. Sheep roamed in the flower garden; cattle were feeding in the mealie lands. The front door was shut, and the windows were all closed.

We both got down from the car to investigate. A small boy opened the front door when we had repeatedly knocked.

'There's no one about, Uncle,' he told me, dolefully. 'I'm looking after father who's dying, and mother died this morning.'

Sister Hassall took his hand in hers — he was a very small boy and looked forlorn though he bore himself like a little man. 'Come along,' she said briskly, 'I daresay things are not *quite* as bad as all that.'

Fortunately they were not. The mother was sleeping. The father, in another room, was gasping for breath, struggling with that horrible congestion of the lungs that was a feature of that epidemic, his face already tinged with the magenta colour that was so deadly significant. The boy was the only nurse they had had for three days; the natives were all down with the disease, and three corpses were lying in the huts for no one could bury them. I left Miss Hassall in the house, and motored for assistance, not easily to be obtained. When I came back, hours later, she had produced semblance of order out of the chaos. The three white patients — for the boy, too, had been put to bed — had been made comfortable; hot water was available; she had visited the huts and induced two of the natives, more or less convalescent, and two others, who were not sick at all but who had lain down with the rest out of sheer sympathy or fright, to act as orderlies and undertakers. It was mainly due to her assiduous care and nursing that all three white patients recovered, and that the mortality among the natives on that farm was not higher.

These are a few instances out of many. Our odyssey through those outlying districts was made under the most trying conditions, for there were few helpers, and for the most part it was impossible to save many patients who were obviously dying when we reached them. No medicine or drug had the slightest effect on the disease, though good nursing and good treatment, husbanding strength nearly exhausted, helping hearts that laboured despairingly against heavy odds, and easing discomfort and pain by suitable means, saved many patients. No nurse ever worked harder, under more trying conditions, than did Miss Hassall. The conditions were really appalling, for the epidemic raged with astonishing virulence, and medical and nursing assistance could only be adequately given in the larger urban centres. The rural districts had to struggle as best they could. Miss Hassall's success was in many ways an eye-opener to me, for it proved how much could be done by one devoted nurse working with zeal and sympathy, to save what could be salvaged.

My work with her during those dreadful weeks was

salutary to me in another way, for she was a constant reminder that one must never lose patience with the sick. For years I had been out of touch with acute sickness, such as one sees it at the bedside; my work had lain with the defective. Here, suddenly, I was called upon to minister to men and women acutely ill, or, what was infinitely worse, acutely apprehensive. Where one saw around one so much real suffering, that pleaded loudly for help, one could be pardoned for losing patience with the cowards who imagined themselves sick and who more loudly clamoured for immediate relief. Miss Hassall dealt with these latter as sympathetically and as ably as she did with the real sick though I confess that I sometimes forgot that fear is, after all, a disease and was far less kind than I should have been. We came home one night, tired out after fifteen hours' work, and were just drinking a cup of tea before going to our rooms, when there was an urgent summons to attend a dying patient. It was the local pastor, who was said to have been ailing for some days. His son came to fetch us in his father's car and explained that there was no other medical help available. We went and saw the patient, almost pulseless and cyanotic, lying gasping on the sofa of his study. He whispered, 'Am I going to die, Doctor?' as soon as I bent over him, and was obviously much agitated. But he had no fever and his condition was certainly not due to influenza. We gave him some brandy and water, which he took under protest, stating, whisperingly, that he was a teetotaller, but it restored him amazingly. His symptoms puzzled me. They were evidently due to some acute poisoning, but I could not think of anything likely to produce the same effects in the same conditions. So I asked him what he had taken.

'Nothing at all, Doctor,' he said, his voice now much stronger. 'I have only swallowed two aspirin tablets every half hour as a preventative against this awful influenza.'

Altogether he had taken the contents of two bottles of tablets, and he was suffering from aspirin poisoning. He had never visited his sick parishioners at the bedside; he had stood outside on the stoep with his handkerchief over his mouth and nose, and comforted them from there. Sheer funk was the cause of his indisposition. I am afraid he found me very unsympathetic, but Sister Hassall put him to bed and he afterwards told me that she was a most understanding Christian-like woman. I quite agree, but in certain circumstances it is difficult to feel charitable even when one is in duty bound to be kind.

Nurse Hassall went back to her routine school inspection when the flare of the epidemic had subsided. She had had experience of district nursing under conditions almost unparalleled in the history of district nursing in South Africa, but she did not even ask for leave. There was too much to do in the schools. She interested herself in the establishment of our first School Clinic at Johannesburg. Until her death she was the superintendent of the Clinic, and the best work that it has done was under her supervision and management. Administrative matters kept her at headquarters, and she had no time to go afield into the Bushveld. When we had a regular staff of school nurses, one or two of these replaced her in the malarious districts, although she occasionally accompanied Dr. Cleaver, my woman assistant Medical Inspector of Schools, on her trips to outlying districts.

Her hard work aged and weakened her. As a nurse she knew, or could at least suspect, that she was no longer a well woman. But, like so many of us who are, from professional experience and by training and education, well aware what the premonitory signs of disease mean, she was disinclined to admit that meaning. That is a lamentable fact of which every doctor is cognizant — the curious dislike which we have to face dreadful possibilities of diagnosis, the equally curious aversion we have to finding out what is the matter with us, and the desire to temporize when, as we preach to the laity, it is imperatively necessary to consult a doctor at once. She died of cancer that she had permitted to develop too far for surgical skill to avail her. There is a plaque to her memory on the walls of the School Clinic. The new generation has forgotten her. But I like to imagine that the thousands of Bushveld children to whom she was the first school nurse whom they had ever seen, a Government woman who quaintly misused words when she spoke in the Taal, who had shared her sandwiches with them and had bearded angry Mrs. Douws in the sanctity of their homes, still remember her with some gratitude for the honest health work that she did with so much self-sacrificing zeal.

CHAPTER VII

PUBLIC ENEMY NUMBER TWO

NEXT to malaria, the greatest tribulation of the Bushveld comes from a small worm, so insignificant that few people have ever seen it. Like the fever, whose history stretches into the far remote past, the symptoms caused by this worm have been known from very early times. The Egyptian Pharaohs suffered from it, for the eggs of the worm have actually been found in their mummies. It causes the disease known as redwater or 'endemic haematuria', from which Napoleon's troops suffered severely on the expedition into Egypt. No one then knew what caused the disease. It remained for a German scientist, Bilharz, who worked at Cairo in 1851, to discover that the symptoms were caused by a parasite, a small worm which he described. To-day the disease is known by his name, bilharziasis, but the worm that was formerly known as *Bilharzia haematobium* has now been rechristened *Schistosoma haematobium*. In Egypt, and also in South Africa, there are two species of this worm, *S. haematobium*, and *S. mansoni*. A third species occurs in Japan, where it causes Katayama fever and is known as *S. japonicum*.

The schistosomes are tiny worms that lay small oval-shaped eggs. From such eggs emerge an embryo or infant with a waggly tail, which science calls a miracidium. This miracidium has to enter a mollusc, generally a water-snail, before it can develop further. In the snail it grows into a small bag, known as a sporocyst, from which in time come numbers of small wriggly bodies with forked tails — for all the world like the imaginary manikins Spallanzani drew of human sperm bodies — that escape into the water and infect anyone who bathes in it. They pierce through the skin of the bather and get into the blood, reaching the lungs by way of the large vessels, finally settling in the large liver vein, where they breed out into worms, reaching full maturity after a few weeks. Their sharply pointed eggs are borne by the blood-stream and reach the kidneys, which excrete them through the urine. On their way out they scratch the lining of the ureters and colour the urine red with extravasated blood. Hence the name 'redwater'.

Like all parasitic worms in man, the schistosome worms produce symptoms by poisoning, but they also cause debility through loss of blood and sometimes grave disturbance by interfering with the function of the kidney machinery. Generally the victim knows what ails him; the blood in the urine is ocular evidence of the disease. But long before that sign appears his constitution is undermined and his health suffers.

My Bushveld school-children were gravely infested with schistosomes. It was easy enough to diagnose the condition. A few drops of urine spread on a glass slide and shoved under the low power of the microscope showed the characteristic oval-shaped eggs with its terminal spine of *S. haematobium*. The more dangerous form, *S. mansoni*, has a lateral spine, and I never encountered it in the Bushveld, although it probably also exists there. But the terminal-spined species was common enough, both among boys and girls, though the boys, who swam more frequently in infested pools, showed by far the higher incidence of the disease. Most of the little patients had a characteristic appearance — a peculiarly anaemic, pallid complexion, not to be mistaken for the sallow cachexia of chronic malaria, with sunken eyes and widely dilated pupils. One could diagnose the disease from the smooth velvety skin, with a tendency to weal formation on the slightest pressure, and the intense fatigue that it caused. Where malaria co-existed in the child, the malaria, of course, overshadowed the bilharzia, but where the latter alone was present, the absence of an enlarged spleen, of intermittent fever, and of the peculiar malarial cachexia made diagnosis easy, and examination of the urine could always clinch it by the evidence of the eggs.

So great was its incidence among the boys of some schools that it was almost impossible for the teacher to get any effective response from his pupils. They were far too fatigued to do school-work. The disease caused such an intoxication that their whole system suffered under it. Frequent headaches, sickness, lassitude, cramps in the limbs, disturbances of vision, and intense weakness were the main symptoms complained of, and as everyone knew that these were the concomitants of redwater, and that redwater was incurable, no great attention was paid to them. At that time the disease was really incurable. No one had yet discovered a drug or a method of treatment that killed and expelled the worms, but in time the pests seemed to die without any medical help and the sufferer recovered. No one ever, so people told me, died of redwater. That was not strictly true. The disease has been known to cause death by bleeding, by clots blocking the ureters and causing uraemia, by producing stone in the kidney and bladder, and by so weakening the patient that he easily succumbed to an infection which normally he would just as easily have overcome. But as in the case of malaria, this immunity from sudden and dramatic death accounted for the apathetic way in which the Bushveld regarded redwater. It was, like malaria, an inevitable disease; the boys were bound to get it, and it was best that they should get it early in life and get over it as quickly as possible. That I found was the general attitude of both parents and teachers.

We knew little about its causation then. But enough was known to be dogmatic on two points. One was that the intermediate host of the parasite was a water-snail, and that infection was through contaminated water; the other was that a sufferer from the disease, excreting ova, was likely to spread the disease. With regard to the first point, the common notion was that one got the disease by drinking water — an unlikely method of infection for the wriggly bodies with forked tails, known as cercariae, are killed by any acid fluid, and the gastric secretion is acid. A little experience taught one that the usual mode of infection was through the skin, and not, as another popular theory supposed, through the natural openings of the body. This theory was widely prevalent, and the natives protected the opening of the urethra by wearing a covering over it when they bathed. Experiments proved that the cercariae wriggled their way straight through the skin. When one bathed in infected water, one felt, on coming out, a tingling sensation and the skin was reddened. When the snails were proved to be the intermediate hosts of the parasite, the rivers and bathing-pools were systematically searched for these molluscs, and I spent many hours in dissecting our finds and trying to discover what species of snail was the chief offender. There were two kinds in the Bushveld streams that nearly always held sporocysts, and where these were found we could take some precautionary measures. But the parents never, I believe, quite credited the hypothesis that the snails were responsible for redwater, and the children thought so little of the disease that they were quite prepared to swim in pools that had been placed out of bounds. Swimming was about the only recreation that they could indulge in, and none of them was grateful to the teacher for pointing out that such enjoyment might be dangerous to health.

We were further handicapped by our want of an effective remedy against the disease. I do not think I ever experimented with so many different drugs as I did to find a cure for bilharzia. More than a hundred different remedies were mentioned in the textbooks and the articles that dealt with schistosomiasis. Most were drugs that had an effect upon the urinary secretion, and among those turpentine, which was dangerous, and the citrates, which were not more useful than cinnamon or hot lemonade, were thought to be the most active. I found them absolutely useless. Then from India came information that in *Cassea beriana*, a yellow flowered shrub, one had a good remedy against the disease. So we tried cassea, again with most disappointing results. All I could recommend to teachers and parents was that prevention was the ideal to be aimed at, but as I could not definitely say what methods of prevention, beyond the absolute prohibition to bathe in pools or streams whose border sedges held snails, should be tried, that advice was not of much practical use. My Department published a pamphlet on the disease, describing the life-history of the parasite so far as it was then known, and laying stress on the fact that the intermediate hosts were the snails. We suggested that the school should select a suitable swimming pool, preferably one in which the water was not stagnant, and clear it of all weeds, and periodically free it from all snails, and that the pupils should bathe nowhere else. That was done at a few schools with encouraging results, but it was plain that we could not conquer bilharzia in that way.

The treatment of children actually suffering from the disease was what doctors call 'symptomatic treatment'. The layman is under the impression that medical science has 'cures' for all sorts of illnesses. As a matter of fact we have cures for very few. We can eradicate the germs of syphilis by giving the sufferer arsenic or mercury; we can cure a patient who has tape-worm by giving him male fern extract to swallow; we can certainly and with very little trouble cure malaria by giving quinine, anthrax by injecting salvarsan, some cases of poisoning by promptly administering an antidote that makes the poison harmless. Then we speak of a 'specific' drug or method of treatment, which in ninety-nine cases out of a hundred can be relied on to produce the effect we want. But for most other diseases — and there are many hundreds of them — we have no such specific cure. We have no specific against a common cold, against pneumonia, against measles or mumps or heart disease, or eczema or cataract or small-pox. The layman jeers at us for this — 'Bah, he cannot even cure a common cold', forgetting that a common cold would not be common unless it were the most baffling and complicated of all diseases. But we do, as a matter of fact, cure many diseases by judicious treatment of their symptoms, thereby helping the sufferer to husband his own resources, the *vis medicatrix naturae* that is in each of us, and through such help to fight the disease and to overcome it. We do that first by good nursing, which is three-quarters of every battle against disease, and secondly by easing strain on bodily organs by drugs and treatment that relieves such

128

strain. In pneumonia, for instance, we make the patient comfortable, reduce his temperature (when necessary) by sponging, relieve his pain and his cough (again when necessary, for sometimes it is good for him to cough) by drugs that are known to give him relief, and help his heart and his lungs by giving good food, oxygen and adrenaline. That is symptomatic treatment, and it is the treatment most often and most advantageously used when we have no certain and infallible specific remedy against the disease.

In bilharzia, then, we treated the school children symptomatically. They were given tonics, the best of which was good food with an abundance of fats and vegetables, plenty to drink and adequate rest. They were allowed to rest when they felt fatigued, and some were taken to holiday camps from which they returned much benefited but still passing blood in their water. Then came the news that Christopherson at Cairo had found in antimony a drug that really and truly 'cured' bilharziasis. We tried it, and the results were so encouraging that many children were treated by the new method. To-day antimony is universally used in the treatment of redwater, which is now as curable by it as malaria is by quinine. The drug is given by injection, and a total of ten to fifteen grains of antimony is needed to kill the worms and prevent a relapse. It is not a home remedy, for antimony is a poison, but must be given by the doctor; and the patient must be watched. The Education Department has now established 'bilharzia camps' where the doctor attends and treats many school children who suffer from the disease. These camps have been very successful, and a continuation of this policy of mass treatment will undoubtedly, in time, rid the Bushveld schools of bilharziasis. The disease will, however, always remain endemic in the Transvaal. Every stream that harbours water-snails is an infected stream, and washing in or merely wading through its water is sufficient to infect a human being. Preventive measures aim at ridding the pools of snails, or, as an accessory, killing the wriggly cercariae by poisoning the water with small amounts of copper sulphate. Neither measure can be relied upon, and so long as there are swimming-pools, small boys will be infected with the fluke-worm. But they need no longer remain infected. In antimony we have a sure, a specific, cure of the disease, a remedy that can be relied on to kill the worm and rid the small patient of all his symptoms, leaving good food and rest and recuperation to bring him back to normal health.

The story of bilharzia contains a lesson that should be taken to heart. It tells how a disease, which on my first acquaintance with it seemed hopelessly incurable, whose effects in causing national degeneration were so evident that one stood aghast and despairing in contemplating them, and which had so profoundly impressed all who came into contact with it that it was an inescapable evil, was conquered by the discovery of a specific against it. The regular use of that specific has changed a large percentage of Bushveld children from sickly weaklings into healthy, hale pupils who can benefit by the class teaching they receive. To the medical man, still struggling with many diseases for which he knows no cure, these facts are encouraging. They enliven the hope that he constantly cherishes that science will ultimately find more such specifics, and that even what we consider to-day an incurable disease will in time be ranked with bilharziasis and malaria as both preventable and curable.

CHAPTER VIII

THE OLD PRESIDENT

They talk of him with affection, tempered with respect and a tinge of awe. For Bushveld men knew him as one of themselves, forthright, haggardly honest with the honesty that presupposes an equality of aim and objective, even if both be to get the better of an opponent. They could assess him at their own primitive values, which acknowledge and admit no differentiation by place or position.

History has not yet placed him, for he has been unfortunate, like Cecil Rhodes, in his biographers. Not, perhaps, quite so unlucky as his great sometime contemporary, he has been able to give, bowdlerized, his own version of things that happened. But his real life, such as the Bushveld men know it to have been, is still hidden from the world, which has only heard the political side of it, and that as if through a gramophone, just as it has seen that broad flat face distorted alike by the stained glass which would make him a martyred saint and the coarse flashlight that would picture him as a cunning and obstinate old cuss ineffectively trying to drag his beloved Republic away from the appalling chaos of progress and culture. In sober truth he had much akin to these men of the Bushveld, for he had their lovableness, their rough charm and that completely logical sense which makes them so absurdly out of date against a background of mining company shares and mine headgears.

When he was still *de facto* and *de jure* President, though an exile in the little villa on the Maliebaan at Utrecht, I was privileged to spend six hours in his company, the first and last time that I met him. When I speak to the Bushveld people of that interview, they nod their heads and blow out giant clouds of smoke. Not enviously, for there was no special honour or favouritism in chatting with President in the old days. Most of them have been so privileged. They could come, any morning when they happened to be at Pretoria, to the low, ungainly dwelling-house opposite the equally ugly church with its imitation Flemish spire, and pass an agreeable, if somewhat taciturn hour with him on the stoep, drinking many cups of coffee and smoking many pipes, telling him of what happened far away from the railway line, and getting in return hints about high diplomacy. Everyone could do that — the veriest stranger could walk up and accost President. They tell the story of the young advocate — now one of the most-respected and best-known men in the Union — who dressed up for the occasion and came in a carriage, halting before the stoep on which the old man sat in the favourite chair, and bowing, with his hat in his hand, at every yard of his advance into the presence. The President bowed in return, once, as courtesy demanded, and went on smoking, presuming that the visitor would stride forward and take the vacant chair at his side. But the young man was too respectful; he continued bowing, scraping the ground with his hat. 'Mighty,' said the President, whose expletives were colloquial rather than resentful, 'if you do that again, man, I shall spit upon your head!'

That is a true version. The other story is less well authenticated. At an interview with another great man, so it runs, the old man was received in a drawing-room floored with a thick Turkey carpet. He smoked, and the other great man nodded to a flunkey who brought forward a magnificent cuspidor, one of those relics of Batavian metal that nowadays fetch preposterously high prices at auction. It was cautiously shoved next to the President, who edged away from it. He continued smoking. The cuspidor was again pushed into prominence, and again he pushed his chair backwards. And went on smoking. A third time the cuspidor was forced towards him, and then he lost patience. 'If you don't take that silver thing away,' he told the footman, 'I shall spit into it.'

Less well authenticated, I say, for Paul Kruger was not a boor. He had hobnobbed with potentates and governors from early manhood onwards, and however direct and forcible he might have been — and undoubtedly was — on occasion, he was not capable of gaffes like that.

This Bushveld was his territory, his hunting ground, the scene of his early triumphs, the place, too, where he suffered his first and perhaps most poignant defeats. It was the last that he saw of his country when he left it, an exile. In the Rustenburg districts he built his first church, so absorbed in the masoning that he worked until he had made the walls so high that he could not climb out before he had unpicked part of the bond. Here he lost his finger, in an affray with his own gun; here, for many years he served his people as a humble commandant and field cornet. Like van Riebeeck, the first Governor of the Cape, he had power and authority before he had reached his thirtieth year. When sixteen years old he was a field cornet; when seventeen he was married, losing his wife and his first child before he was legally of age. Physical and mental prowess, in a community where the former quality was too common not to be appreciated and the latter too valuable to be ignored, gained him a standing that he never lost, but strengthened as time went on until, finally, he became the acknowledged communal leader. Of his physical feats the Bushveld people still tell wonderful tales — how he outpaced a native runner, how he fought and beat the strong man of his commando, how he tirelessly rode for days when on duty, even when racked by that curse of the Lowveld, malaria.

I had found him past his prime, a broken, saddened old man, reflecting with resignation that he could take no part in the negotiations that were even then shaping the peace that was made at Vereeniging. His health, undermined by fever, had broken down; his eyes were weakened, and though he was allowed to fondle and fill his pipe he was never permitted to smoke it. Yet he passed the tobacco to me, brusquely telling me, 'Smoke, son, smoke. They won't let me, but I like to see a pipe going'. Then we talked, he animatedly, I listening, all on the understanding that nothing was to be divulged to the newspapers. In his big chair he slumped down, a huge body and a large head with the face much crinkled and the full lips sagging. One could hardly imagine him as an athlete, as a skilful leader of men with whom personality counted for far more than descent or cultural acquirements. Yet on occasion there flashed into his eyes a look of strength, and his low voice vibrated with the remnants of a passionate soul that could still soar and suffer and was not ashamed to show feeling. A deputation of German students came in, bearing bouquets of wild violets, and he listened impassively to a long harangue on freedom and their sympathy with the Boers. 'Tell them I thank them,' he asked the interpreter to translate, and when the deputation had left, he threw the violets on the table, replaced his top hat on the carpet, and resumed where he had left off, 'As I was saying, son . . .'

Here, in his own territory, the remembrance of that interview thirteen years before came back to me when I found myself among men who had known him all their lives, to whom he was an outstanding figure whose massive proportions overshadowed every other competitor for local fame. He was not yet a legend, for his reputation was too recent to be encrusted with fables although there are plenty of apocryphal tales about him. Whatever men might think of the manner in which he had managed the political affairs of his country, there are few — and those for the greater part knew him in his official capacity rather than in private life — who think of him with feelings of rancour. Time has softened the very harsh asperities of party politics that were so frequent when Chief Justice and Commandant-General dared oppose him at his elections. Men speak of him now with reverence, not without pity indeed, but with a softness like that with which we recollect something of which we are proud, even though our pride may be chequered with regret for lost opportunities. For the Transvaal, for the Bushveld especially, he remains the patriarch who earned men's respect by his long years of public service and their appreciation by his rugged massive personality.

That physical robustness is figured by van Wouw's statue of him at Pretoria, a stiff and unimaginative representation of the man. At Rustenburg there is a better bronze, which shows him in a more likable mood, but the best statue of him is that modelled by his own grandson, which has not yet found an abiding place anywhere in the country over which he presided for half a hundred years.

Tourists visit his old home, which is now a museum, dedicated to his relics, restored out of recognition of what it was in his own time. The two marble lions that Barney Barnato gave him — an incongruous gift to one who had killed so many of these big cats — are still in position on the stoep, but there is little else that recalls the days when he used to sit there and give counsel, always practical, sometimes even Solomonic (for he was a shrewd old fellow and knew humanity far better than anyone who has since succeeded him in the limelight) to his visitors from the Bushveld. It was there that he talked to Cecil Rhodes, who found his stolidity and imperturbability too wearying to be long endured. Yet both men had something in common, and if they had been, the one less impatient and eager for immediate results, the other less suspiciously watchful for the imagined attempt to outwit him, the course of South African history might have been altered for better or worse.

Stephanus Johannes Paulus Kruger was typical of the Bushveld, but he was not a product of the Bushveld. Indeed, the Bushveld cannot produce such men, for types like that are laid down in the mother's womb, and time and education can add but little to what was there fashioned and stamped. He was born in the old Cape Colony, of German immigrant stock, and in the Dutch Reformed Church vestry at Cradock practically all that we know about his birth stands recorded. 'The child born October 1825 and christened on March 19, 1826, Stephanus Johannes Paulus; father Casper Jan Hendrik Kruger; mother Elsie Francina Styn; godfathers and godmothers Carel Petrus van Wyk; Hester Hendrina Catharina Styn, Jan Hendrik Steenkamp, Catharina Maria Syun; field cornet A Pretorius.' Yet there is a tradition, still very much alive, that makes his birthday to be the tenth of October, on which date its anniversary is still kept in the Transvaal.

So are the facts of history distorted.

He followed with his people in the wake of the first Trekkers. He gained his baptism of hardship and privation

136

at an early age, among people who regarded physical courage higher than its moral counterpart. From boyhood no one questioned his bravery, but it was the bravery of the flesh rather than of the spirit, a hardihood that made him daring, at peril of his life, but which was not strong enough to overcome the depression of malaria from which, like all his fellow-citizens in the early days of the settlement, he chronically suffered. His letters, lately collected from the forgotten files of the archives as a labour of homage and love by Dr. Engelbrecht, are curious reading, now abounding in optimism, now tumbling into something akin to despondency. I have before me a diary, kept by one constantly in his company during the anxious days following Majuba, when he fought, perhaps more strenuously and more persuasively than ever before or after, for the ideals that he cherished. It recounts how in the evenings, coming back from a tiresome interchange with Sir Hercules Robinson and Sir Henry de Villiers, he used to throw himself into an animated discussion of men's muscles and qualities of physical resistance of pain and fatigue. 'He told me', says the diarist, who afterwards became one of his most trusted officials though often differing in opinion from him, 'how in his adolescence he had matched himself in running against the fleetest natives and outpaced them by sheer determination not to give in and by dogged pertinacity of purpose.' How he had competed with giants in his own community in a game that even in his staid Presidential days he still had a hankering for, the pinching trial which consists in seeing how hard a man will allow himself to be pinched on the soft inner thigh flesh without wincing. These feats gained him notoriety, but it was not that reputation of endurance that made him leader and beloved. It was his knowledge of his fellow-men, his native shrewdness and fixity of aim, and his tried and tested capacity to give of his best, in personal service, to his country and his people. These qualities were his passport to fame, the hall-marks of a character so many faceted — with some of the facets highly polished and others, again, as rough and opaque as the surface of newly splitten quartz — that those who have written about him have been dazzled by the reflections from shining smoothness or irritated by the unevenness of the cleft matrix. In time some historical lapidary will deal with him correctly, showing that the unpolished facets were capable of as much splendour as those that shone so brightly. But to do that, fairly and justly, one will have to take into consideration his temperament and constitution, and make allowance for the aura of mysticism that sometimes came upon him, and forced him to retire, like the anchorites of the desert, into the caves of the Magaliesbergen to commune in silence with himself until he shook off that dreadful melancholy and despondency that are the aftermath of intermittent fever. For no historian of the Transvaal can afford to neglect the influence of disease and climate upon the men who played a conspicuous part in shaping that history. It may be that future historians of South Africa as a whole will have to pay equal attention to these factors to be just in apportioning blame or praise to those who are yet to play their parts.

To the Bushveld, to the Transvaal, the old President remains the chief, the central figure of a stage so crowded with events and episodes that no one can as yet take an objective view of it. The play is too recent, the personality of the actors is too fresh in the memory, and the fall of the curtain on the first act caused such poignant grief to those who had shared the old President's aspirations and believed in his ideals, that it is impossible for them to see the affair in its proper perspective. They discuss it with restraint. When they talk of the old President, as they often do, on the stoep or round the camp-fire, they like to dwell on their personal relations with him, to think of him as one of themselves, a rock-staunch upholder of custom where custom seemed good, but not necessarily one opposed to all neoteric influences nor a despiser of what was vernal simply because it was not patinated by tradition. Nor, if one follows his career closely and with some sympathy, can the latter accusation, though often enough made, be sustained against him. He was responsible for many innovations, some of which were resented by his contemporaries whom he had to cajole into acquiescence and never succeeded in persuading into co-operation. Like all strong men, in whom the capacities of leadership are well developed, he was sensitive to a degree that aroused a suspicion of vacillation. His old Secretary of State, Dr. Leyds, can tell many stories to illustrate this innate delicacy of feeling, this fine susceptibility and consideration for what even an opponent felt. Here are two of them.

'When he found that tobacco smoke was distasteful to me, that the fumes from his short pipe worried my eyes, he always put his pipe aside when I came into the room. "I can go on afterwards, Doctor, when we have done",' he would say.

'The one occasion when I saw him on horseback was late one night. I had gone over to his house, and we had discussed a matter in which I had urged a certain policy with which he was not in agreement. I argued and pleaded, but he stuck to his point, and we parted with some feeling of mutual friction between us. I went back to my house, at the other end of the town. Late that night — it was raining and cold — I was awakened and told that the President was waiting for me. I went out, and found him sitting on horseback in the street. "I have come, Doctor," he said, "to tell you that I think, after reflection, that you were right and that I was wrong. I should not like you to wait until morning before I told you, so I had to come down.'

I myself experienced some of this consideration at my one and only interview with him. We had been chatting for several hours, I only too eager to listen, although the interview had been granted on the distinct understanding that I was not to make use of anything he said for the paper I represented, he, I can only suppose, liking to discuss the past with a youngster who displayed a sympathetic and curious interest in what he said. Both of us forgot that the luncheon hour was long past, though one of his secretaries, the late Mr. van Boeschoten, kept running in and out of the room, every advance of his being stayed by the old man's brusque exclamation, 'Wait, Boeschoten, wait! I have much to tell this young man.' Suddenly he halted in the middle of a sentence, and took up his pipe, which he was not allowed to smoke but merely to fondle. 'You must go and get something to eat,' he said. 'Young fellows must not be starved. Go and come back and we can continue.' I protested that I did not need luncheon. 'You yourself, President . . .' but he broke in, 'I am an old man. I take my cup of soup. But you — go, or I shall . . .' and his thumb and forefinger intimated how severely he would pinch out any disobedience to authority.

I have kept the notes I made afterwards, when that interview was fresh in my memory. They are interesting, and would have been doubly so at that time, when the negotiations that led up to the Vereeniging pact were pending, for he spoke freely, paying me the honour of trusting my word that, though a journalist, I would not publish anything he said. I have been told — I was told then by his entourage — that he was a broken old man, not to be compared to what he had been in his prime, but I saw little in him that betrayed senility, except the physical signs of advancing age, the slight tremor of the fingers, the fatigued slant of the head, and the weakened eyesight for which he had to use stronger glasses. His voice was sonorous and powerful, his vocabulary rich and forceful, his talk vivacious and interspersed with homely similes that reminded me of conversations with my father's elders. He was a rugged, rough-hewn primitive old gentleman, with an innate courtesy and a certain indefinable charm of mannerism that were singularly attractive.

That is the memory of him that abides with me. I found that my Bushveld community also remembered him in that light. Something of the admiration that Milton felt for Cromwell, and expressed so eloquently in the 'Second Defence', they felt for him, though they could hardly put it in such well-sounding words. If they knew it they would probably agree that Milton's praise, exaggerated as it may sound, can fittingly be applied to the old President.

Of his person, his looks, his characteristics as an individual their recollection is not very clear, for it has become tinged by legend and hearsay. Those who were privileged to be in close contact with him can tell you, more or less accurately, what he looked like, but no two descriptions wholly agree, although one could fabricate a reasonably passable passport composite picture from both. All who knew him were impressed by his large, blunt-featured face, with the small, slanting eyes and the heavy chin. Most of those who worked with and under him will tell you that he had a massive head, but heads are difficult to measure without callipers, and

Kruger's head was neither abnormally broad nor uncommonly large. Round the camp-fire, one night, the talk turned on heads, and someone instanced Rhodes as a person who had an unusually large head. I knew the statement was wrong, for I had met Rhodes frequently, talked to him, listened to him, ridden with him on the mountain-slope, and had never taken him to be a massive headed man, though his shock of unruly hair might have given that impression at a fleeting glance. Among my personal archives I have a copy of the original note made by Sir Sinclair Stevenson on the morning of March 27th, 1902, at the cottage at Muizenberg, where Rhodes's body lay, prepared for the post-mortem examination. It reads: 'Preliminary examination on the late Cecil Rhodes made at 11 a.m. at Muizenberg in the presence of Drs. Jameson, Smartt and Stevenson, Dr. Syfret operating and Sir Charles Metcalf and Mr. Walton present in the house at the time. Head measurements; frontal, ear to ear, $11\frac{3}{4}$ inches; root of nose to occipital protuberance; $9\frac{1}{2}$ inches; circumference of head $22\frac{1}{2}$ inches.' The real post-mortem examination, it is interesting to note, took place six and a half hours after death at 12.30 on the same day at Groot Schuur, and Sir Sinclair Stevenson's notes are equally clear and explanatory. In the old President's case, too, a careful necropsy was carried out, and the report of it exists, in the writing of his personal medical attendant, Dr. Heymans, now the Union's representative at Rome. It shows that the last decade of his life must have been one of physical suffering that weakened a constitution, which though naturally robust, had been much undermined by malaria. His future biographers will have to take that disease into account in considering his character and temperament if they wish to do justice to his greatness and to deal equally fairly with his faults.

CHAPTER IX

THE MABOLEL

THE great Limpopo rises in the hills of the western Transvaal, a little muddied stream that runs north-west for some distance before it becomes a real river. Then it bends eastwards and continues evenly in its course to the Indian Ocean, gathering on its way the waters from great tributary rivers like the Sand, the Palala and the Magalakwen. Before the last pours its waters into the main stream, the Limpopo is a large sluggishly flowing river, full of many deep holes, ramparted on both sides, but more especially on the Transvaal side, by high banks of alluvium and an outer, empty moat that is again banked by sand-dunes. In flood time the river overflows the first escarpment and its waters enter the parallel moat, so that it is a broad, white-crested mass of turbulent water, vastly different from the placidly flowing and rather attenuated stream that one sees in winter time.

There are many large 'holes' in the Limpopo, popularly known as 'hippoholes' (*seekoeigate*), parts of the river where a dike of limestone or dolomite has dammed up the water so as to make a lakelike expanse, usually a hundred yards wide and a couple of hundred yards long. But there are some holes that are much larger. Among them the Mabolel is the chief and from the naturalist's point of view by far the most interesting.

I saw it first in late winter, when the river was low, and the surrounding veld garbed in its leafless coating of russet and grey, with clumps of chrome-coloured aloes to relieve the monotony of these neutral tints. The approach to it is through wild and desolate country, sparsely populated by white men, but more frequented by natives, whose little groups of huts, 'towns' or '*stads*' as the Bushveld calls them, appeared now and then set in an environment of badly cultivated mealie lands. Although the area had been well surveyed and many farms were demarcated, few settlers were to be found there. On the map one saw many farms, but they were for the most part tenantless. Some of them bore quaint names, for the surveyors had to mark their maps somehow and gave fancy names to the farms they triangulated. The largest farm, now almost a small settlement, was 'Beauty', although it has no special features that make it more scenically striking than its neighbours. Another was called 'Kiss-me-quick-and-go my honey', an allusion to an old ditty popular when Johannesburg was more blatantly a mining camp than it is to-day; such names as 'Three buffaloes shot here', 'Fear of leopards', 'Lions' scrapings' and 'Mother-of-pearl' occurred, and there were many native names, probably far more apposite than these coinages of itinerant land surveyors. Adjoining the river were the 'pont farms', originally given out as free grants by the Republican Government in the early 'eighties to burghers who undertook to look after the drifts or crossings, at one of which there was originally a pont.

The country through which one passed on the way to the Mabolel was typically Bushveld. On both sides of the road, within a distance of some yards from the road itself, extended the bush, a dense half-jungle of thorn and other trees with a carpet of high grass, sometimes so high that when one walked in it one could not see over the haulms. It was easy to lose oneself in that scrub, and I took great care never to wander off the road unless I had a native guide with me. My brother Inspectors had insisted on the danger of wandering away from the road, and had related tales, gruesome tales, of travellers who had been lost in the scrub and had died there of thirst and starvation. The stories, when I heard them first in the comforting atmosphere of the club, had seemed to me to be slightly exaggerated, but when I realized how easy it was to lose all sense of direction when one walked into the bush, I had less difficulty in believing them. The attraction of that immense park on both sides of the road, especially to one who wished to study the bird life with which it abounded, was strong, and it was fatally facile to yield to it and to enter a tangle where after a few minutes

la diritta via era smarrita

for like Dante's wood, the bush is indeed 'selvaggia ed aspra e forte'.

I blazed my way carefully on entering it, and took compass bearings, but never ventured far into it alone. With a native guide I had no qualms, for the native seems to have an instinctive sense of direction, and picks his way with almost arrogant assurance for miles through the scrub. The white man finds it difficult to imitate him. In my Bush-veld experience I know of two cases in which white children were lost. The one case was that of a little girl who had wandered away from an encampment, and had been almost immediately missed. Although search was made for her, she could not be found. For several days search parties scoured the bush for miles from the spot where she had last been seen, but they failed to find her. Ten days afterwards her body was discovered, on top of a rock not very far from the camp. She had climbed up and probably lain down on the cool rock surface to get some palliation for her frightful thirst, for she had stripped off her clothes and when her body was found her head was resting on the little bundle. A tiny, dried-up, shrivelled little body it was, desiccated by the sun that for days had scorched down upon it and coloured it so darkly that one had some difficulty in recognizing it as that of a white child. She must have wandered distractedly for days, circling back on her tracks, within easy reach of help but unable to find it, and one's imagination shudders at the thought of what she must have suffered before she fell into that coma of exhaustion that ended her tragedy.

The second case was that of a schoolboy who had similarly disappeared into the bush and had wandered many miles away from the spot where he had entered the scrub. After three days' search he was found, exhausted and delirious, naked and much scratched by the thorns through which he had struggled, and fortunately recovered without any lasting ill effects. The psychical shock of such an experience must leave its mark upon whoever has gone through it, and the fact that this boy had stripped himself naked — probably in the attempt to assuage his intolerable thirst — and was delirious when found, showed how great must have been the distress that he endured, physically and mentally, during the time that he was lost in the bush.

These tragedies were formerly more common, and the Bushveld can tell of many. In some cases the bodies of the lost were found; in others the men or women vanished and left no trace. One of the most curious cases of the latter kind was that of a young man who went into the scrub to fetch back a strayed ox; he took with him his gun, and left the camp early in the afternoon. The ox came back, but the young man did not, and although the bush was systematically searched, by search parties that had the help of expert native trackers, his body was never found. Weeks afterwards his gun was discovered, not far from the spot where he had left the open road. It is difficult to account for such complete disappearance, for there is some concensus that wild animals do not touch the dead bodies of those lost in the bush. Even where the body is eaten by wild dogs some remains of it are usually found. A possible explanation is that this young man was attacked and carried away by a vagrant crocodile. That crocodiles wander far from their haunts in the river pools, sometimes being found miles away from water, seems an undoubted fact, and it is not unreasonable to suggest that they may catch their prey on such excursions and drag them to their water-holes for leisurely consumption as is their manner of feeding. In the Mabolel country, indeed, crocodiles are credited with amazing cunning and cruelty. The big pools hold many, and all are aggressive. One specimen, known as 'King of the Fishes' has become almost a legend in that region. He was supposed to have killed and eaten more than a score of natives and at least two white men, and many efforts were made to kill him. His invariable custom was to swim quietly submerged in the water, and approach his victims while they were drinking or washing, swipe them into the water with one tremendous blow of his tail, and drag them off to his lair, a muddy, sedge-surrounded hole at the extreme eastern edge of the biggest pool. The bodies of his victims were never recovered. Many traps were laid for the 'King' but he always managed to evade them, and his audacity and cunning became bywords among the natives who regarded him with great fear tinged by some reverence and respect. They invested him with miraculous powers, and sturdily believed that he could travel miles on moonlight nights to hunt for prey on the veld.

He was finally shot and his carcass measured twenty-three feet in length and ten feet and some inches in girth.

The road to the Mabolel crosses the Magalakwen river by a deep, sandy drift through which the car has to be assisted by a crowd of native women and children. The river itself is splendidly deep, with well-wooded banks. Here the trees are tall, imposing, much wreathed in a tangle of a cucumber-like gourd whose golden-yellow fruits glisten against the dark foliage. Flocks of parakeets inhabit these riverside trees, and when they are clamouring and chattering one can scarcely hear the shouts of exasperation made by the troops of blue monkeys that compete with them in raucous dissonance. After the drift there is a stretch of almost level country, thickly wooded, through which the road winds with frequent turns and twists. The roads in the Bushveld, though narrow, are generally well surfaced, soft and even in winter time which is the dry season, but apt in summer, when it has rained, to become muddy and slushy. One has to look out for projecting stumps in the middle of the road, and at times to take precautions against the central ridge, the 'middleman', which is such an annoying feature of country roads everywhere in the Union, but nowhere more danger-ous than in the Bushveld.

I found a school some miles away from the Mabolel, set in the heart of the malarious area. The children were, as usual, malnourished and weak, showing a spleen percentage of well over 60. Most of them came from the 'pont farms' around the Mabolel, and were able to give me information about the best way to reach the pools. A brother Inspector was at the school, for the ordinary term inspection which he had just completed, and we arranged to visit the river the same evening and to camp on the bank.

On the way we stopped at one of the 'pont farms'. It belonged to the descendants of settlers who had 'trekked' out of the old Cape Colony more than fifty years ago, and there were signs that the original owners had cultivated it with some system, though now it was clear that it was no longer well farmed. There was a grove of orange trees, all seedlings, planted many years ago, loaded with fruit. The Transvaal orange, which is extensively cultivated in the Bushveld, is either a navel or a 'Valentia late', beautiful to look at but not to be compared in flavour with the seedling orange. Here the seedlings were luscious bags of well-flavoured juice, and their large size and thin skins enhanced their excellence. In the garden were several old-fashioned fruit trees, mulberries, quinces, clingstone peaches, and almonds, the last already in bud.

My brother Inspector, who knew his Bushveld people intimately, for he had worked that circuit for several years, told me that this particular farm was owned by a family whose men-folk had all been killed by lions. That, at least, was the tradition. 'You must humour the old lady,' he said, 'for, as Kipling remarks, that is their doom and pride. Her husband was killed by a lion not so very long ago, and his father and uncle were both mauled, fatally, by lions. That is as far as I have been able to trace the tradition, but doubtless, if you are interested, she will tell you more about it.'

He left me at the farm while he went on in his car to arrange our riverside camp. I strolled back to the house with the young man who had done the honours of the garden and treated me to the seedlings. He was the youngest son of the family, had long left school, and much wanted to go to some town where he could be employed in a garage. My car attracted him powerfully, for it was of a different make from that of my brother Inspector's which was so far the only motor car he had seen. He was a powerfully built, upstanding youngster, the type that would have made a good policeman, slow witted but reliable. There are many such in the Bushveld. The pity of it is that nothing is done for them. John could not leave the farm; he was his mother's manager, but it was evident from his talk that his heart was not in the business of farming, and that he hankered after the fleshpots of the town.

The long low house, more solidly built than most houses in the Bushveld, stood under some spreading *mopani* trees, whose far-flung branches overshadowed the stoep. In the *voorhuis* or dining-room-lounge combined, the principal room, the old lady waited for us, with the coffee and biscuits that are always ready for the visitor. She was a sad-faced old lady, lean and wiry, placid of voice, with a homely dignity such as most of the Bushveld women have. On the floor and on the leather-thong seated couch were lion skins; on the wall hung two large lion skins. There were lion skins everywhere about the house.

'Yes, Doctor,' she said, when I mentioned what my brother Inspector had told me, 'the Inspector is right. We have a feud with the lions. My people have killed hundreds of the vermin, and the beasts have killed some of my men-folk. My husband and my two sons have been killed by the lions, and I have a presentiment that Johnny, too, will be killed by a lion.'

'Don't fret, ma,' said Johnny, and in an aside to me, 'Ma has killed a lion herself, but she is still frightened of them.'

'Have you many lions hereabouts?' I asked, for on our way we had neither heard nor seen a lion.

'Not this season, Doctor,' she replied. 'There's too much food for them across the river. But there are a few couples, and belike Doctor will hear them to-night. They growled last night, but far away.'

She told me much about lions, for her experience of them was large and varied. Her own kill had been made on the farm itself, when a lioness had calmly walked towards the garden, and she had snatched up a rifle and shot the beast. Its skin was one of those on the floor. Her husband had been killed by a lion when he was on a game-shooting expedition in a neighbouring district. The two sons, elder brothers of Johnny, had been killed on neighbouring farms where they had followed up a wounded lion. From what she told me I judged that they had been incautious and rash, but I did not like to say so.

'A lion,' she said, 'is the most cunning and the most villainous of all vermin, Doctor. There are those that call it the king of beasts, but I've never held that opinion. An elephant, yes, or a buffalo ... but a lion, no! Doctor may think I am prejudiced, but I don't like them. I should not mind if they were all destroyed. Then we shall be well rid of them.'

She took me to see her vegetable garden, nicely laid out and well stocked. Adjacent to it was a large pond, its surface covered with greenish growth from between which peeped some flowers of the water hawthorn.

'We had more of it once,' she said. 'We brought some from the old Colony, but it does not accord with our climate here. It wants winter rain, and our rain comes in summer.'

I noticed an old mother Muscovy duck, carefully shepherding her brood of ten ducklings away from the water. Whenever the ducklings swerved towards the pond, the mother intercepted them and poked them with her bill, sometimes even using her wing to urge them to remain on dry land. It was something new to me, and I was interested. 'It's the water tortoises, Doctor,' said my hostess. 'They bite off the duckling's legs as soon as they swim, and that's why the old duck won't let them go in.' She showed me the water tortoises. Three of them, each as large as a dinner plate, lay wallowing in the mud. I remarked that they were good eating. 'Eating?' she said, scornfully. 'Who'd eat a water tortoise? You must think we are uncivilized here, Doctor, if you imagine that we would eat such rubbish.'

A few moments later I had another revelation. In a corner of the garden a young duiker buck was tethered to a pole. The animal was quietly browsing on the grass within length of his rope, and was quite tame. I ventured to ask why it was tied up. Usually tame buck were allowed the freedom of garden and house, and never strayed into the veld, or if they did they invariably came back to the homestead.

'That's because he eats the ducklings, Doctor,' said the old lady. 'He's eaten four of them already, and if we let him loose he'll try and gobble up the rest.'

I said good-bye to her, and drove back to where we had arranged our camp for the night. A year later I heard that Johnny was in hospital, badly mauled by a lion. He had tracked the animal and shot it, and he and his dogs had followed it up into the river reeds — a singularly reckless way of doing things. The lion had sprung out and the lad had missed his shot and tried to climb a nearby thorn tree, but the lion had followed him and severely ripped the flesh from both thighs. The natives and the dogs had succeeded in beating off the lion, but the boy was so badly injured that he died in hospital from septic poisoning.

My brother Inspector had selected a camp site within a few hundred yards of the Mabolel itself. It was a picturesque grass-grown glade, ringed by huge monkey thorns, sixty feet tall, and within sight of a bend of the river where the banks were heavily studded with giant sedges. From the glade ran footpaths to the riverside, or what I took to be footpaths. Our cars we parked behind the trees, and the natives had already laid out our kit, rigged up the mosquito nets and made our beds. I started off to look at the Mabolel.

The Mabolel is a huge pool, which in the late afternoon, with the sun glinting upon its wide waters, seemed much larger than it really was. I judged it to be about half a mile long and about two hundred yards wide. Where the bank shelved down to it was a ledge of smooth rock, past which the water flowed slowly eastwards down the river. On the opposite bank was another similar shelf of rock. 'Don't go too near the water,' my brother Inspector warned me, 'and look out for crocodiles.' I did not see any crocodiles, but in the pool itself were two hippopotami, playing with a calf, and disporting themselves in full view of the audience. They seemed quite tame, but a hundred or more yards of water separated them from us, and there was no reason why they should have been frightened. The beautiful pool — for the Mabolel is really beautiful — was overhung in part along the sides by the high trees — karree, wild fig, thorns of various kinds, wild orange and others whose names I could only guess at, and the well-trodden paths down the sides showed that this was a favourite drinking-place for game. It was a paradise for the ornithologist, for the trees gave shelter to many different kinds of birds; on the sand banks in the river itself, plovers and waders strutted, and on the surface of the water far away were water birds which I could not identify without a glass. I determined to spend at least a day in such ideal surroundings, an arrangement that I knew would suit my colleague who wanted a day's game shooting. There was plenty of game in the neighbourhood, for on our way to the river we had passed large troops of wildebeest and zebra, seen a herd of hartebeest, flushed many coveys of partridges, and come across such diverse fauna as kudu, reed buck, impala, and duiker, while the clacking call all around us meant that guinea fowl were somewhere near by.

Before sunset I improvised a rod and tried some fishing in the pool. Although the tackle was rough and ready, I caught half a dozen river mackerel within as many minutes; the water was teeming with fish. I had no proper spoonbait for tiger fish, but the Mabolel is probably one of the best spots for tiger fishing in the Province, and tiger fishing is the best that the river angler can ask for. The tiger fish is a fighter, more valiant and impulsive than any salmon. But its interlocking teeth bite through any fishing-line, and to fish for it one needs strong piano-wire traces.

When we came back to the camping-spot, the sun had already set, in a splendour of gold and green and red, and our evening meal had been prepared. We sat round the camp-fire and chatted, and when the moon rose retired under our mosquito nets. After the excitement and fatigue of the day it was easy to fall asleep, and when my companion shook me by the arm I thought it was morning and time to get up. But the moon was still overhead; it could scarcely be later than eleven.

'Just listen,' said my colleague, with a shade of anxiety in his voice. I had no need to strain my ears. From what seemed a few yards beyond where we were lying came the sound of

horses neighing — a short, curt neigh, that had something
of a grunt in it, to me an utterly novel sound that I could
not place.

'I am afraid its the hippos,' said my companion. 'We're
directly in their track. It was stupid of me to select this
place. You see, they are very inquisitive, and the moon's
shining on our car lamps — there, look. They'll come and
investigate, and they may damage the cars. Let's get out of
this.'

We got up and went to the cars, where the natives were
sleeping. They too had heard the noise and were much
disturbed. 'It's the sea-cows, Baas,' they whispered. 'If
Baas were to make a noise . . . shoot, anything that might
scare them . . .'

'It's more likely to enrage them,' said my colleague, 'but
you might try throwing stones into the sedge. And we'll
turn on the lights.'

We did. As soon as the beam of light played on the
sedges, they became violently agitated, and from them sprang
several large shapes that plunged with a splash into the
river. But we deemed it wiser to move a few hundred yards
farther away from the glade, well outside the tracks that led
from the river. The next morning we found that the animals
had been feeding within fifty yards of our sleeping-place; the
young sedges had been pulled up and their soft ends chewed
off and the 'spoor' of the hippos could be plainly seen on the
sand.

Before sunrise I settled down on a soft sandy spot, hidden
by a large clump of reeds, to watch life on the Mabolel. On
the opposite bank were all kinds of buck, that had evidently
been drinking and were now browsing peacefully. In the
branches of the trees the monkeys were already chattering,

and flocks of parakeets flew shrilling from tree to tree. The call of partridge and guinea fowl was incessant, clamorously repeated, and the finches and chatterers were swarming round their nests, adding to the din. I watched a crocodile quietly emerging from the water and sidling up the flat rocks, where he lay in the sunshine while the egrets came and picked his teeth for him. They seemed to have no fear of the animal and at times half their bodies disappeared between his lazily opened jaws. A 'lazy snake' (python) glided into the water on my side of the river, quite close to me, and swam across, its head held well above the surface, and vanished in the underwood. Darters and herons — among the latter the lovely black heron (*Melanophoyx ardesiaca*) was conspicuous by his inveterate habit of shading his fishing-place with his wings to counteract the reflection from the water — tufted umbres and several kinds of duck, appeared on the scene. I counted forty different kinds of water birds, and as many land species, and overhead circled a couple of sea eagles. But the sun was high up before the hippos appeared. Then they suddenly popped up in the middle of the pool, the family of the day before with their infant, and two others. The pool held half a dozen, and with the exception of the one baby all were full grown. They too allowed the egrets to settle on their backs and to attend to their teeth.

I have rarely found a better observation spot than that sandy nook on the banks of the Mabolel, and in the Transvaal there is, I believe, no place that holds more variety of natural interest. I visited it again on more than one occasion, and always saw something new, something that was worth noting. But for many years now that district has been plagued by drought. The vast troops of wildebeest and zebras have quitted it to seek sustenance in the less harried eastern parts of the Province. The landscape itself has changed. The big ugly boabab trees (*Adansonia digitata*) alone remain in their pristine grotesqueness, immense minatory excrescences against the skyline that defy drought and tempest alike.

The tragedy of the Bushveld is the inconstancy of its seasons. They are either super-abundantly bountiful or pitifully lean. For a succession of years the summer rainfall may be copious enough to make the veld a verdant park, so exquisitely laden with lush grass that one feels it to be the ideal ranching country. Then may come year after year, first with a little rain that suffices to sprout the grass but does not suffice to prevent it withering after a few weeks, then with no rain, or with merely local showers. In the years that I knew it, the western Bushveld had good seasons; I saw it at its best, a lovely country, densely grassed and wooded, swarming with game and birds and insect life because there was so much food. Now it is almost a desert, and the Mabolel has shrunk to half its size, while its surroundings are denuded of most of the glory that I saw. In the eastern Bushveld the years of drought have not been so severe. There is still plenty of game, and the veld in summer is still park-like. But nothing there can compare with the Mabolel country in its prime, and I like to recall the days that I spent watching life on that big, silent pool, and heard the legend of the family at feud with the lions.

South Africa already has twenty-two game preserves. The best known of these, the large and much advertised Sabi Preserve, known as the Kruger National Park, it owes to the efforts of an already forgotten South African. Mr. Charles Marais, who died a few years ago, was one of the first Government land surveyors appointed by the old Republican Government. In his tours through the eastern Bushveld, he was struck by the variety of game and the ruthless extermination that was going on in practically all districts. He told me how he had come to Pretoria, after a six months' trek in the Sabi, determined to interest the old President in the matter. 'One man,' he said, 'assured me that he had shot two hundred kudu, merely for the sake of the skins, which fetched some small price when sold to the stores at Volksrust. One morning I strolled over to the old President's house. He was sitting on the stoep, and called for coffee. "How did you find the people, Marais?" he asked me. "The people are all right, President," I answered, "if they would only not poach so much." "What do you mean?" he asked, in his quick, domineering manner. "They shoot the State's property, President." "What does it matter if they do, Marais? There's plenty of wild things. If they didn't shoot them, the lions would get the game. Do you know what a lion eats every year?" "No, I don't, President, but I don't think the lions destroy half so much as the poachers do." "That is because you know nothing whatever about lions. A lion eats when he is hungry and he is hungry every six days. So he kills sixty head of game every year. And how many lions do you think there are in the Transvaal?" "I have no idea, President. Let us say twenty thousand." "Many more, man, many more. But twenty thousand and sixty head of game for each — come, you are better at ciphering than I — after all that's your business. How many's that?" "A hundred and twenty thousand, President." "Well, do you think the people destroy more than that?" "But President, the game is an asset of the State. We have more kinds of game in the Republic than they have anywhere in Africa, and I've just seen a man who boasts that he shot 200 of one of the rare kinds — kudus, President. . . ." "Who is the fellow, Marais?"

I told him, and he blew out a cloud of smoke. "That man is a boaster," he said. "I know him. I don't believe a word of it. Well, Marais?" I suggested that he should make an effort to preserve the game ... I talked for an hour and told him what I had seen. "I must go down to the Raadsaal," he said at last getting up from his seat. "I'll see what I can do. If things are as you say. . . .""

'The old man was as good as his word,' Mr. Marais said when he told me the story. 'He couldn't stop poaching — its still going on; it'll never be stopped until the public realizes what an evil it is — but he did attempt to preserve the game.'

The whole Bushveld area is subject to periodical droughts that make conservative farming a farce. Under such conditions there is no hope for its community, unless the present methods are altered and a system of small proprietors who can farm on small plots in selected areas is introduced. The rest of the country might very well be made a huge game reserve. That is one way of looking at the matter, and it is a way that many people, who have experience of the Transvaal, favour. But there is another aspect — the more national aspect — of preserving the integrity of the community that now struggles to maintain the old traditions of rural settlement. That old tradition is of value to white South Africa. How valuable, in comparison with game preservation, time will show.

CHAPTER X

BUSHVELD BIRDS

THE bird lover, visiting the Bushveld for the first time, may be pardoned if he quotes Ferdinand in *The Tempest* and exclaims

> Let me live here ever
> So rare a wonder . . .
> Makes this place Paradise.

And on better acquaintance, the liking grows, for nowhere in the wide continent of Africa are the conditions for the study of bird life more convenient, plentiful, or advantageous. That is because in the first place there is such diversity of environment, and secondly because the opportunities for observing birds at close quarters and in their natural habitat are so frequent. There is bird life all around. There is no need to build a shelter and patiently to lie in wait for hours for the chance to spy, through strong prismatic glasses, upon a bird family likely to resent such close inquisition. Here the birds give you the freedom of their haunts. Like the little tree squirrels, that manicure and toilet themselves brazenly in close propinquity to you, they welcome your attentions, so long as you are peaceably disposed. Only when you become aggressive, are you no longer tolerable to them, and they fly away reproachfully, some with screams and squacks of splendid indignation, others with shrill, plaintive cries like those that have been betrayed by their best friends.

Where there are so many species, and so great a diversity of form, colour, kind and conduct, it is difficult to assign to any one the palm for interest and attractiveness. My first favourite still holds pride of place with me, for a more captivating bird it would be hard to find even among so many that are charming in their habits and behaviour. It is the crimson-breasted bush shrike, *Laniarius atrococcineus* of Burchell. Ornithologists are so unstable in their nomenclature that it is quite likely that my old friend's name has been changed since the time when I first made his acquaintance, but these vagaries of classification need not prevent anyone from recognizing him, for he is one of the most conspicuous of all the bush shrikes. All are handsome, gaudily but harmoniously coloured birds. The crimson breast is clothed in velvety black, so intensely dark that it shines in the sunlight, as glossy and iridescent as the blackest jet. All but the breast and neck, which are a brilliant crimson, in startling contrast to the polished sable of the rest. I first saw this bird sitting on a low bush, playing idly with a grasshopper that it had caught. Its sheer gorgeousness of colouring, set off by the slate grey of its environment, made one gasp with admiration. When I came to know it better, I found that its vivid hue was not, as is sometimes the case, a compensation for a drab, uninteresting bird personality but a dress worthy of so intelligent and attractive a bird as its owner. It is by no means a shy bird. Like all bush shrikes it possesses a fund of curiosity that amounts to impertinence, and with the least encouragement it becomes friendly, without, however, too blind a trust in humanity. With such encouragement one that favoured my camp, hopped into the motor car to investigate the bright cup of a thermos flask that had attracted its attention, and liked the thing so much that it flew away and came back with its mate to resume its investigations. Both male and female have the same gaudy garb, but the young are a fulvous grey, and only get their glossiness when they mature. Two such young ones were bought from an itinerant bird seller (those were the days when bird snaring was common and when one could purchase for as many pennies half a dozen Bushveld birds caught by liming) and placed for the night in an aviary with some fifty small birds, mostly of the finch tribe. They sulked on their perch and refused all nourishment, though enticed by minced fresh meat and an assortment of crickets and grasshoppers. The next morning that aviary was strewn with the disbrained corpses of half of its inhabitants, while the survivors shuddered in a bunch in the farthest corner. The young shrikes had indulged to the full in their sadistic taste during the early hours of morning and pecked open the skulls of their fellow-prisoners, or of as many of them as they could get at, and had eaten the brains for breakfast.

By themselves they were attractive birds that could even, on occasions when they seemed to be in a sportive mood, indulge in the rudiments of song, a low-toned trebly repeated call, quite unlike that uttered by their green-coloured cousins, and dance upon their perches in a kind of ritual dance. One of their cousins, the Bakbakiri bush shrike, is quite a good dancer, and those who are fortunate enough to catch him at his courting, which is usually done in the strict privacy of a bush clearing, can count on as fine an exhibition of terpsichorean art as any bird can show. Like some of the more sombre-coloured of his genus, too, the crimson-breasted bush shrike is pugnacious and over-bearing, bullying his own species that gives in to him, and

harrying the smaller birds in the bush. But when he displays
the better side of himself, and flits about in his gaudy livery
of sable and crimson, you forget his faults out of sheer
admiration for his beauty.

Two adult — or adolescent — representatives were almost
tame companions in one of my first bush camps. They were
both males, and kept company as attachedly as ever did
Damon and Pythias, resenting the attentions of the female
shrikes that wished to play with them. Their own friendship
was sufficient for them, and held an element of homosexuality that was as interesting as it was sometimes ludi-
crous to witness. They sat side by side on a swaying branch
and shamelessly petted one another. Then one would fly
down and pounce upon a beetle or grasshopper and carry
it, still alive and struggling, to his friend, who would jerk
it up and down until there was no further reaction to any
stimulus that could be applied, when both would proceed
to spike it on a sharp thorn.

The constant observation of these two bush shrikes,
confirmed the conclusion I had already drawn from the
habits of the ubiquitous grey-backed shrike, whose custom
of impaling some of its victims has been explained on
various theories. Wherever there is a barbed wire fence in
the Bushveld, one comes across dead and dried small
animals and insects, neatly transfixed by one of the barbs.
That is the work of the grey-backed shrike, which is said
to be a cruel and spiteful bird. I have never been able to
convince myself that he spikes his catches for the mere sake
of watching them writhing in agony. As a matter of fact,
most of them are quite dead when impaled. My native
constable assured me that they were hung up to dry, so
that the bird might have a stock of provision for an empty

day. On the Bushveld one cannot talk of a 'rainy' day, for on such rare days in summer there is plenty to eat for every bird that is insectivorous. But I have never seen the shrikes return to their so-called larder for the purpose of eating anything that it held. They alight quite close to a dried lizard or frog, and take no notice of it whatever. The supposition that they impale what they catch as a solemn warning is too absurd to be entertained. There must be some other reason.

The most gorgeous bird I saw in the Bushveld, I saw but once, and realized immediately that I had seen a splendid rarity. It was a ground thrush, a Pitta (*P. angolensis* Vieill.) usually regarded as inhabiting the tropical regions of Africa, but certainly coming much farther south than Pretoria. It is a most harmonious and at the same time striking combination of glossy green, white, buff, carmine and blue, in which the colours merge so sharply that every twist and turn of the bird's body presents you with a new spectrum. A very kaleidoscope of a bird, so astoundingly variegated in hue that its garishness appears almost pathological.

Colour is still one of Nature's mysteries, and the colour of birds, more especially such outrageous combinations as the Pitta presents, can no more be explained by the current theories than can the sadistic habits of the shrikes. Where both male and female have vivid colouring, there is nothing to be said for the sex-attraction theory. Where in the spring the male bird's colour becomes more sharply defined — as in the finches, the doves, and the parrots — the sex-attraction theory seems plausible, until one finds that males stripped of their finery mate just as easily as their more fortunate fellows, while some of the latter never get a wife and do not seem to want one. Protective colouring is usually pattern colouring, such as we learned to employ during the war. At its best it is seen in Hartlaub's quail, in the small ground partridge, and among the owls. The vivid colours of the Pitta, the love-birds, the shrikes, the hyacinthine finches and many others, are certainly not protective; they are in sharp contrast, usually, to the birds' surroundings. Yet they may be protective in another sense. We know little, as yet, about the influence of humidity and light rays upon the glandular system of birds, and it is quite possible that these glaring colours are protectors against the intensity of the light rays. All feather colouring is dependent either upon pigmentation or upon refraction. Pigmentation is due to the presence in the structure of the feathers themselves of definite coloured chemical compounds, of which the chief are eumelanin, which gives rise to black and brown, and the lipochromes — zoonerythrin, which causes a red coloration and zooxanthin which gives a yellow tinge. Variations of black, red, yellow and brown, and in a few birds, like the turacos or bush lories, whose wing and breast feathers contain the green pigment turacoverdin or the copper compound turacin, are therefore essentially caused by chemical substances. Such colours are painted on or in the feathers, which may be said to be dyed. In some cases the colour may be washed out when the feathers are steeped in alkalies. The majority of bird colours — green, blue, white, grey and their variations — are not caused by definite pigments but owe their intensity, and more especially their iridescence and sheen, to the structural conditions of the feathers that refract or break up the light rays falling upon the plumage. 'Structural colouring' accounts for the splendour of the sugar birds, humming birds, and perhaps also the pittas. It also accounts for many of the colour changes that the plumage undergoes with the change of season. The magnificent 'courting' coat of the scarlet-bishop finch is not, as was formerly supposed, a different dress assumed for the purpose of attracting the female, but merely the shedding of a coat of feathers that prevented the winter sun from irradiating the lower range of feathers and through refraction giving the bird its glossy scarlet colouring.

Recently Goernitz has shown that feather colouring is to a large extent dependent upon climatic conditions, and the researches of this ornithologist have considerably modified our views on mimicry, protective colouring and natural selection. Von Lucanus, in his review of the various theories of bird colouring, sums up the present position fairly when he remarks:

'Wir sehen immer wieder, wie schwer die Frage nach der Entstehung der Faerbung des Gefieders ist, und dass die frueheren Anschauungen, die alles so leicht und einfach zu erklaeren schienen, heute nicht mehr bestehen koennen, nachdem sie durch das rastlose Forschen der Wissenschaft ueberholt wurden.'

The unceasing researches of science have not, however, elucidated the problem, and we still do not know why some of our Bushveld birds possess such startling, even provoking, colours. The attraction theory I have long ago given up. Birds, like human beings, find sexual attraction more likely in form than in colouring. The bizarre ruffs and ear feathers of some species are obviously secondary sexual characters, and one can understand that they exert an attraction. But decolorized, or dyed or disguised male birds mate as readily with responsive females as do those in their so-called 'courting plumage'. There are species in which the female is much more gaudily coloured than the male; there are many species, again, in which both male and female are indistinguishable by colouring alone. It seems much more likely that the colouring is of physiological, rather than of psychical importance, in that it protects the body glands against the disturbing actinic rays. There is no great mystery about the part that pigment, especially blood pigment, plays in our own bodies. Even the writers of thrillers have made use of the now well-known facts about haematoporphyrin, while the importance of pigmentation in preventing fatigue, heatstroke, and irritation of the skin is generally acknowledged. The distribution of vivid colouring on the bird's body favours the assumption that such colouring is either stimulative or protective, for the most conspicuous patches of colour are usually over areas below which lie the most important nerves or hormone secreting glands. This assumption does not contradict the view that colouring may be of sexual importance, for the stronger colouring seen in some birds during the mating season may be directly stimulative to the sex glands.

The fact that birds in tropical areas are generally more vivid in colouring than those in less humid and colder parts, strengthens the supposition that climate and solar radiation are factors of considerable importance in determining the degree and distribution of colouring. There is no justification for assuming that brightly coloured birds are less easily seen in an environment of tropical foliage than the dun coloured. The glossy starlings, that are among the most most beautifully coloured birds of the Bushveld, are easily seen, even when they perch in the shadows; the gaudily coloured blue jays, the green and blue parrots, and the multi-coloured finches are just as easily discernible against whatever background they choose. The suggestion that birds nesting in cavities are strikingly coloured because they have no reason to disguise themselves, scarcely needs consideration, for there are many species — the dun-coloured toucans, for example — that are cavity-nesting, and there are bright coloured species like the green pigeons that nest in the open. Equally invalid is the argument that vivid colouring — or rather particularly brightly coloured patches — may serve as a guide for stragglers of the same species. Von Lucanus lays stress on this point in attempting to explain the gaudily coloured patches on some species of ducks. These patches are completely submerged when the birds are swimming, but are clearly visible in flight, and it is supposed that they guide errant followers when the main flock leaves its hunting-grounds for the roosting-places. With gregarious birds that is a possibility, were it not for the fact that there is considerable doubt whether or not birds can distinguish colours with the same ease that human beings can. Experiments with captive birds have not cleared up this point satisfactorily. Black and white, when in sharp contrast, can certainly be distinguished; greens and blues also. But yellow and red appear to be more or less the same to most birds, and they seem to take no notice if these colours are interchanged.

Frank Chapman, basing his opinion on bird studies on Barro Colorado, suggests that bright colours are found more commonly on birds that favour high levels, while the more sober-coloured ones are ground frequenters, but he admits that the pittas are striking exceptions to this rule. 'The relation between colour and habitat in these species (the brilliantly coloured ones)', he remarks, 'would seem to support William Beebe's suggestion that bright colours are associated with bright light, and that consequently the most brilliantly coloured birds inhabit the forest canopy where the studies of Allee show that the average light intensity is twenty-five times greater than that in the shade on the ground.' He discusses the effects of humidity upon bird colouring, and devotes several paragraphs to colour protection, but comes to the final conclusion that in general it is habit, and not colour, that is protective — a conclusion with which most field naturalists who are acquainted with birds in tropical or subtropical conditions will probably agree.

The mystery of bird colouring becomes, if the old theories are right, more perplexing when one sees brilliantly coloured species living in community with exceptionally dull ones. The environment of both is exactly the same; to some extent the habits of the two are similar. On a large thorn tree I found the nest of the social weaver, the size of a small hayrick. It had many separate entrances, and some hundreds of its owners who were sharing their quarters with a flock of gorgeously coloured love-birds. The carmine and green of the love-birds contrasted strongly against the yellow grey grass of which the nest was composed, while the drab colours of the finches blended so well with the grass that I had difficulty in detecting a bird that sat quietly in the entrance of one of the galleries and made no attempt to fly away although I stood within a few feet of it. Equally interesting and inexplicable is the presence of pairs of brightly coloured finches in a flock of inconspicuously clad members of a different species, and their nesting in the same bush. The variations in plumage colour that several of the most brightly coloured species show when they are placed on diets containing abundance of mineral salts or an addition of certain drugs, also strongly suggest that colouring — which is, after all, nothing but a skin reaction as the feathers are epidermal structures — is dependent on metabolic changes.

When I started my work in the Bushveld very few birds were protected by law. The privileged ones were the game birds, the plovers, the secretary bird, and the blue jays, and a few others. The rest were, as it were, outlawed, and a thriving trade was done by fanciers who exported thousands of the smaller varieties to Europe and America. One such exporter had his collectors all over the Bushveld, and at his depot many thousands of birds were to be seen in the aviaries. The Bushveld attitude towards birds was not aggressively hostile but certainly not friendly. The farmers guffawed at the suggestion that birds were useful, and pointed to their crops which, they said, were annually much damaged by birds. They admitted that a few species were not only harmless but actively helpful. The secretary bird destroyed snakes, and the 'locust birds' had been known to stay a flight of these destructive insects. But bird catching and bird killing were favourite sports among the Bushveld children, who ruthlessly snared, limed and shot birds, not always for the sake of preserving the gardens, nor for the pot, but simply because small boys in an environment where birds are so plentiful, find it exceedingly difficult to desist from such practices. Once a party of three youngsters sold me forty-two small birds for a six-pence. They had spent the day at the riverside, and I met them on their return. Their bag consisted of seven Namaqua doves (*Oena capensis*), five grenadier waxbills (*Ureginthus granatinus*), ten blue-breasted waxbills (*U. cyanogaster*) and twenty-four common waxbills (*Estrelda astrild*).

The last they had captured in a way that was new to me. They had tied pieces of sacking to the two ends of a heavy stick which was thrown into the middle of a flock of the little birds, just when they were rising from the grass. The stick killed one or two, but half a dozen were brought down by the sacking and the children ran up and secured them. They told me that this was by no means an exceptional bag; at times they had caught over two hundred small birds. Some they ate, most they killed, and a few they sold. A sixpence was more to them than forty-six birds; they could buy almost a quarter of a pound of sweets with it at the coolie shop.

Such an attitude towards birds does not imply wanton cruelty. The Bushveld dwellers are not more cruel than similarly situated communities in other parts of the world. Their outlook was simply that of people who had not learned to associate the useful with the beautiful, and who were essentially utilitarian. Now the legislature has stepped in and forbidden the capture, sale and export of all South African birds. No longer can thousands of Bushveld finches be exported to Hamburg, where they will probably find a domicile much more pleasant than they had at home. No longer will the Bushveld children be permitted to catch *Oena capensis* and exchange him for sweets at the coolie shop. But there is no prohibition against killing, and I am afraid that the new laws are not altogether in favour of the small birds, and that sooner or later there will be a reaction against them. It is always a mistake to try and promote culture by act of Parliament, and the Parliament that passed this special legislation did not enjoy a high prestige. I much prefer to see the Bushveld children leave the small birds alone because they recognize the charm and beauty and interest of birds rather than because they are afraid of being fined for keeping *Ureginthus granatinus* in a sedge cage without a permit from a Minister who does not know the difference between *Ureginthus* and *Laniarius*.

So rich is the Bushveld in birds that in this chapter I can merely mention a few, not of the most interesting, for all birds are interesting, but of the most common species. My long list totals several hundreds, among them a few out-of-the-way rarities of importance to the ornithologist, but hardly likely to be recognized by the ordinary observer. The variety is to be accounted for by the unusually variegated environment that the Bushveld offers. After the summer rains there is abundant food and shelter for birds, and only the larger, ground-loving types, like the bustards and partridges, are exposed to perils from their false brethren, whether mammals or reptiles. There is plenty of cover for nesting, and the grassy flats, well-wooded pans, and above all the scrub, provide them with the best food and shelter they can wish. It is possible, too, that they find the climate much more to their liking than farther north. Avian malaria is prevalent, but it does not appear to limit their numbers, and probably the smaller birds have acquired an immunity to it, although that is a matter which needs much more investigation before any definite opinion can be expressed upon it. We know very little about epidemic disease among birds, especially in their wild state. I was interested in a small finch, which I found in flocks on the bands of the Sand River, on the western side of the Transvaal; it was new to me, and I was anxious to obtain some specimens. I was told that it was comparatively easy to get hundreds of them at night; they roosted in the tall sedges of a dam quite close to the homestead. I visited the dam one evening, with my flashlight, and obtained several specimens, but I found that thousands of small bodies lay scattered on the grass, and that in the nests there were many dead birds, both adult and featherless. My host, the farmer, said that the cold had killed them, but the temperature was mild, and I can only surmise that some infectious disease had attacked them.

The most conspicuous bird in the Bushveld is undoubtedly the ostrich. He roams in the grassy plains on the banks of the Limpopo, usually in pairs although I have seen coveys of six or more attendant on a herd of zebras. Moderately shy, he gallops off as soon as he spots the observer, running away at such a speed that it is impossible to see the action of his legs; he looks like a ball of black, if a male, or of brown if a female, moving horizontally across the landscape at tremendous speed without any connection with the earth. At one school the children led me to a nest, with a clutch of sixteen eggs. The female bird was absent, but the male was busily employed in turning the eggs with his beak and did not see us until we were within a few yards of him. He rushed away with flapping, protesting wings, but halted a few hundred yards off, regarded us dubiously, and came back and settled on the nest when the observers had retired. Within a foot of the nest were two clutches of plovers' eggs, laid between some stones on the bare sand, and the birds to which they belonged hovered around with shrill cries while we examined the ostrich eggs. The variation in the colour of the neck skin, about which so much speculation has arisen, was not visible in this male ostrich; his neck was the ordinary grey, although he was in full plumage and his primaries were exceptionally glossy. In the scrub he is difficult to see, but one often hears him, for his harsh, raucous cry, which the uninitiated sometimes mistake for the growling of a lion, especially when it is heard after sunset, is frequently audible above the minor cries of the veld. Formerly he was hunted for his feathers; nowadays he is immune from the poacher, for his flesh is tasteless and rank, only palatable when made into *biltong*.

Flamingoes I saw on the lower reaches of the Magalakwen River, but they are rare migrants in the Bushveld. This troop was a couple of hundred in number, containing both young and adult specimens, and the water was much too deep for them. It was the first and only time that they had been seen there. Their southern haunts are the *vleis* in the Cape Province, where in a good rainy season thousands of them may be seen, even in the Cape Peninsula. On Lake Ngami they are said to be plentiful, but their real habitat and breeding-grounds are in Kenya. Their loveliness and harmonious colouring make them, when seen in a troop, an unforgettable sight, but as individuals they are ungainly, disproportionate birds. In flight they are magnificently beautiful, and for the table there is no bird that excels them, for their flesh is deliciously tender, like that of a magnified golden plover. One of the early travellers testified to this fact, but he embellished his description by stating that flamingo flesh was, even when cooked, scarlet in colour, and that soup made from it resembled Russian bortsch. In sober reality it is black or dark brown, like duck's meat, and flamingo consommé differs in no respect from that made from any other water-fowl.

The toucans or hornbills are, after the ostrich, the most distinctive birds of the Bushveld. The largest of them, the ground hornbill (*Bucorax cafer*) known as the bush turkey, is seldom seen, though its droning cry is often heard. It wanders about in coveys of four or five, and is as useful a vermin killer as is the secretary bird. The crested hornbill (*Buceros cristatus*) is supposed to be entirely tropical, but I saw a specimen perched on a dry thorn tree, keeping company with a pair of crowned hornbills (*Tockus melanoleucus*) near the Palala river. The most common species is the yellowbill (*Tockus flavirostris*), a bird that in flight and when perched looks magnificently glossy and smooth and when captured turns out to be amazingly skinny and overrun with ticks. The nesting habits of the hornbills have been a matter of much controversy. Many museums contain specimens of their nests, a hole in a tree trunk walled up with mud with a small aperture through which the male bird is supposed to feed the female who never leaves the nest during the incubation period. I found many nests, with eggs or young in them, but none that was walled up, and I cannot yet credit the statement that all hornbills keep their wives so jealously sequestrated while they are hatching their eggs. Sometimes the hole in the trunk is so shallow that the young birds drop out and are found lying on the ground, with the parents jabbering on the branches above, and it is quite possible that an experienced hornbill, who has had a death in the family in such circumstances, provides against a similar happening in future by walling up the hole. A young hornbill makes an interesting and amusing pet, and I found several in the homes that I visited. On one farm there were two which had become deeply attached to the domestic cat and followed her about, waddling on the ground with a queer, lopsided gait. They used to visit the fowl runs and steal the eggs, flying to a wire fence with their prey, which they tossed expertly into the air and caught end-on in their huge beaks and swallowed with relish. In the evenings they would roost beside the cat in the kitchen, and when the milk boy brought the milk bucket in the early morning they were always ready to take a sip. They were shy of strangers, and squacked and snapped at me, but they allowed the children to handle them, and even displayed signs of affection, after the manner of parrots, by running their ugly beaks up and down the child's face.

Among the most beautiful Bushveld birds are the bee-eaters. The common *Merops apiaster*, usually regarded as a migrant, is probably domiciled in the Bushveld; one meets him at all seasons of the year, flying low over the ground in silence, or high up and uttering his monotonous, dismal croon that reveals his presence even when he is so high that the eye cannot track him. Beautiful as he is, he is not to be compared to his Bushveld cousin, the magnificently coloured *M. nubicoides*, a comparatively larger bird, with a carmine throat and breast and a splendidly red tail and back, or even to the smaller *M. bullockoides* which is less brilliantly tinted. The small *M. pusillus* is a harmony in green and yellow, a gregarious little chap that is sometimes very friendly and allows of a much closer acquaintance than its shyer but more resplendent cousins. Equally showy are the jays or rollers, of which the European *Coracias garrula* is often to be seen sitting on the high tree tops, while the tailed roller, *C. caudata*, a much shyer bird, which has yet a propensity to frequent the open spaces near Kafir huts, is as common as the drongo shrike. Both species are frequently shot for their wing feathers, and it is rare to see an adolescent Bushveld boy without a wing of one of these beautiful birds stuck in his hatband. Another glossily iridescent bird is the red-billed wood hoopoe (*Irrisor erythrorhynchus*) a study in purple and green, barred with white and black. It is a shy, retiring bird, frequenting the deep shadows of the scrub, but betrays itself by its jarring cry, and, to a patient watcher, by its inquisitiveness. Even more gaudily iridescent is the lory (*Corythaix porphyreolopha*) whose general colour is dark iridescent green, with steel-blue reflections on the back, wings and tail, with wings of brilliant carmine glossed with purple. Its first cousin is the ubiquitous go-away bird (*Schizorhis concolor*), a hoary grey bird, crested, most vociferous, gregarious, and by no means shy: and incidentally excellent eating. It is essentially a Bushveld bird, although it wanders occasionally to the Highveld. It is probably one of the most useful birds, for it is insectivorous as well as frugiferous, but it is not popular as it is supposed to scare away the game when the hunter approaches by giving its raucous warning cry. The cuckoos, too, are striking in colour, and both the golden and the emerald cuckoo are among the most beautiful birds of the Bushveld, while the bush shrikes, starlings, and many coloured finches and weaver birds display every variety of colour imaginable. Compared to some of them the parrots are sombre coloured. The Bushveld harbours all the various species known south of the Limpopo. Of these the largest is *Psittacus robustus*, Le Vaillant's parrot, which is a comparatively rare bird, usually found solitary or in pairs in the depths of the forest. It makes a tame and interesting pet, and some specimens can be taught to speak quite glibly. Meyer's parrot and Ruppel's parrot are the two most common in the Bushveld. Both are brownish-green birds, the former with slightly more yellow in its plumage, the latter with much more blue. On the banks of the Limpopo they are to be found in flocks of hundreds, and notwithstanding their 'protective colouring' they are easily spotted in the thorn trees. When perched they are quiet, well-behaved birds but in flight they are garrulous and almost always seem to be at play. To watch an assembly of these parrots performing what is obviously some intricate game is one of the most interesting occupations for the bird lover. They form themselves into two opposing groups, each group occupying different trees. From both groups come forward a couple of birds, to perform, in mid-air, various antics, gyrating round and round, or looping spirally round their fellows. After this exhibition both groups join in the play, which is performed with much chattering, and at times becomes so wild that the birds brush against each other, either by accident or design. Suddenly, as if at some given signal, the evolutions stop, and both groups fly back to their trees. The performance reminds one of the dancing of the bush shrikes, which is supposed to have some sexual significance, but the parrots play in unison, at all seasons of the year, and it is difficult to imagine that they indulge in anything but a game, whose rules and conventions are rigid enough to make every performance practically a repetition of its predecessors.

Where parrots are, one may nearly always find their smaller kinsmen, the love-birds, although the latter seem to like open country better and are often to be seen far away from water. The rosy faced love-bird (*Agapornis roseicollis*) is the most common specimen of the parrot tribe on the flat lands where the scrub is scanty, and usually hunts in pairs, though it invariably roosts in community. It is a pugnacious and domineering little fellow, and I have seen a pair attack a drongo shrike and drive it away from a tree which they had apparently selected for their own domain. This is one of the few birds that the Bushveld regards with real friendliness; although it is sometimes captured, to be made a pet of, it is rarely killed, and the presence of *papagaaitjies* near a homestead is regarded as auspicious. In captivity it is a perky, chattering little bird, breeding freely, and becoming tame enough to be allowed its liberty outside the cage without attempting to fly away.

Perhaps the most interesting, and the least well known, of Bushveld birds, are the doves. The most lovable of them is the small emerald spotted dove (*Chalcopelia afra*) whose plaintive cry is one of the first sounds that impress the stranger to these wilds. It is found everywhere where there are tall trees, for it is a high flyer, seldom settling on the ground, a shy, secretive shadow lover, very typical of its kind. The various species of turtle dove are far less shy and the little Namaqua dove (*Oena capensis*) is perhaps the tamest of all. The much larger speckled pigeon (*Columba phaenota*), which is essentially gregarious and to be seen in hundreds on the mealie fields in late summer, is a strong flyer, difficult to approach, and ordinarily the shyest of the family. Yet I have seen two pairs of them consorting with tame pigeons on a farm, and breeding in a loft, where they permitted the observer to come quite close before they flew up. The two finely coloured green pigeons (*Treron calva* and *T. Wakefieldii*) are forest loving birds, haunting the wild fig trees, and are much sought after because their flesh is esteemed a delicacy. Like the speckled pigeon they are strong flyers, and gregarious in habit, although it is not unusual to find solitary specimens far away from their beloved fig trees.

There still lingers the superstition that tropical and sub-
tropical birds, however much they may excel in colour, are
deficient in song. Anyone who has spent a summer in the
Bushveld will be able to correct this impression. There are
a few birds who have a sustained, melodious song, lasting
for several minutes. It is a matter of opinion how these
notes compare with those of the bullfinch, the nightingale
or the bulbul. My own opinion is that bird notes are not,
strictly speaking, comparable. Each species has its own
individual charm, whether in the cadence or in the melody
itself, and it is unfair to judge a songster, whose vocalization
one hears for the first time, by comparison with the achievement of one with whose music one is already perfectly
familiar. Nor is it possible to determine by dissection if a
particular species is superior or inferior to another in
vocalization, through the possession of a syrinx or specially
constructed musical box, such as all songsters are supposed
to possess. Even without such an apparatus many birds
contrive to utter sounds that are rhythmical and when
repeated constitute 'song' in the ordinary acceptation of the
word. The melodious call of the wood partridge, the low
whistling notes of the woodpecker, the assonance of the
cuckoo, and even the strident piping of the finches, have all a
quality that entitle them to be classed as musical. Nor are
these sounds of tropical birds always monotonous. There is
much diversity in the cheerful twittering of the weaver
finches swinging over the pools, and there are many
different notes in the chattering of the parrots at play.
There is also imitative variety, which all bird observers in
the Bushveld take into consideration. I have heard a bush
shrike imitating a cuckoo, and the love-bird practising the
warble of a finch, while there are many bird sounds which

I have never been able to trace, although some of them are so commonly heard that they must be uttered by well-known birds. Sustained melody, with a gamut of some length, is heard much more commonly than is supposed, and not merely from the high-flying larks and thrushes but, curiously enough, from some of the ground-loving species. The fact is that song, like colouring, is still much of a mystery. A great deal has been written about it, and much sentiment has been woven into the discussion, while the popular theories of selection and sex attraction have been dragged in to explain why birds sing. Delamain, in his well-known book translated under that title, goes so far as to credit the Oscines or songsters with definite artistic aspirations: 'Musical art is born of the satisfaction which a being experiences in expressing his life by a sound. The golden fly, buzzing, loves the noise of his wings; the cicada, in the ecstasy of his vibration, forgets the enemy watching him. A bird enjoys the note modulated by his own throat. But if he attains art it is because, endowed with a sense of the beautiful, he is able to choose among his notes the clearest, the purest, and the fullest, to link one to another, to find the rhythm, compose the phrase, transpose the tones, thus achieve pure music, and make a song gush out from a cry' (*Why Birds Sing*, p. 58). The premises here are not such as to warrant the syllogistic conclusion, and the facts are probably all wrong. Buzzing flies buzz not because they enjoy it, any more than an animal enjoys panting when it runs, but because buzzing is the natural result of structural function. The cicada stridulates only when he is quite sure that he is out of danger; his musical ecstasy does not conquer his instinct for self-preservation. And there is no proof whatever that a bird spontaneously 'chooses', from the gamut available, notes that increase the cadence or influence the rhythm beyond the range of the melody that evokes a tribal response. Song in birds, so far as my observation has enabled me to form any opinion, is primarily a stimulus to exertion, whether such exertion be demanded from the songster himself or from his mate or mates. It is similar to the rhythmic chantys that the natives use when they do work, or to the vociferous play of children. The finches, for instance, sing best and most sustainedly when they are building; the usually quiet grey shrike warbles quite skittishly as encouragement to the wife when she is laying down the smooth lining of the nest. Courting phrases, that birds undoubtedly use — one has only to listen to the emerald-spotted dove bowing and scraping before a coy female to detect the difference between his courting and his businesslike crooning — are entirely different in rhythm from the ordinary 'stimulative' song, sometimes so different that one is astonished, on hearing them for the first time and seeing the bird that utters them, to find that they emanate from a songster whose usual notes are a key higher or lower. Indicative notes — commands, warnings, directions, long-distance signals — are again different. Among the starlings (*Spreo bicolor* and *Ophrys morio*) these indicative notes are so varied, and occur with such regularity, that one can only suppose that they have some directing significance. Similarly varied are the admonitory calls of the go-away bird, which has a repertory of more than thirty different notes which it uses in twice as many combinations of, usually, two notes. Protective cries are easily distinguished, and are uttered by all birds, and vary from the sharp hiss of the brooding hornbill — onomatopoetically uncommonly like the sound made by a puff-adder — to the shrill, excited squack of the disturbed parrot. They are expostulatory sounds, sometimes heard in bird play, and sometimes also when there is, apparently, nothing near to frighten the bird, and they may be likened to human swear words or more innocent expletives. My red-breasted bush shrikes, the two males that wandered about by themselves, used to utter such expletives frequently, and to fly apart and sulk on separate twigs for a while until they made up their tiff and swore friendship again over the carcass of a mantis.

Dr. Ellis of New South Wales thought that birds, like human beings, possess 'an inherited emotional factor which finds its expression in musical sounds', and he went to the length of postulating that bird song is related to bird colouring, on the assumption that the musical sense in birds is analogous to the colour sense in human beings. Colour-blind people react differently from normal non-Daltonic persons to musical sounds. That difference, however, is probably not a colour difference but a constitutional difference. The colour-loving Mozart whose music is bright and joyous, was an example of an extrovert personality; the gloomy Beethoven, deaf and comparatively indifferent to colours, was an introspective introvert. 'As a rule the female is appreciative of the emotion of music and not creative of music itself, and in birds colour and music are usually apart.' These statements are not quite true; they certainly do not hold for Bushveld birds, but the subject, like that of mimicry, selection by sex, and many others, demands further and fair-minded investigation. At present all our notions about birds and beasts are largely coloured by old-fashioned and quite un-proved theories, mostly offering some teleological explanation of facts that may possibly have quite another meaning.

For the bird lover, indeed, the Bushveld is an ideal field for such study and observation, especially in summer when food is plentiful. The diversity of species — more than three hundred in all — comprising most of the natural orders of African birds, and ranging from the vulture and the ostrich to the tiny wrens and fascinating sugar-birds, the comparative tameness of most of the species one meets in the bush, and the excellent opportunities for investigating such problems as the two to which I have specially referred, song and colouring, and others like nesting, communal habits, mating and migration, are attractions that every field naturalist will cordially appreciate. To me they were doubly stimulative and inspiring, for there is nothing that conquers fatigue and depression so quickly as to lie at ease under the shade of some tree and to watch the birds. The contrast between the care-free cheerful feathered folk and the care-worn harassed humanity among whom my work lay was disturbing at first, but in time I came to forget, temporarily, the ugly side of Bushveld life and to revel in the fascination presented by its animal wealth. In a tropical environment such contrasts will always appear, and no thoughtful observer can ignore them. But if he happens to be interested in Nature, he will find ample solace from the depressing thoughts that they bring by devoting his attention on occasion to the wild life about him.

CHAPTER XI

BLACK AND WHITE

THE white man has continuously inhabited parts of the Bushveld for more than a century. The oldest families now living there are the direct descendants of men and women who emigrated from the Cape Colony, at the time of the Great Trek. Younger houses are the descendants of those who came north much later, and probably the majority of Bushveld whites belong to families who migrated from the higher lands farther south, and for various reasons established themselves in this malarious country. On the whole, with exceptions that are beyond the pale, the white settler has kept himself reasonably pure in blood. He has not consciously bred a race of half-castes, although hybridism is not altogether unknown, and is probably more prevalent than is admitted.

When the first emigrants from the old Cape Colony came into the Transvaal they found there a white father and several white sons, who had all married native wives. The father was one Conrad Buys, a descendant of free burghers at the Cape who had served the old East India Company well, and had been granted lands in the eastern part of the settlement. When the Cape was occupied by the English, ostensibly in the interests of the patriotic party in Holland, Conrad Buys was living on his farm beyond the Gouritz River, in a picturesque environment of rocks and forests. He had already disregarded the orders of the old regime, and he thought fit to disregard those of the new Government. Adventurous, daring, physically of exceptional strength, he was a man of undoubtedly strong character, of a sturdy independence that made him by nature a rebel against all authority except his own. He had already journeyed into the Kàfir country and learned native dialects, and he was both respected and feared by those with whom he came into contact. He was a married man with several stalwart sons when he determined to wander beyond the limits of the new Government's jurisdiction. He went north, into the wilds, and on that journey his wife died. As there was no white woman with whom he could mate, he took to himself a chief's daughter, and married her accord-ing to native custom. His stalwart sons also found wives for themselves among the native women. After wandering through what is now the Orange Free State, the Buys family crossed the Vaal River and settled beyond the Magalies-bergen, where the level expanse of the Springbok Flats is broken by the red sandstone tor now known as Buyskop, or Buys' Hill. There, or thereabouts, the emigrant farmers found the Buyses when they trekked into the Transvaal in the early 'thirties of the last century. Old Conrad was the patriarch of a clan already numbering several score of individuals, and he and his sons were definitely, irre-proachably white, and therefore on an equal footing, socially, with the new-comers. They could shake hands with the Immigrant Boers without loss of dignity on either side; they could smoke and take snuff, and discuss with the Trekkers with interest and from personal experience the disadvantages of living under any government whatsoever. But their progeny complicated the situation. Conrad's own children by his native wife — or wives, for he had several — were not pure white, and his grandchildren were equally non-white. They were 'coloured', and the cleft that divided the pure white from the coloured was in those days, communally and socially, racially and politically, as deep and as unbridgeable as it is to-day. Not perhaps traditionally. The Dutch settlers at the Cape had been as liberal in their outlook as their fellow-settlers in Java — originally. There are many recorded instances where Dutchmen, farmers or officials in the Company's service, married — properly married — black women, usually slave women, though sometimes aboriginals. On May 21st, 1656, Jan Wouters, a white man in the Company's service, married Catherine of Bengal, a black slave woman. In September of the same year Anton Muller, another settler, married Domingo Elvingh, another Bengal slave. Both were wedded with the full consent and approbation of officialdom. Nor were these men among the least cultured among the settlers. Van Meerhoff, a surgeon, married Eva, van Riebeeck's interpretess, who was a pure Hottentot and who had been brought up as a protégée of the Governor. When her husband died, Eva's morals were so deplorable that she had to be exiled to Robben Island, but she retained her status as the wife of a white man and was accorded almost a miniature State funeral when she, too, died. For the Dutch were very logical in their outlook upon such matters. If the marriage between white and non-white was legal, the non-white party was granted all the rights and privileges of citizenship, and the offspring, no matter how variegated in colour, were looked upon as Netherlanders. Where white and non-white bred without legal and ecclesiastical approval, the children were regarded as natives and treated as such. Later on, when there was no dearth of white women in the settlement, marriage between white and non-white became a rarity, and in time the descendants of those who had approved of and countenanced such marriages, and of those who had profited by such approval, united in raising a caste barrier that is now to be met with throughout South Africa. The slave, the aborigine, and the offspring of slaves, no matter how much white blood they could show, were treated as belonging to the native class, inferiors who could never attain to even the semblance of equality with the white man. The coloured individual was kept in his place. He saluted the white man respectfully, spoke only when spoken to, volunteered no remarks of his own, and drudged and did such work as the white man deemed unfitting to do himself. Openly he called the white man '*Baas*' or 'Master', and the white man referred to him as 'Creature' or '*Skepsel*'; in private he spoke of the white man as a '*Maaksel*' or 'manufactured article' — as an artifact, made, not created, by God. He shared this distinction — or disgrace — of being a 'creature' with the native, who looked somewhat askance at him, but who realized that he had something, whatever it was, in common with the white man, and stood, accordingly, a trifle higher on the scale.

Wherever there are white men and native women, living under conditions that make miscegenation not only possible but easy, such miscegenation will occur, and South Africa is no exception to that rule. It has a large coloured or half-caste population. How large nobody quite knows, for it stands to reason that the upper and lower limits of such a community are exceedingly difficult to define. I have known two brothers apply for work at the mines, where one was taken on and the other refused as 'not of pure European blood'. The ocular evidence in the one case was so strong that it impressed; in the other it was not to be noticed. The one boy had a clear white skin, blue eyes and fair hair;

the other had curly black hair, thick lips, a flat face, and a dark, coppery complexion. This is not an isolated instance. Every school teacher can quote cases where it was impossible to decide if the child was 'coloured' or European. There is no mixture in the schools, but many times I have examined obviously coloured children who attended a European school and who for all practical purposes ranked as Europeans. On a very few occasions I have had a converse experience, where the child was light skinned and manifestly, merely to judge from appearance, European, but where the parents and brothers and sisters were clearly non-white and where the child attended a mission school. There is no generally acceptable test that can be applied, which is perhaps just as well for all concerned, for public opinion is very touchy on points of colour, and indeed it is held to be slanderous to doubt the non-Europeanship of a white citizen who, despite his appearance, insists on being taken for one of the old red sandstone brand. Blood grouping tests, however interesting from a scientific point of view, would scarcely be tolerated; they might upset so many preconceptions that one shudders to think what would happen if courts of law or school boards insisted upon them. The school doctor soon learns by experience how to differentiate in a rough and ready way. The half-caste has anatomical peculiarities that are typical in the first generation — and may be as typical in succeeding breeds — but that are generally 'bred out' in the grand or great grandchildren. The first is the constitutional slenderness, the leptosomic-asthenic type of the child, associated with a non-typical facial development. The experienced can tell, by gently feeling the child's nose, 'if he has black blood in him', the test being to feel for the niche at the tip ordinarily present in the European child but rarely felt in the half-caste. The peculiarities of the palms, nails, and ear lobes, which elsewhere I had been told were points of differentiation, I soon came to look upon as of much less significance than the constitutional type and the rounding of the end of the nose. Colour and shape and growth of hair, that are distinct signs, are rarely conspicuous in those cases where a difficulty of classification arises. When they are present, anyone can tell that the child is non-European.

Let us, for the moment, return to Conrad Buys. The Boer settlers had no notion, when they entered their new country, that they would there find a group of already established settlers, about whose paternity there could be no shadow of doubt. Old Conrad made no secret of his matrimonial adventures. He was secure, inasmuch as he had both feet solidly planted, being friendly with the natives with whom he had contracted blood alliance and of the same race as the new-comers. These facts demanded a special adjustment of relations. With the solid common sense that marked their communal resolutions, the Boers frankly admitted that the Buyses merited preferential treatment, and they gave it them, not grudgingly but generously. The Buys boys were allowed to carry arms — a great privilege — and to purchase or barter for powder and lead; those of them who were passably white were certainly granted greater privileges. A tract of country was set aside for them, and they were allowed to govern themselves, as they had done before the Trek Boers arrived on the scene, subject to the condition that they had to respect the authority of the new Government and refrain from dabbling in communal politics. The arrangement worked excellently. Old Conrad ruled his clan in patriarchal simplicity, and with a paternal authority that was, apparently, never questioned by his rapidly increasing offspring. He dealt out primitive justice, and there are legends that ascribe to him almost Solomonic sagacity in settling complicated disputes among his own folk. At last he died, nominally a Christian, but never a real burgher of the new state. His clan multiplied. At the end of the last century there were several thousand *Buys Kafirs* as his descendants were popularly called. In 1914 their number had dwindled, and the 1918 epidemic of influenza raged so severely among them that their race was almost decimated. Their remnant is to-day one of the most interesting objects in the Bushveld, that should well repay detailed investigation.

So far as can be gathered from local sources, they lived then and still live as a family clan, intensely conservative with a conservatism that has blended together both European and native custom and tradition into something definitely original, a self-contained community, barely in touch with their native or white neighbours. They are an excellent example of fairly strict endogamy, although it is clear that from time to time there has been an admixture of new blood, white or native, from without. In physique they approximate closely to the half-caste coloured, but their stature is an inch or two taller, their weight is generally heavier for their age group than coloured folk of the same group can show, while their complexion is definitely much lighter. Some of them may easily pass for pure Europeans. The first Buys woman whom I saw had a smooth white complexion, regular features, long auburn coloured hair, light brown eyes, and a much more Nordic than Bantu figure and gait. One beautifully developed, sixteen-year-old boy would have passed easily as of pure European descent, but in physique and in normalness he was a conspicuous exception to his brothers and sisters. He had a perfect set of teeth, a rarity in his clan, and a good intelligence quotient.

Want of good food, economic disadvantages, disease and poverty are playing havoc with the Buys Kafirs. Tuberculosis and pulmonary infection find them an easy prey, and as a clan they are ravaged by malaria and redwater. They are dying out, and if anyone wishes to study their anthropology in detail, he should lose no time in setting about it. Such a study should be undertaken, for nowhere in Africa can one find such interesting material for the investigation of hybridization among human beings. As an experiment in miscegenation their history is unique. Old Conrad and his sons were excellent examples of physically sound Nordic types, and to judge from the old gentleman's success in his many adventurous undertakings, he must have been a pycnic, well endowed with those mental and moral qualities that conduce to success and fit a man for leadership. The women they mated with were also admirable types of their race, descendants of chiefs and headmen, physically perfect specimens of Bantu womanhood. Some of the old men of the tribe whom I met were men with fine faces, rugged looking, with shrewd, wary eyes, and their talk gave one the impression that their mental faculties were not staled by ostracism but rather sharpened by their isolation. Custom and habit have forced them to accept their position as social and political inferiors. They tacitly admit that they are below the white grade, but they do not willingly mix with the aborigines, and adopt towards the latter much the same air of condescending superiority that the white man adopts towards them. The majority of the white Bushveld settlers scarcely know of the existence of these half-castes.

The territory is so vast and so sparsely populated, that this is not to be wondered at, for the Buyses live in an isolated location, beyond the Salt Pan Mountains, far away from white neighbours. Moreover, the white settlers have enough to attend to without bothering their heads about a decaying, almost-expiring clan, whose presence, when all is said and done, is not something to be inordinately proud of.

Indeed, it is a subject to be approached with infinite tact, for colour prejudice is very strong in South Africa. Intermarriage between white and non-white is everywhere deprecated; by law it has been made a criminal offence in the Transvaal. Yet, as statistics show, such intermarriage does take place, and by no means infrequently. No human laws can stop intercourse between white and non-white where circumstances conduce towards such intercourse, as I have already said, and there is ample evidence to show that it prevails everywhere. In the better populated urban areas, it is of course more common; in the rural areas it should be unknown, and would, at least, be comparatively rare if the white community staunchly maintained its traditional policy of isolation that connoted a moral as well as an economic and social superiority. That moral ascendancy it must obtain from its cultural and not merely from its traditional outlook on life.

I come from a missionary family. Hereditarily, if there be anything in heredity, I am of those that can see no specific distinctions in the human race and that recognize all mankind as belonging to one family, however diversified by colour, custom, or creed its various components may be. One of my great-grandfathers was a missionary. Both my grandfathers were missionaries. My father was a missionary for many years among the cannibal Battas at Prau Sorat on the Toba Lake in Sumatra. From childhood to early adolescence I lived in a missionary atmosphere, imbibed missionary tradition and culture, learned to regard white and black not as different species but as the same race separated by a cleft that in time could, and, as I was told, inevitably would, be bridged by a common civilization. The cement for that bridge was Christianity, the great civilizing factor in European history. The native who was still heathen was to be regarded as a lost brother, but none the less a brother, one to be won back by precept and example, not intimidated and bullied into hypocritical subservience. In short, my whole education was, consciously or unconsciously, designed to foster in me what my fellow-citizens to-day would call 'a scandalously Negro-philistic attitude of mind'.

I have not altogether outgrown that attitude, although experience and knowledge have considerably modified it. My father, after ruining his health in the Sumatran jungles, came back to South Africa, and accepted an appointment as pastor to a Dutch Reformed Congregation in the south western part of the Cape Colony. He exchanged the liberal Lutheranism with its rich store of old Catholic tradition behind it, for the more rigid and unlovely Calvinism systematized by the Synod of Dort in 1618. Calvinism, as Professor Haarhoff has remarked, is Roman Stoicism without its redeeming features. Its symbolization holds nothing that appeals to the aesthetic sense; its philosophy is harsh and hard; its regimen is the crystallization of intolerance. In South Africa its pioneering exponents were highly cultured men, who brought with them a good knowledge of human nature, and who adapted themselves to their environment, and laid more stress on a liberal interpretation of the essential postulates than upon the strict observance of their many taboos. As in Holland, the Dutch at the Cape were singularly liberal and broad minded. They attended Divine worship punctually and regularly, and they were staunch enough in upholding the 'religion' but they had no objection to indulging in practices, such as card playing and dancing, which were anathema to the stricter brethren. When, at the beginning of the last century, Scottish pastors, who had been taught their Dutch in the most rigidly strict Calvinistic circles in Holland, came out to take charge of parishes in the Cape Colony, a change came over the scene. The strictest orthodoxy was insisted upon, with the result that later on, the more unyielding portion of the Reformed split off and formed their own congregations.

My father's congregation was composed of the original Reformed — now generally known as the Dutch Reformed — and his parishioners were by no means unduly bigoted or illiberal. They had their own, perhaps peculiar, views as to what was fitting and godly. They danced until the small hours to the accompaniment of a native orchestra. They played casino, and sometimes lost much money at it. They had been slave owners but humane ones, who treated their chattels as human beings, with the result that when emancipation came most of the slaves in our district elected to remain with their former masters. In my youth I knew some of the descendants of these slaves, and heard much of what went on when man held property in man. But I cannot remember that I heard anything that shocked or outraged my juvenile feelings, even though I had been brought up in a missionary household and could have been — and perhaps undoubtedly was — more sensitive on such points than my white playmates who constantly referred to their coloured contemporaries as 'black things'. Nor can I remember any incident that showed the whites to be less humane, more prejudiced, or more 'anti-native' than my own missionary kinsmen were supposed to be. My recollection is that while everyone admitted that there was still a wide chasm between white and black, no one emphatically stated that it was a permanent division that could never be annulled. The relations between white and black were friendly, protective and paternal on the side of the whites, respectful and pupillary on the part of the coloured. The latter were all nominally Christian, and before a separate church was built for them in the village, they attended the European church, where they sat discreetly on the back benches. But they were counted as members of the congregation, although they never 'presumed' on their privileges.

Similar relations existed throughout the Cape Colony, practically in all congregations. The emigrant Boers, when they trekked across the border, took with them many of these coloured people, their former slaves or children of slaves. These coloured folk shared their adventures, their deprivations and their pioneering hardships. They, too, were massacred by the aboriginal natives; they, too, had a share in laying the foundations of the Boer colonies beyond the Vaal. And yet, for all that, the chasm remains as wide as it ever was, and in the north it has grown wider and deeper with the years.

To a South African so much out of tune with his time, it seems strange that there should be so wide a divergence of opinion on this question of white and black between the south and the north. In the Bushveld, amidst that white community that lives so far apart and that continues to struggle against so many odds, one learns to appreciate, if not altogether to sympathize, with the 'northern' view. A community that from the first has had to struggle, without outside help, against aboriginal strength numerically much greater than its own, may be pardoned if it insists upon retaining such advantages as it has gained, even if it has to go to the length of enforcing class legislation that in itself is an absolute denial of its ideal republicanism, just as much as it is a negation of its Christian creed. To understand what appears to be so crassly illogical, one must study the historical background, and realize that intolerance is founded on fear, on an apprehension which the south has never experienced, certainly never in its crude, savage reality, but which the north has had before it from the time when the pioneers first settled there.

'But, Uncle,' I said to a Bushveld farmer over the coffee cups one day, when the talk had veered from hygiene to politics. Conversation always flounders into these political bays, no matter how carefully one steers. My host, on this occasion, was a violently 'Anti-Botha man'. He held firmly, honestly, that if Botha had declared the independence of the Transvaal in 1914, there would now have been a republic, embracing the whole of Africa south of the Zambezi.

'But, Uncle, you know a republic means liberty...' He nodded vigorously, in full agreement... 'And equality... and brotherhood. Are these possible when three-quarters of your citizens are natives?'

He carefully refilled his pipe. 'You do not understand, Doctor,' he said, patiently, as if explaining to a small boy. 'We were a republic in the old days. ...'

'Scarcely that, Uncle. You were an oligarchy... a state of whites ruled by an Executive Committee elected by the whites alone.'

'And that is what I mean, Doctor. The native cannot be a citizen. He must be a ward. You would not give the burghership to children, now?'

'And if the natives grew up, Uncle?'

'Aye, but that will not happen in your lifetime, Doctor, nor in mine. Nor in our children's children's. And we must adjust things for the present not for the future. . . .'

That is the view. It has been the 'northern' view from the time when the north was settled. It is the short view, that takes the present into consideration and ignores the future. It has been productive of much that does not benefit the Bushveld, or South Africa at large.

I attended a meeting of a school committee. The question before the meeting was if the widow A——'s children should be allowed to attend. I had examined them at school, and there was no question in my mind as to my inability to certify them as 'pure European'. But the widow A—— passed as such, and the committee decided that the children should remain. 'For the present,' remarked the chairman. 'Later, we may have to make a plan.'

I walked back with the chairman, and suggested that the children should go to a good mission school, many miles away. He shook his head. 'I don't hold with that. It would be un-Christian for us to do that.' And then, doubtfully, 'I daresay when the Inspector arrives we may be able to make a plan'.

'Our ways of educating the native are the result of experience,' another patriarch of the Bushveld told me. 'You see, Doctor, you must impress his mind. If you don't do that, you don't educate him.'

'But the school try to do that, Uncle.'

'Not in our way, Doctor. Let me tell you what I mean. I

198

had a native who was new and untrained, and when I came
to the kraal in the morning he did not say, "Morning, baas",
as he should have done. I said, "Morning, Mysikinya" the
first day, and told him he must greet me, so he said, "Morning, baas". The next day I waited but he did not greet me,
so I said, "Morning, Mysikinya", and he replied as he should
have done. On the third day I came and he said nothing, so
I knocked him down and he jumped up and said, "Morning
baas! morning, baas! morning, baas!" And since then, as
soon as he sees me he shouts out, "Morning, baas!" That's
how one must impress them, Doctor.'

On my latest trip into the Bushveld, I chanced upon one
of the old teachers, living in retirement on a small farm. We
sat on the stoep in the twilight, and discussed world politics.
Far away the zebras barked, and the nightjars flew around
our heads, swiping at the big hawk moths that came to feed
on the hibiscus flowers. Before us lay the scrub, bathed in
moonlight, a mosaic of russets and darker purples.

'And you still hold your missionary views, Doctor?' he
asked me.

'Not altogether. I can make allowances for you,' I replied.
'But you yourself don't think quite what you used to think.'

'No indeed, Doctor. I have been reading and considering.
Do you know what one hears about Russia — the things they
have done there since the war, Doctor, impress one. And
after all, it is our business, isn't it?'

'Quite. Do you remember what Milton said to Salmasius?'

'No, I can't say I do. What was it, Doctor?'

'You know when the English started playing at republicanism, they chopped their king's head off. All Europe was
terribly scandalized, and Holland — your Holland — most of
all. Salmasius was the world's wisest man at that time; had

the Nobel Prize existed he would undoubtedly have been a Nobel prizeman. He was the great oracle of Europe; he knew everything. So they set him to write a book to show the English how very wrong they were to cut off their king's head. He wrote very forcibly, and he argued, according to his lights, very soundly. But Milton refuted him all along the line, and the best part of Milton's reply was the remark, "What the devil is it to you what the English do among themselves?"'

My friend appreciated the retort, and chuckled. Then became grave.

'Is it not strange, Doctor,' he said, ruminatively, 'that we should have been upset over that first republic? It showed the fallacy of one great, universally accepted principle, the divine right of kings. And later on came the French Revolution, as you may remember, Doctor, that showed the fallacy of another assumption, that a man's worth depends on his birth. If I remember rightly, the English were as much upset about that as we were about them chopping their king's head off.'

'You may parallel that,' I said. 'The Russians have demonstrated the fallaciousness of a third principle — that a man's worth depends on the amount of money he possesses. And our friends, the French, were very much upset about that.'

'So I suppose the next revolution will show the fallacy of our principles, that a man's worth depends on the colour of his skin,' he remarked, meditatively. 'I am afraid, we'll be just as upset about that as the French were about Russia.'

'Quite. But what the devil does it matter what we do among ourselves, Teacher? We can always quote Milton as our authority.'

Very flippant, no doubt. But there is a grain of truth in it.

Quite recently a non-Aryan friend came to me to ask me to join in an organized protest against Nazi legislation against the Jews. I pointed out that the Jews in South Africa had never protested against similar class legislation here, where it is directed solely against those whose skins do not conform to the regulation old red sandstone colour. No native boy can enter our medical schools — and yet we have a crying want of native medical men, and our native territories need medical service urgently and imperatively. No native woman can be trained in our hospitals, because public opinion shudders at the thought that a non-white should nurse a white patient. In the present state of public opinion, it is useless to rail against our class legislation, however illiberal and intolerant it is. The majority of our citizens regard such legislation as the least that can be done to safeguard the interests of white civilization. To my missionary mind it seems hopelessly wrong, just as it seemed hopelessly wrong to Salmasius that a Christian community should forget that kings rule by divine right; to Castlereagh that a 'lousy plebeian' should presume to be the equal of one born an aristocrat, or to the thrifty French peasant that money should not be allowed to count for anything in the scale of human values. We may all be quite wrong, and nobody can justly blame us for expressing an opinion in conformity with our convictions. But we cannot really take it amiss if folk who think differently from us and who happen to be in the majority, should hurl Milton's retort at us, 'What the devil is it to you what we do among ourselves?'

CHAPTER XII

BUSH MAGIC

ONE of the earliest 'human documents' in the history of South Africa deals with magic and the mysteries of divination. When the white settlers came here, in the middle of the seventeenth century, they found peopling the coastal belt native tribes who were still under what St. Thomas Aquinas called the influence of a potent, ordaining and controlling spirit. The Bushmen or Khoi-khoi, had no conception of a devil, certainly not of a devil as a personal entity. They acknowledged a Supreme Being, one Heitsi Kabib, romantically born by direct obstetrical intervention of the stars, a specialized superman, who lived and died as a man, but whose ghost now pervades all humanity, turning whatever there is of evil to good through natural forces that may be directed by one who knows how to do it.

When I was a lad I heard much about Heitsi Kabib, almost as much as I heard about Jesus, and in my young mind I inevitably compared and contrasted the two. I was much more impressed by Heitsi. *He* never disputed with the doctors in the Temple, but he ran races against the sun, and he had a wonderful and alluring dog, whose name I have forgotten, but whose adventures were exciting enough to rouse wild enthusiasm. An old Bushman shepherd taught me to throw stones at wayside graves — a way of propitiating Heitsi Kabib that is traditional among the Bushmen. It is no disgrace to throw the original earth upon those you have loved. They came from it, and they went back to it, and piety and reverence demand that you should cover them with a portion of it whenever you can do so. That was the simple philosophy of my shepherd *Outa* who had violently protested, in his adolescence, against having 'water thrown on his head' and in spite of all temptations had remained, though nominally a Christian, a faithful follower of the wonderful Superman with the equally wonderful dog.

His ancestors had venerated Heitsi Kabib in the days when South Africa knew no white men. When van Riebeeck came, a new gospel and a new conception of life were brought to their notice. Van Riebeeck himself was certainly not fanatically religious. He was a member of the Barber Surgeons' Guild, which was supposed to be secretly materialistic and merely in externals responsive to the appeal of religion — a supposition that is still popularly current about every medical man. What is much more pertinent, he was a most inquisitive and inquiring man, who was continually trying to find out what others thought about things. Like all sensible men, he wanted to know particularly what strange folk thought about the hereafter. What really happens when you die?

That intruding question — to some people the most important question that a man can ask — had doubtless been answered for him by his native friends at Tonkin, where he spent much of his official time before he came to the Cape. As a medical man he must have recognized that the Buddhist conception of what happens after death, as explained in the *Bardos*, agrees more closely with what science has observed of death and dying than either the Christian or the Khoikhoi interpretations. Both Christianity and Bushman-religion reject 'the most ancient and widespread belief of the *kuklos geneseon*', although both, curiously enough, make a formalistic exception for one individual, God or man as the case may be, who undergoes or suffers reincarnation. My old Bushman protestant told me that Heitsi Kabib would sometime return, 'as surely, little Master, as that ewe over there will have twins this year, though I can't rightly tell the little Master when, not knowing things like a magician does'. Van Riebeeck, in his talks about religion with the native chiefs, through the medium of Eva the interpretess who afterwards embraced Christianity and became, though legally the widow of a white man of high professional standing, a common prostitute, heard much about Heisti Kabib, but from his remarks in his Log one concludes that he thought that deity of comparatively little importance. It was not that the Bushmen's Superman was deficient in those supernatural qualities that inspire respect; the legends that have encrusted round his personality are interesting and many of the episodes related of him are exciting. But he lacked a philosophy. He had established no ritual — except that of throwing clods of earth or karroo nodules at a grave when one passes it — and had done nothing to systematize his creed. To a Hollander well versed in the intricacies of predestination, foreordination and free-will, such lamentable carelessness must have seemed grotesque, and to merit the cheerful contempt with which our first Governor refers to him.

Indeed, to the first white settlers in Africa the simplicity of the natives' theology must have appeared childish in comparison with their own intricate and complicated systems, that included witches as well as saints, and were buttressed by the pronouncements of that amazing concensus of prejudice, the Synod of Dort. The settlement at the Cape had not been established for many months when the new-comers showed that, however superior they might have been in formulating abstractions, they were in practice on a level with the 'wild and brutal folk that pretend that their God was once upon earth'. Van Riebeeck's surgeon, a dare-devil of a fellow who grumbled about his pay, practised divination to find out if it was feasible, and expedient, to murder the Governor. The records of the trial state that divination by 'book and knife' was the method used. An open knife was laid on the pages of a Bible, certain questions were asked, and the movements of the knife indicated the answers. The witnesses had no doubt whatsoever that the knife turned this and that way. Their credibility was never impugned. The offending doctor was condemned before trial, for in those days Grotius and Sir Thomas More believed in witchcraft, and the settlers at the Cape, common folk of no great culture and no less and no more superstitious than their kinsmen in Holland, saw nothing strange in the statements that were elicited — probably by judicious application of a hot iron — from the principal accused. Van Riebeeck, to his credit, thought less of the divinatory accessories than of the attempt to obtain extra pay for services that were properly scheduled, and his sentence on the obstreperous surgeon was much more humane and lenient than it would have been in Holland.

This is the first recorded case of occultism in South Africa, but needless to say it has not remained isolated. Native belief and imported superstition became allied, and in time blended into a strange jumble of traditional credulity. Among the imported beliefs, that of Malay magic was undoubtedly the most influential. When the slaves came, and the exiles from Java — that great repository of occult wisdom that has assimilated the combined philosophies of animism, Hinduism, Brahmanism, Buddhism, Lhamanism, Mohammedanism and Christian Gnosticism — the occult 'apperceptive massas' offered to the white population rapidly increased in number and grew more potent in suggestibility. Death and dying became suffused with a haze of legend, that was perhaps more persuasive and compelling because it was necessarily kept secret as denying the direct implications of the Shorter Catechism with which every civilized person was supposed to be familiar. That tradition has lingered till to-day, much attenuated from what it was in the old days when the slaves made ju-ju in their quarters, and the 'old masters' were scared at the sight of a dried ostrich foot, but still strong enough to be ranked as a factor of some importance in the cultural life of the white population, especially in communities living at the periphery. For proof of that one has only to lead conversation round to the subject of the supernatural. Of the existence of ghosts, for instance, Bushveld dwellers, white as well as native, have no real doubt. The Malay who can make *paljas* or magic, and the Shangaan witch-doctor who throws his *dol-os* bones, meet on a level, and the white *baas*, who in public derides both, is privately a little afraid of what either might be able to do. That is probably the reason why he does not protest against the absurdity of punishing the practitioners of these occult arts when they happen to be natives, and of allowing them untrammelled liberty of action when they masquerade as spiritualists and give paid séances in the towns. In his heart he feels that there is something mystic in these practices. On occasions he has found the methods of divination practically useful, while on others he has been astonished by happenings that he cannot explain except by assuming that they are para-natural.

To the sceptical, cynical and sophisticated stranger, the crude conceptions of the Bushveld may at first sight seem unworthy of more than a scornful smile of derision. To the sympathetic observer, however, they reveal much that is helpful in understanding the relation between mind and material things. In an environment such as this, where outside suggestions are rare, and the influence of the past is strong, where conservatism and tradition still claim their due, and old, innate thoughts creep to the surface through even the welter of modern irrelevancies such as the wireless and the gramophone, there are whimsically naive conceptions in which are blended the primitive superstition of the savage with the cheerful realism of the child. Ordinarily they are suppressed, and not allowed to obtrude themselves when life is flowing evenly and placidly. But in days of difficulty and doubt, their influence is apparent, even when it is purposely obscured by conventional ideologies and out of respect for the inhibitions imposed by the churches. Naturally the doctor comes more often into contact with these convictions, for it is when pain and illness harass us that we involuntarily turn towards the dimly remembered but unconsciously still operative beliefs of our forefathers. Even the doctor is not exempt from such atavistic introspectiveness, and medical men, strictly between themselves, can tell of numberless examples where their colleagues, despite their experience and training, have succumbed to the temptation. It is the doctor therefore who can and should sympathize with that human failing, for he best knows how despair and doubt can drive man or woman to do that which knowledge and common sense can only deprecate.

In the Bushveld, where doctors are scarce, my presence was invariably taken as an invitation to submit physiological or psychical perplexities to the arbitrament of an expert. It was useless for me to point out that I was in the first place a 'Government doctor' and had no desire whatever to compete with my colleagues in practice, and secondly that I was interested in children alone. Where circumstances were urgent, and immediate intervention was called for, I could not refuse whatever help I could give, but the majority who demanded consultation could just as well have gone to the nearest village, however far away it was, for their perplexities — with the exception of some cases already referred to — were neither grave nor peculiar to themselves.

There came, one grand morning when I had finished inspection and had arranged to go botanizing with some of the class, a patriarchal farmer who insisted that he should have half an hour in strict privacy with the doctor. For the first twenty minutes he discussed the iniquities of the Government; ten further minutes were occupied in telling me how much he had lost through the *wildebeest* breaking his fences. By that time I had learned that one loses by haste, and much sooner reaches one's objective if one tries to emulate the father of the most beautiful Jemima and exercise unbounded patience. So I listened, with suitable monosyllabic interjections, which is the customary Bushveld method of showing interest in what is being told to you, and at last was rewarded by an explanation. Many years ago my visitor had been 'magnetized' by a Cape boy whom he had thrashed for some dereliction of duty. Since then he had suffered from vague pains in his inside that no treatment could cure. Did I think that if he went and saw the new Coolie doctor at Pretoria, whose marvellous cures were advertised even to the far north, he might get 'demagnetized'? He was detailed in his description of how the curse had originally been put upon him. The scoundrel had mixed iron filings with his coffee and he had inadvertently drunk the coffee. Three hours later he had had his first bout of indescribable pain.

Although he said it was indescribable, he proceeded to try and describe it, and gave a very fair account of what one would have expected from a patient who suffered from tape-worm.

I advised him, as a preliminary to consulting the Coolie doctor, to take a decoction of pumpkin seeds. My patriarchal friend assumed an expression that might have done credit to the Commander-in-Chief of the King of Syria when the prophet told him to wash seven times in the river Jordan. I expected him to emulate the Field-Marshal, who, as the Vulgate has it,

Iratus recedebat, dicens . . . Cum ergo vertisset se, et abiret, indignans.

But he remained. 'Is that a sure remedy against magnetism, Doctor?' I told him that for *his* magnetism it was a proved remedy. If it failed he could always try the Coolie doctor. But I put as much confidence in my voice as I could when I told him that it rarely failed. That white lie will be forgiven me. I cannot tell my students that pumpkin seeds are a sure remedy against tape-worm infestation; I can only state that they very often succeed in expelling the brute, and are at least safe and can be tried at home. He left, much comforted. I met him by the roadside, several months later, when he more than repaid me by extracting my car from a slough with his donkey team. The tape-worm had been conquered and he was no longer plagued by inside pains. I thought it advisable to comment on the uncertainty of permanently curing cases of magnetism, for tape-worms have a nasty way of recurring, but advised a repetition of treatment should the magic start working again.

One of my attendance officers, a burly, sensible fellow who

as a youth had gone on commando with the Boer forces, been captured and exiled to the Bermudas, told me when we were lying under a common mosquito net at our camping-place that the farm on which we were was a 'ghost' farm. Strange balls of lurid light — he had seen them himself — gambolled over the grass and left a sulphurous smell behind. He had chased one on his bicycle once, but had hurtled into an ant-heap before he could get close enough to investigate what it was. 'But I have no doubt', he assured me, 'that it is something supernatural. A man was murdered here, some years ago, and it is quite likely that his spirit is restless.' He took it as a matter of course that there are ghosts. Under what conditions they manifested themselves he could not explain, but he related several personal experiences that had convinced him that the restless dead return. He told his stories without much emotion, and his personal credibility was excellent, but there was no way of testing his facts. He had been a transport driver, and on one occasion had been asked to convey a rich prospector's dead body to the coast. He consented on condition that the body was suitably coffined. The deceased had been very corpulent in life, and there was no skilled assistance to embalm the body, so it was decided to lay a bed of tar in the large coffin, put the corpse on that, and fill the coffin with tar, after which the lid was securely screwed down. But on the long, hot journey through the Lowveld, the tar melted, and dripped from the seams of the coffin. The native attendants became aware that something out of the way was being carried on the ox-wagon, and deserted.

'I was left alone that night,' said the Attendance Officer, 'for not a soul would come near the wagon. I had to tie up the oxen to prevent them ranging, and then I had to walk miles to a native location to get other men. There I found that my own natives had already been there and spread the news that we were carrying a dead man, and no one would volunteer to come with me. I trudged back, and when I came in sight of the wagon — it was a fine moonlight night, Doctor — I saw the dead man sitting by my fire. A frightfully fat man, Doctor, and all black, covered with tar, and with the same old hat that I had seen on his head when he lay in the coffin. But I was so tired, Doctor, that I did not care to turn back, and although my heart was in my boots I went up to him and said, "Good evening, Uncle—if you sit so close to the fire you'll burn with all that tar on you." "Tar?" he said, just like that, Doctor. "Tar? There's a smell of it about, yes, but it's from your wagon, and from what I hear . . ." and would you believe it, Doctor, it wasn't my dead man at all but an old chap who had outspanned beyond the ridge. Very good he was to me, too. His boys helped me out of my difficulty, and I brought the corpse safely to Durban. But whenever I smell tar, Doctor. . . .'

The mosquitos droned outside the net; it was much too hot to sleep.

'So that wasn't a ghost. Where, then, have you seen one?'

'Several times, Doctor. Not exactly a ghost, for the person wasn't dead yet, if you get what I mean. When we were going down by train to Simonstown, from where they shipped us to Bermuda, you know, I saw young Elias Swart. He was a commando mate of mine, but we'd lost touch, and when I was captured he was somewhere with Ben Viljoen's commando in Rustenburg. But he came and sat next to me on the seat. I naturally thought that he was one of our batch, and began to talk to him, but he only shook his head, and then the others started laughing at me for talking to myself as they said. They hadn't seen him. When I explained, one old uncle told me that Elias had been captured long ago. "He's just as much a prisoner as you are, son," he said. "Then where is he?" I asked. "I don't rightly know," he replied, 'but belike we'll meet him.' We did, Doctor. When we arrived at Cape Town, the parson came to meet us, and he told us that there were lots of our fellows at the Green Point Camp. "I've just come from conducting a funeral," he said. "A young Rustenburger. He died of measles. Perhaps some of you may know him; his name is Elias Swart."

'And how do you account for it, Doctor, that the natives can foretell things? I can take you to one who will do it for you. He'll make a fire and put powder on it, so that it smokes, and in the smoke you'll see all sorts of things. I've seen them myself. . . .'

I was not impressed. A few months later the late Mr. Justice Morice, whose credibility was at least as good as that of my Attendance Officer, told me that he had seen a picture of the Union Buildings on Meintjies Kop some years before the plans had been drawn. 'The Kafir made a fire and threw something on it that made it smoke, and as I looked the smoke was thick and smooth like a frosted window. I saw on it a clear picture of a rocky hill-side, where people were excavating and erecting scaffolding. That vanished and I saw part of a building, with the same background. A wisp of wind carried the smoke away, but when it re-formed I saw a finished building in or upon it, with two funny little turrets. I remember I thought those turrets were quaint — out of keeping, somehow, with the rest of the building. The smoke made my eyes smart, and I turned away. When I looked again there was just smoke and nothing more. Then three years later, I noticed men at work on Meintjies Kop and I remembered what I had seen, for what I saw was exactly like the second picture in the smoke. And when I saw the Union Buildings finished, they were just like what I had seen that evening. Even the quaint little turrets were there, and I've always thought them rather ugly.'

Judge Morice told me this experience in the dining-room of the Judge President of the Transvaal Supreme Court, the late Mr. Justice (later Chief Justice) de Villiers, a man of great experience and generally regarded as one of the best lawyers we have produced. He agreed cordially with his colleague. 'You may sneer at it,' he declared, 'but that sort of thing needs investigation, and you doctors should try and find out what it means. I've seen the fellow myself, and although there's a lot of humbug about him, he certainly does seem to have a gift of clairvoyance, and what is more, he seems capable of transmitting it to others. He made a fire for me, too, and I saw in the smoke something that had happened in the past — as a matter of fact, I saw myself just at the time and in the circumstances when I was wounded. So far as I could see, the conditions and surroundings were quite similar to what I remembered of them.'

In the Bushveld I met some who had been 'born with the caul', and could be regarded as seers. From the Middleveld came the prophet, Nicolas van Rensburg, who reaped some reputation in the Boer War because he foretold events that happened days afterwards. When I met him he was already old and arthritic, with a face and personality that impressed even those who did not believe in his gifts of clairvoyance and clairaudience. He was certainly not a 'medium' in the ordinary acceptance of that word, but rather a mystic, an introvert much occupied with his own musings which he tried to explain symbolically. Constitutionally he was the asthenic, leptosomic type, with long thin fingers and relatively long limbs, a person easily depressed by weather changes, and like all introverts, highly emotional. I could not find evidence of any psychic gifts in him, and the few 'foretellings' that he made proved of no more evidential value than that he had studied the political situation with some care. But, although he was an uneducated and uncultured man, he had an innate sense of the beautiful, and looked upon life with the far-seeing eyes of a poet. His rhapsodies were the result of deeply felt emotions that he could not express in appropriate language because his vocabulary was not large while his visions were extremely variegated. He had the habit of using one word to express two different meanings, and of repeating the same phrase, slightly inverted, over again, not to emphasize it but as if he delighted in its assonance and rhythm. Schizoid personalities have that habit, and he was a typical schizoid — a divided mind — whose imagination was so vivid that he had no difficulty whatever in persuading himself that what he imagined were realities. So long as that type remains like that, mildly critical but at no time anti-social, it is comparatively harmless. There are many dreamers and fantastics in every community, and to some of them we owe what is best in literature and art. Unfortunately, Nicolas van Rensburg lacked the technique necessary to give form and substance to his dreaming, and his memory survives merely because he was an exceedingly kind-hearted old gentleman who 'saw' events that lay in the future and sometimes, apparently, prophesied correctly.

I met another 'seer', a strong, virile, middle-aged man, who found his gift entirely unpleasant and wanted something to enable him to get rid of it. As a child he had seen his uncle being engulfed in a quicksand, and had come running to his mother, in a great state of excitement, to tell her. He had been soundly whipped with a quince stick, for his uncle on that day had been mildly interested in a case before the circuit court, and had laughed heartily when informed of the boy's 'dream'. A month later, however, the uncle crossed a drift, when the river was in flood, and missed the fairway. His horse floundered in a quicksand and its rider only saved himself by swimming to shore. After this the boy enjoyed the privileges and the miseries of a prophet on a small scale. His school-fellows plagued him to foretell what questions would be asked at examinations; his elders asked him to predict the state of the weather. In several cases his 'foretellings' proved to be accurate anticipations, but as he grew older he became less able to foretell. 'Since I married, Doctor,' he said, lugubriously, 'I only see things in a dream, occasionally, but it's very disturbing, and it upsets both of us. Mostly when folk are to die. Yes, Doctor, they sometimes do die, but of late years I've not dared speak about it. If Doctor could give me something for it. . . .'

There was a young man, altogether unsophisticated and quite unaware that he possessed special gifts, who in trances could communicate with those who have passed over. The District Surgeon, who knew him well, confessed to me that the youngster was a puzzle to him. 'He had a bad attack of malaria, very bad indeed, with cerebral symptoms, but he pulled through it all right, and a year or two later he began to get these attacks. He goes rigid, but if you ask him anything he responds, usually not in his own voice. They've had séances with him, and he has really said the most amazing things. I've made notes of some of them, but you'd better judge for yourself.' I met him watering a patch of beans in the parental garden. He was a tall, thinly boned youth of nineteen, shy and awkward, with an intelligence quotient of about 85. We arranged that he should come and be psychologically tested, for he certainly seemed to be 'psychic' and to possess the gift of mediumship, but he never turned up, and I lost sight of him. Possibly, in time, he may develop into another 'seer' and win some of old Nicolas's reputation.

Among the natives such gifts of wizardry are firmly believed in. I have met several of the native *inyangas* or herbalists, and of their more esoteric colleagues, the *isanusis* or diviners. The former are of no great importance; they accomplish whatever success they obtain by means of the application of shrewd common sense or of familiar drugs inextricably mixed with a variety of native remedies. Epsom salts and powdered nitre were the standard ingredients in their mixtures that I tested. In the Bushveld they have no legitimate standing, but in Natal they are properly licensed and can compete with the registered medical men, who have, indeed, more than once complained about their competition. Very few of them possess the rudiments of diagnostic skill, and they far too often forget the Hippocratic admonition 'nil nocere' so that their practice is not altogether beneficial to the natives. The properly initiated and trained *isanusi* is a much more interesting individual. The first one I met had a great reputation in his district, and I owe my introduction to him to the good services of the native driver who took me, in the spider hired by the School Board, to a school that I could not possibly reach by motor car. The native driver was a Cape boy, of mixed Hottentot and Bushman ancestry with a dash of white blood in him. My grandfather had baptized him on a mission station, which created, as he naively put it, a bond between us. I found him most communicative, and when I halted the spider, to collect a fine specimen of *Eulophia speciosa*, a terrestrial orchid with splendid chrome yellow flowers that grew in a swamp some yards away from the roadside, his interest quickened. 'Does the *baas* gather it to make medicine with?' he asked. I explained, and we chatted cheerfully about simples and philtres, and discussed whether one could by magic influence the course of human events. 'The *baas* must meet the *isanusi*', he said, finally, and cracked his long whip to emphasize what a fine thing it would be if the *baas* and the *isanusi* could discuss such things in a friendly fraternal spirit.

In due course his friend turned up. A fine, upstanding old man, who in his early adolescence must have been an inspiration to any sculptor. A finely moulded face, and clear, shrewd, understanding eyes; long, shapely hands, now slightly tremulous from senility, but still strong, with the extensor tendons sharply defined in ridges. Unfortunately, our interview had to be conducted through an interpreter, for to my shame, I have no Zulu. And as the native driver knew so much about me, and about my grandfather, collusion could not be guarded against. The old man threw his bones for my benefit — the phalangeal bones of a monkey I made them out to be, although there was one human cuneiform among them — and most correctly described some of my past history. When it came to 'foretellings' he was much more diffident. I made careful notes of the places — he could not foretell the times — when this or that was to happen to me. There were six items in the catalogue, none of them particularly exciting. One — the third prophesied — occurred on the journey home; the fifth happened fourteen years later. Of the others I have as yet had no experience, but there is still time for his prognostications to come true. Later on I saw some of the 'practice' of this particular *isanusi*. It confirmed my original impression that the old man was very wise, very shrewd, and very observing, with an astonishing knowledge of human nature and considerable experience of psychiatry. In comparison with him the *inyangas* I have met were tyros, 'yet but in the lower school'. Yet it was neither an *inyanga* nor an *isanusi* who in my Bushveld wanderings startled and perplexed me the most. It was a nondescript native, with so many strains of diversified humanity in him that it would be difficult to classify him in any racial category. He was the person who made one see things in smoke, and was said to be able to speak with the dead, a veritable wizard of Endor. I had much difficulty in tracing him, but at last ran him down on a farm where he herded cattle. His master testified to his extraordinary cleverness, but doubted if I would benefit by it. 'He's so old and decrepit that he wont do anything now. We just let him imagine that he is of some use.'

I found him at the huts, a wizened little ochreous-coloured fellow, whose great age was evident in his everted eyelids and almost total absence of buttock flesh. He could speak Dutch, and many native dialects, and knew a few words of English, for he had been born in the old Colony, of slave parents, possibly himself a slave. He could not tell his age, and had no interest in it. I judged him to be between eighty and ninety. He was so frail and skinny that it seemed hopeless to test him. But in conversation he displayed an astonishing agility, a quickness of perception and a readiness in reply that showed him still to be highly intelligent.

Yes, he said, in answer to a direct question, he had shown the big *baas* from Pretoria things in the smoke. That was many, many years ago. Of late he had not done such things. It took a deal out of a man to do such things, and he was no longer strong. How could one continue to be strong and healthy if one did not, occasionally, get a drop of the sap of the vine? And here, of course, it was a monstrous crime to give even a drop of the sap of the vine to a creature. Yes, on occasion he had spoken to some of those who had passed over. Yes, he doubted not but that he could still do so, did necessity arise, and were he to have a drop of the sap. . . .

'I'll give you some as medicine' I interrupted. 'I am a doctor, and if I think you need it, there can be no question of crime.'

A doctor? But that altered the case. And the *baasie* so young looking. Was the *baasie* married? Perhaps . . . after all, he was old and weak, but for a doctor! It needed a terrible lot of strength to call up the spirits, and he could not rightly say that he could manage it, not having had proper nourishment for days and days, and without a drop . . .

'You shall have whatever you like, *Outa*. I promise.'

Then, perhaps, it might be managed. But not here. Not on the farm. The farm was not the proper place to call the spirits to.

'I will take you where you wish to be. There's the car. Can you come along now, *Outa*?'

Now? But most certainly not! Even a doctor — no, pardon, he meant no offence, but a doctor most of all should know that such things could not be managed on an empty stomach, nor in broad daylight. If he could prepare himself . . .

I felt his pulse. It beat slowly, fewer than forty beats per minute — a Napoleonic pulse or that of extreme old age. From the 'medical comforts' in the car, I prescribed two

tots of sweet wine, one *statim sumendum*, the other *si opus sit*.
Technically it was unlawful. I was not the man's medical
attendant, and my prescription was a real placebo.

Then I arranged to fetch him that night, after supper, and
take him a few miles into the veld. It was stipulated that
I should come unaccompanied, for 'folk say all sorts of nasty
things about me, and I am an old man and all for peace'.

I drove back to the homestead, not much edified by the
slightly flippant tone of the interview, and in doubts whether
I should keep the appointment. My host, the farmer, was
but mildly interested. The old native had enjoyed a reputation years ago, but was now rarely consulted, and few knew
about his magic powers. There could be no harm in trying
him, but I must not expect anything but some hocus-pocus.
That was all that had occurred the last time, some years
back, when the old creature had been invited to display his
powers on the farm stoep. To be sure, the old creature had
said that with so many folk about one could hardly expect
the spirits to come, but that was all in the way of excuse.
Still, if I was really interested in such things ... and my
host shrugged his shoulders to intimate that he had no
further concern in the matter.

I called for the *Outa*. He bounded into the car with
alacrity, and was as interested in its fittings, especially the
electric switches, as a schoolboy. He was dressed in an old
coat, ragged and much too big for him, and trousers so
plentifully patched that it was difficult to distinguish the
original cloth. He wore no shirt, and his feet, of which the
arches had dropped, were bare. He asked for a bit of tobacco, but placed it in his pocket and said he would chew it
later. He chattered cheerfully, almost like a child, about
many things, but refrained from any allusion to the business

for which I had brought him. When we came to a gate, he hopped off and ran with his wizened little legs to open it, climbing back like a monkey. We drove on a by-road, deeply rutted on both sides, and as it was dark, we had to go carefully for fear of damaging the differential against the 'middleman', the central ridge between the ruts, which was grass grown and might have hidden protruding stones. A few miles from the homestead, where some thorn trees grew, he invited me to stop. I drew the car into the open veld, away from the road, and we got out.

The old fellow's demeanour now was quite different from what it had been when we were driving. He walked slowly over the veld until he came to a spot where the grass was low and thin and the ground stony. He gathered a few dry sticks and bits of grass, asked me for a match, and lit the little pile. Then he wandered around and gleaned more firewood, piling it on the blaze, and adding the still green twigs of the thorn trees to make it smoke. I turned off the car lights.

'Well, *Outa*, what now?'

'The master must squat there' — he pointed to a tuft of grass — 'and the master must look into the smoke, and see what pictures there are in it. Sometimes the pictures come, and sometimes they don't. Who is it the master would like to call up?'

'Can you call up anyone, *Outa*?'

'Not anyone, master. Not those who have just passed over. They are not used to it yet, and it is difficult even for the old ones to come when one calls. The master must not mind if they do not answer. When I was younger, it was easier. Now I don't know. But master must tell me who it is that master wishes me to see.'

'All right. I want you to ask for *Baas* Theophrastus von Hohenheim. He's been dead many years. . . .'

'Was he a missionary, master? I don't think that will do. Missionary and pastor folk — they are difficult to call up. I don't think, master, they like it. . . .'

'This *Baas* wasn't a missionary — far from it, *Outa*. And he's been dead hundreds of years.'

'The name is like that of a missionary, master. And I doubt . . .' he shook his head, and sat down, bending almost over the fire. He put his chin in both his cupped hands, resting the elbows on his knees. The smoke blew on his face, but his eyes kept open and he did not blink. I got up — he had not told me to remain squatting — and felt his temporal artery; the pulse in it was beating very slowly; the artery itself I felt thickened and hard under my finger. I touched his eyeball — he had lost his conjunctival reflex. He was in a trance as complete as I had seen in any medium.

The fire crackled, as if in protest against the uninflammable thorn twigs that made it smoke. The smoke itself grew in volume, but I could see nothing in or upon it, and when I came too close it made my eyes smart. Then I saw the *Outa's* hands drop, and his chin came forward. His features, wizened and wrinkled, stood out clearly as a spurt of flame leaped up and illumined it. He began to speak, in a queer, sing-song voice, in German. A draggled German, curiously clipped, but understandable, with consecutive sentences. He gestured with his hands, clenched his fist and struck his knee with it as if to emphasize a particular word. Then his chin fell on his breast and he muttered a few words whose import I could not make out. His German sentences had been clear and lucid, and although I could not recollect them from my reading of Paracelsus, they were astonishingly similar in style and construction to what that empiric might have written. My professional interest overcame my surprise, and I attended to the old native, whose breathing seemed to have almost stopped. His pulse was still slow and good, so I shook him, and he started up.

'Did master see him?' he asked, eagerly, and when I shook my head he was plainly disappointed.

'Such a fierce *baas*,' he explained. 'Nothing like any of the others that I have ever called. And he talked such outlandish stuff I could not make head or tail of what he said.'

'He talked quite understandably, *Outa*. What did he look like?'

'Why, nothing like what people look like now, master. No decent trousers or a hat, but with a sheeps-skin on his head. And so fierce, master, he almost frightened me to death.'

I made a note to find out if Bombastus wore a wig, ever. I am not sure on that point yet. When we drove back, after I had given the *Outa* another drink, which I felt he had earned, I tested his knowledge of German.

'What's an *auerhahn*, *Outa*?'

'I don't know, master. Is it something one can drink?'

'Didn't the fierce master tell you what it was?'

'No, *baas*. I couldn't understand what he said.'

'Did he tell you anything about pheasants or partridges, *Outa*?'

'Oh no, *baas*, he just blackguarded me, I think, he was so fierce. But some of them don't like to be disturbed for nothing. It is a pity master did not see him in the smoke.'

I have since traced some of the sentences that the *Outa* spoke that evening, although I can find nothing about an *auerhahn* in Paracelsus. There is a passage about pheasants that runs somewhat like the *Outa's* but it is much less precise.

CHAPTER XIII

DINGAAN'S DAY

The one day upon which the Bushveld relaxes, completely and wholeheartedly, is Dingaan's Day.

It falls on December 16th, and commemorates the victory of the Emigrant Boers over the Zulu chief at the battle of Blood River on the historic Sunday, December 16th, 1838. The anniversary of that day is celebrated as a public holiday in accordance with the vow taken by the Boers that if God granted them the victory, that day should in perpetuity be consecrated to the honour of God. For many years the custom of remembering the day was observed sporadically, but with the re-birth of national consciousness after the Boer War, it gained support and popularity as the one typically Afrikaans festival of the year. With Union it was given official recognition. Dingaan's Day, December 16th, was made an official holiday for all the four Provinces.

There are to-day no fewer than eleven official holidays in the Union of South Africa — New Year's Day, Good Friday, Easter Monday, Ascension Day, Empire Day (formerly the birthday of Alexandrina Victoria of happy memory), Union Day, May 31st, the anniversary of the day on which the peace of Vereeniging was signed as well as of the day on which Union was declared, Arbor Day, the first Monday in October, formerly known as Wiener's Day after the member of the old Cape parliament who had been responsible for its introduction, Dingaan's Day, Christmas, and Boxing Day. The first promulgated official holiday, April 6th, the day of van Riebeeck's landing, has been forgotten, and is kept merely by a few enthusiasts who honour the Founder's memory. Four of our public holidays are church festivals, whose meaning and significance are not very plain to a population that is preponderantly non-Christian, but as the consummation of Union was taken, by the Christian minority in the land, to be a definite gesture on the part of the Almighty, or is so declared to be in the Union Act, the inclusion of these church festivals in the list of our holidays may be taken as a grateful recognition of the Divine kindliness. The selection of Dingaan's Day as recognition of the Afrikaans national sentiment is more difficult to explain, especially when one considers that the object of celebrating it is not to honour the degenerate tyrant of the Zulus but to commemorate the breaking of his power and prestige and the liberation of the Boers from the ever-present fear of his reprisals. Nor, if the truth must be said, is the event that is remembered on that day of such vital importance to all South Africa as it was to the party of emigrant Boers at the time. As a child the story of the Blood River fight made no great impression on me; I was much more stimulated by the death ride at Mars le Tour, the Armada, the siege of Leyden, Ivry, and such like episodes. Told baldly, as Cory tells the story, there is indeed little in it to arouse a child's enthusiasm.

'Full daylight showed the Boers that their camp was being surrounded by many thousands of Zulu warriors. Their approach, though frightful, presented a beautiful appearance . . . they came forward in thirty-six regiments each consisting of from nine to ten hundred men. This estimate may seem very high, but when it is remembered that Dingaan saw his power and perhaps his existence threatened, he would send the largest force he could against the danger, thirty thousand warriors may not have been under the mark. The fight was most furious on both sides, but with regard to the results, it was exceedingly one-sided. The Zulu guns were absolutely useless against the Boers, not one was hit. And their assegais, though hurled in thousands, were scarcely more effective, for only one man in the camp was wounded. But, on the other hand, the Boers entrenched in their wagon stockade, mowed down the Zulus in hundreds as they came within shot. Added to this, the cannon gave the Boers an advantage which more than counterbalanced the superiority in numbers of the enemy. After this fight had continued for some time, Pretorius, fearing the ammunition might run short, gave orders for the gates of the camp to be opened, and a large body of Boers to rush out and charge the diminishing ranks. This was done. For a time the Zulus stood firm, but the increasing carnage among them caused them to turn and flee — scattering in all directions. The Boers chased parties of them for about three hours when further numbers were shot ... Two wounded outside, together with the casualty in the camp, were the only casualties on the Boer side. On the side of the Zulus it is difficult to estimate the number, but three thousand has been put down as the number killed without reckoning the wounded. The grounds around the camp were thickly scattered with corpses, and many were in the ditch and the river, the blood-stained water of which on this occasion was the origin of the name Blood river' (Cory: *The Rise of South Africa*, vol. IV).

That is the plain unvarnished story. Compared to the trials and dangers of other pioneers — the trek of the Mormons to reach the safety of Salt Lake, for instance — the privations endured by the Voortrekkers seem almost trivial; they can, at all events, be matched by the deeds and derring-do of the men who colonized the frontiers of the Cape Colony and fought against the Bushmen with their poisoned arrows and against the frontier Kafirs. There were other exploits, beside Blood River, that deserve commemoration, and in the honour and glory that the pioneers reflect, not only the Transvaal shares but the older Province also. That in itself makes the claim for Dingaan's Day as a general holiday an arrogation that could be, and sometimes was, resented by those who are of opinion that we should remember all the Voortrekkers, all our pioneers, from van Riebeeck onwards, and not single out a special, and after all not especially magnificent victory over the natives, for particular remembrance and celebration. Nor is it advisable, or expedient to signalize a victory obtained with so little sacrifice. Let us rather, say those who object to Dingaan's Day, honour the Voortrekkers by holidaying on a day to be known as 'Voortrekker' or 'Pioneer' Day, preferably on a date that has no relation to massacre and victory, and make our homage to these intrepid men and women something in which all sections of the community, white and black alike, can share, hurrahing them not because they killed and conquered but because they endured, accomplished and achieved and laid the foundations of a civilization that should be common to all so far as its benefits and its culture are concerned. To that the reply has always been that Dingaan's Day is no ordinary festival, but the observance of a solemn obligation laid upon the descendants of the Trekkers to give thanks to God for deliverance from great danger — a religious more than a community festival, a day of prayer and worship altogether different from an ordinary holiday. As such it should give no offence to native susceptibilities, for the crushing of Dingaan's tyranny released the Bantu from an oppression more savage than we nowadays can contemplate. The native, however, may not think so. He is not so democratic as to believe in the doctrine that every man has the right to oppress himself; he still believes that it is the chieftain's function to do whatever oppression there is to be done, and he may prefer one of his own race to be the oppressor rather than one of alien extraction. And blood kin of the Trekkers in the other provinces may think that their own forebears, who did not trek but stayed and worked out their own salvation, obtaining self-government and a liberty as complete and as rational as that which the Trekkers found north of the Vaal, deserve special commemoration, apart altogether from the festival that remembers the fight of Blood River. Logically, too, the feat to be remembered is the first and most pioneering effort of white men in this country—their landing on the shores of Table Bay in the autumn of 1652, for that was an adventure as great and as daring as any of which South Africa may justly feel proud. The Bushveld has not thought much about the ins and outs of the matter. It is content to honour the obligation yearly, and to hold festival on the sixteenth of December, without caring what logic or common sense may say.

On that day people from all neighbouring parts gather at some central spot convenient for such an assembly. Wagons and donkey carts are arranged in circle; where possible the old Trekker custom of forming a *laager* is followed, though those who can afford to do so bring tents and marquees for their better and more comfortable accommodation. The day opens, when the eastern sky begins to be flecked with the light of dawn, with a salvo fired by a commando of mounted men and boys. The religious nature of the holiday is recognized by the programme, which provides for prayer meetings and service in the early morning, and possibly for another short sermon in the early afternoon. Sandwiched between these services are sports, entertainments for the children, and in the evening the general meetings round the camp-fires. On such occasions the Bushveld turns out in its live-liest, gaudiest garb; one sees it at its best, for there is little of the drab, monotonous calm of daily life; everything is lively, animated, joyous, vociferous, friendly, companion-able, exuberantly tolerant. The midday meal, served in the open, on trestle tables spread under the shade of giant trees, is an event of the day. Days of preparation have been spent in making it something to be looked forward to and some-thing to be remembered. Cates and comfits, baked meats and ample supplies of vegetables, and for drink coffee and tea and a modicum of peach or wine brandy, are taken from the wagons, each visitor bringing a share and everything going into a common stock to be served out by the women who are kept very busy with the work of providing for so many guests. At my first Dingaan's Day meeting, I took notes of the variety of viands provided, for I have always been interested in food and feeding. A community's cookery is some index to its culture, perhaps a better one than its crime or its educational progress. And among the Bushveld women there are still excellent cooks, who have had good training and who have behind them the culinary tradition of both the East and the West. But no cook can triumph with bad material, and the pity of it is that in the Bushveld the material for preparing a good meal is not generally obtain-able. The beef is always stringy and tough, because the cattle are starved for months during the year and never stall fed. Mutton is fair, and especially succulent in Decem-ber after grazing on the fresh, lush grass that springs up so luxuriantly after the first summer rains. Game too is then at its best, though never, except in the case of birds, too fat. It must be larded and braized, carefully marinaded for some days before cooking, and liberally basted. Vegetables are plentiful in summer, and the method of serving them is that handed down by tradition, steaming or parboiling, followed by simmering in fat or butter until they are thoroughly tender when they are dished up with a sprinkling of grated nutmeg over them.

None of the dishes that I met with at these gargantuan meals were new to me, except one. Many were old Cape dishes, in which both East and West had influenced the preparation. There was the *bredie*, a meat and vegetable stew, similar to the Chilean 'charquican' and the Chinese vegetable chop sueys. There was *soesaties*, globs of mutton and pork, marinaded in wine and vinegar spiced heavily with coriander, pepper, turmeric and tamarind, strung on wooden skewers, baked over the coals on a gridiron and served with 'pap' (undrained rice) and a curry sauce. There was salt rib of mutton, coriander spiced and roasted over the coals; mutton 'carbonades' fried over a wood fire and savoury with the impregnated aromatic smell of the smoke; hunter's stew, made of partridges and young bustards and a haunch of venison put into an iron pot and stewed with lard, without the addition of water, until everything was blended into a succulent, appetizing entrée. There were sucking pigs, stuffed with bread crumbs and raisins; legs of venison roasted and abundantly and most artistically larded; chickens and partridges roasted and served cold, to spare the drudgery and time needed to cook them on festival day. The bread was home-made, excellent and satisfying, baked in ovens scraped out of a termite mound and stoked with veld bush.

The dessert was a variety of sweets, jellies, custards, the tricky 'milk custard' open pies for which the recipe has been handed down through generations, though no one's 'melk-tert' is quite similar to his neighbour's.

The dish that was new to me was ox head, baked whole, with the skin left on, in a large ant hole. It was a most terrifying dish to look at. The immense head, with the horns left on and the hair singed but not wholly burned off, was brought forward on a big piece of wood, carried by two cheerfully grinning natives, and its appearance was greeted with excited anticipatory cheers by the guests. To me it looked both fearsome and unappetizing. Its sunken eyes still had a semblance of indignant glare in them. But there could be no mistake about its succulency. The carver dextrously sliced the thick skin away, exposing the soft cheek flesh, baked to a turn, and handed round portions. Mine was the most delicious meat that I have tasted in the Bushveld; its tenderness was melting, for it had been baked for hours very slowly under that thick protective layer of skin and retained all its juice and savouriness. So much was I impressed by it that I determined on the first available opportunity to try the method myself. That opportunity did not present itself for some months, but later on a farmer friend sent me an ox's head, cooked in his large brick baking oven on the farm. 'All you need do is to warm it up in your own oven, if you have one large enough,' he wrote. My own oven fits a moderate sized turkey but could not manage that monstrosity. The chef at the Pretoria Club thought that his might do, and permission was given to serve the head in the club dining-room, on condition that the party was screened off. General Botha happened to be dining at the club that night, and when he heard of the arrangement, begged to be allowed to assist. 'There's nothing like it,' he said, 'and I've not eaten if for years.' We ate that head to the great embarrassment of the scandalized waiters, but it carried enough meat to allow them, too, to assure themselves afterwards how excellent it was. But it needs some courage to carve a horned ox head whose eyes carry that indignant, reproachful glare.

There was never much drinking at these feasts; although large quantities of coffee and tea were consumed, strong drink was taken in moderation, and one rarely saw anyone the worse for his libations. In the Bushveld much brandy is distilled from peaches or from the fruit of the maroela tree (*Sclerocarya caffra*) or more rarely from prickly pears (*Opuntia tuna*) an imported pest whose fruit, however, is excellent eating when picked early in the morning while it is yet refreshingly cool. Peach brandy is a fiery, almost colourless liquid; when well matured it is drinkable when diluted with water, but in its pristine state it is very powerfully intoxicating. Maroela brandy is a pale creamy liquor, with a peculiar, pleasant-smelling aroma; its alcoholic strength is equal to that of peach brandy, and as it is never allowed to mature properly, its effects when consumed are usually lamentable. Gallons of it are made, and apparently used, but for all that drunkenness is rare. The natives use beer, made from millet grain, a pleasant, sour-tasting drink of a relatively low alcoholic standard. Wine brandy, which comes from the Cape Province, is usually good, but its price prevents it from being generally used. Wine itself is almost never seen; so far as alcohol is concerned, the Bushveld is a spirit-drinking community. Which is a pity, for good, lightly alcoholized wine is a civilizing factor, while its vitamin content is not to be despised. The general opinion in South Africa is that at all costs it must be kept from the native population. The natives may drink their maroela brandy and their beer, but they must not be permitted to drink a light wine. It is a statutory crime to give them wine; a greater crime to sell wine to them. Every year many white men and women are convicted of this heinous crime, for illicit liquor selling is common in all urban and in some rural areas. That has always seemed to me an illogical prohibition, as illogical as it is to forbid wine to a child and create in him the desire to drink it because it is something that his elders drink. It is better to teach the child to use wine in moderation, to let him differentiate between good and bad wine, and to make him sensible to the value of wine as a table beverage. In wine-producing countries children learn at an early age how not to abuse wine; drunkenness in such countries is far less common than in spirit-drinking communities. In South Africa the wine industry is the only industry that can support itself, that needs no bolstering by bounties and that has been carried on through generations by producers who as a class rank among the most cultured among the community. To tell them, as the law tells them, that they are producing a commodity that is rank poison to three-fourths of the population while they are allowed to sell it to the other fourth, is to assert something that neither logic nor common sense can support. The provision of light, unfortified table wine to the native population, far from being a curse, would be a beneficial factor in civilizing the aboriginals, if it is allowed under proper supervision and care is taken that the wine is pure and unadulterated. The present restrictions on wine are absurd and anti-social in their effect, for they encourage the drinking of beer and spirits, put a premium on illicit commerce in spirits, and create in the native a desire for strong drink that, no matter how well the law is enforced, he is bound sooner or later to satisfy. Nothing has retarded his progress so much as this nonsensical prohibition, to him, of something that his white superiors are at complete liberty to buy and use. The fact that his chiefs and headmen are said to clamour for such prohibition leaves me cold and unconvinced. Their attitude is influenced by what they have seen of the evils of spirit drinking, and they are absolutely unaware of what light wine is — they have had no experience of such table beverages, and they cannot know that a light table wine is far less potent, as an intoxicant, than old Kafir beer that has amassed a much higher alcoholic content.

Dingaan's Day is the one time in the year when Afrikaans nationalism displays the best of its culture and makes an attempt to live up to its aspirations. There is a danger that the patriotism for which it pleads, and strives to inculcate, may be of the narrow kind that engenders hatred and animosity towards those whose culture and tradition are not its own. That danger was very apparent when the day was used for political propaganda at a time when party feeling ran high in the Transvaal and the ranks were divided into Botha and anti-Botha folk. Arrangements for holding the festival were usually left in the hands of a local committee, on which the prominent farmers, the teachers, and the clergy all had seats. These committees arranged for speakers for the day, drew up the programme, and collected funds to which everyone contributed according to his means. As there were so many gatherings throughout the Province, the committees had to start work early in the year, and the programmes were often published many months before the event to give those who intended to take part in the festival ample time to provide for their absence from home. Speakers were requisitioned from the towns, and there was great competition to obtain the services of prominent public men for these occasions. The speeches were usually inspiriting, dealing with the history of the Voortrek and the nation as a whole, and uplifting in drawing a moral between the difficulties that the Trekkers had to overcome and the disadvantages of the present.

I, as a new-comer, was immediately pressed into service. The gathering that I attended on my first Dingaan's Day was held at a picturesque farm, in an environment that was semi-tropical in its beauty. There were more than nine hundred visitors, counting grown-ups and children, all very eager and attentive. I was asked to speak on the history of Dingaan's Day, and in my simplicity I spoke for half an hour, telling my audience about what I had heard and read of the trek into Natal and the victory at Blood River. That was in the morning; in the afternoon I was scheduled to address the children. In the interval came the luncheon, and an old gentleman carried his plate towards where I sat, and entered into conversation with me. I found that his father had fought at Blood River and that he himself had been an infant in arms at the time. I felt very foolish, guilty of a gaffe that would be discussed, and conscious that I had elaborated where my knowledge had fallen short. But the old gentleman did not seem to mind. He talked most amiably about the tenderness of the chicken and the rise in the price of tobacco.

When the children assembled, I noticed him in the background, together with other grown-ups. Instead of speechifying to them, I suggested that as we had with us one who knew infinitely more about the Voortrek than I did, Uncle

S—— should tell us about it. The old gentleman was very diffident. He protested that he had lost his false teeth; that he could not 'speak in company'; he made all sorts of excuses, but in the end we gathered round him, informally, and he began to tell us of his own experiences and of what his father had told him. As he warmed to his theme, he displayed just those gifts of narration that appeal to the child. He acted some of his episodes; his voice rang with emotion when he told of the anxious time in the laager, the main laager, where women and children sat waiting for the news of the battle. He told of many exciting escapes, and described how the Trekkers had crossed the high mountains and seen from the top that glorious landscape which is Natal. It was dark when he finished and that night round the camp-fire he told more stories. Listening to his quiet, droning voice, one realized what Dingaan's Day meant to him and those like him. Probably the younger generation, disturbed by the sophisticated interest of the radio and the talking film, does not understand that meaning. For its understanding presupposes personal experience of hardship and suffering, trial and endurance to which the younger generation is a stranger. It connotes an interpretation of life held only by those who have seen its desperate side, where human values dwindle to the minimal in the balance against communal existence. That is an interpretation that often shocks those who forget under what conditions pioneering settlement, in a country teeming with animal and human enemies, is stabilized. It shocked me to hear another old gentleman, a Senator selected, wonderful though it may seem, to represent native interests in parliament, tell of his visit to the kraal of Mojatjie, the vigorous Kafir woman who for generations ruled her tribe with the intrepidity of one of the female sultans of Atjeh before the Cadi of Mecca decreed that no woman could reign over men. 'That night,' he said, 'the native guide tried to stab me. I rolled over and grabbed him, and broke his assegai. Then I bent him across my knee — so' — he made pretence of holding someone down — 'and took out my pocket knife. I had to open it with my teeth, the fellow struggled so, but I managed it all right. I cut his throat, and when we went back, I told the woman that I would treat them all like that if they tried further treachery on us.'

He was an amiable old gentleman, though he played cards very badly, and he had no qualms about cutting a treacherous native's throat.

I found many such old men later on when I attended more Dingaan Day festivals. It seemed that they were not asked to narrate their experiences because most people knew of them; it was a story told before, familiar enough to those who had heard it. But at such gatherings there are many, especially youngsters, who had never listened to these grave seniors and I always urged the committees to choose them to speak on the historic aspect. None is alive to-day — none was alive then — who had actually taken part in the battle, but there were still alive several who had actually experienced the rigours and hardships of the Great Trek. Mrs. Joubert, the widow of General Joubert, a *grande dame* in the true sense of the word, who lived in retirement at Pretoria, was one of those. I have listened to her for hours, when she was in the mood to reminisce, enthralled by the vividness of her descriptions of episodes and emotions. She was a small girl who took part in the Trek, and had seen much of the horrors that were inseparable from it, and she could tell of it in her trenchant homely Afrikaans with an objectiveness astonishing in one who had been dragged through so many miseries and had so vivid a recollection of what had taken place in her childhood.

Some of these personal narratives of survivors of the Trek have been collected; some are preserved in the archives in the shape of letters and log-books. But many are lost, because there was no one to take them down at the Dingaan's Day gatherings where they were told. What remains is enough to give a fair picture of the emigration. Though its details may not compare, in adventurousness or in mass interest, with the stories of pioneers in other parts of the world, they may yet serve as an inspiration and an encouragement. The story of the Emigrant Boers is one that no Bushveld child should forget, and Dingaan's Day, however unsuitably it is named, keeps it alive better than do the schools with their dull disquisitions of what led up to and what followed the Trek. It is a record of courageous achievement of which any community might feel proud, and whoever knows it will find the knowledge useful in judging the character and mettle of the Bushveld men and women fairly.

If it be true that literature is an index of the cultural evolution of a community, the growing Afrikaans literature which is emerging to-day may be taken to exemplify and express what cultural influences there are at work among the people who speak Afrikaans. It concerns itself mainly with facts that are still too strongly blended with primitive emotions to be regarded objectively; it reflects popular views of life that have not been subjected, as yet, to critical analysis; it attempts a record rather than a synthesis of life, and it shuns realities that appear to lie outside the scope of a direct appeal to emotions that it attempts to exploit. One sees in it already the germs of a greater toleration than seemed possible twenty-five years ago, a more charitable interpretation of motive, a more kindly conception of character. The Afrikaans-speaking citizen is gradually learning to readjust his views, to judge more leniently and less sectionally than his father did, with a greater insistence on the common humanity innate in all human nature. As a literature grows it sheds caricature and portrays types rather than peculiarities; it lays stress on rules rather than on exceptions, just as statistics, when mature, deal with percentiles rather than with averages, and take into consideration standard deviation, probable error and distributed zeros. And so far what there is of literature in Afrikaans has grown out of the people. There has been much imitation — some of the best sellers in Afrikaans are ornamented tracings of better things in other languages — but what may be reckoned the best has a cultural influence that it would be difficult to over-value and impossible to ignore.

CHAPTER XIV

THE COOLIE

Mishap upon mishap, one puncture following another so that the tyre covers had to be stuffed with grass to carry me the rest of the way, had dogged me, and in sight of the little town the fan belt — in those days fan belts were made of thin leather and could not be depended on — snapped. That was the nadir of my luck. A cart, driven by a kindly farmer, came up conveniently, and I rode into town behind the heavy ox wagons that carried limestone to the kilns. There was a garage, my Samaritan farmer assured me, and he could recommend its proprietor, though, God be thanked, he had never needed service for a motor car, not having one. Did I fancy the weather? To him it looked much like heavy rain before night.

That was what it looked like to me. Indeed, so threatening had the clouds loomed up from the west that I had hastened, with the usual result that follows incautious haste. But as the garage could be depended on, and as the town probably had lodging house or hotel, a thunderstorm did not matter. It was a Saturday. By Monday morning the rain would have ceased and with chains the roads might be passable.

I climbed down from the cart at the garage, arranged to have my car fetched, cleaned and overhauled and my kit to be sent over to the hotel and walked over to that institution, which, like most of its kind that I patronized in the Province, did not impress me by its comfort, cleanliness or completeness. An outside room, opening on to the back veranda was assigned to me. Its windows and doors were ostensibly mosquito screened, but the wire screening was torn and inadequate, more a danger than a safeguard. I rigged up my camp mosquito netting over the bed, took a bath in water that was indifferently warm, and worked for a while at my notes. The clouds were gathering fast, and long before sunset a heavy purple pall lay across the sky from which lightning, as yet far off, intermittently flashed. When the native waiter came to announce dinner, a few heavy drops of rain, forerunners of the storm, pattered on the iron roof and the low roll of thunder echoed from the hills.

The dinner was similar to many I had eaten at Bushveld hotels, a disgrace to the cook and an offence to a guest. Watery soup, flavoured with marmite, tinned salmon garnished with what was called mayonnaise sauce, venison that was tough, unlarded, and tasteless, with an accompaniment of sodden vegetables and badly cooked rice, and a fruit salad of sliced pawpaw and orange that fortunately even the ingenuity of the native chef could not quite spoil, figured on the bill of fare. The wine list held champagne, preposterously priced, and a few indifferent Cape wines valued at much more than they were worth, so a beer shandy seemed indicated. I was the sole guest at dinner; the permanent boarders were apparently dining out.

After the meal, I settled down in the lounge, a small, cheaply furnished room, whose sole attraction was its high-powered light that made reading less inconvenient than the dim bulb in the bedroom. There was a small cupboard bookcase holding an assortment of old illustrated magazines, railway sixpenny novels, and a few bound volumes. Among the last I discovered a book that I had long wanted to read. Years before John Morley, whose discriminating literary taste I have always honoured, told me that one of the best characters in fiction was to be found in *The Initials*, by an authoress now quite forgotten, the Baroness Tautphoeus. Here, among a miscellany of rubbish, was a Bentley first-and-only edition of her book. I took it down, and started to read it. Outside the wind had risen to something like a gale. The rain came down in torrents, with bursts of vivid lightning, whose reflection dimmed momentarily the strong glare of the lamp, followed by peals of thunder that shook the house and reverberated in descending cadences of monstrous sound.

The Baroness proved readable but not exhilaratingly so. Hildegarde, the heroine, appeared to me to be a composite figure created from too many odds and ends to be really interesting. Literary taste is a queer thing, and no one can account for the popularity of what was once a best seller, such as this book was, and is to-day a rather boring reflection of the manners and modes of Continental Europe in the middle of the past century. The dialogue was vivacious, but it needed an effort on the part of the reader to adjust himself to the atmosphere of the book. Possibly I was grumpy and tired. When one has struggled for hours with refractory tyres and tubes, and had one's equanimity further disturbed by indifferently hot bath water and a scandalously cooked dinner, one is hardly in a mood to appreciate even what John Morley thought highly of. I am afraid I did not agree with that distinguished critic's opinion, and I was just going to lay the book aside and retire to my bedroom, when the native waiter appeared to announce a visitor. No one, so far as I knew, was aware that I had registered at the hotel. I had chosen it by chance, for my intention had been to travel farther that afternoon to reach the hospitable shelter of a teacher's dwelling.

'Who is it?' I asked.

'It's a coolie, *Baas*. He wants a doctor, *Baas*.'

'But isn't there a doctor here? I'm not a doctor . . . not in that way. . . .'

A slight little figure, shrouded in a wet mackintosh, insinuated itself round the waiter. It spoke deprecatingly.

'Please, Mister . . . it is vairy urguent. It is my wife . . . if the doctor would only come . . . there is no other doctor. The doctor that is haire, Mister, he is out to-night and it is vairy urguent . . . please, Mister, if Mister will be so kaind . . .'

There is nothing I dislike more than professionally to be made a convenience of by patients who are too lazy or parsimonious to employ a private practitioner. I reasoned that where one of my colleagues was settled in a district, I had no business to interfere with his private practice, and I made a rule not to respond to calls except where it was a case of dire emergency. Then I could act on behalf of my colleague, report the matter to him, and leave him to book the call as one of his own or to ignore it as he pleased. In any case I could not exact a fee as I was a whole-time Government official. Just because of that I was sometimes called out to patients who imagined that they might get cheap or gratuitous attendance, or who preferred a new doctor to the one who regularly acted as their family practitioner. An emergency was a different matter. No ethical considerations stand in the way of immediately succouring a patient who needs prompt treatment to save life or prevent disablement.

Here there was probably no such pressing need for my services. The inclemency of the weather, my own tiredness, and, I must admit, my utter disinclination to act as anybody's locum, made me procrastinate as long as I could. My caller was a Hindu — a coolie, as everybody of that race is colloquially styled throughout the Transvaal — comparatively young, slightly boned and built, with an intelligent, attractive face. His slender, shapely fingers plucked nervously at his mackintosh button when he spoke and he was evidently labouring under suppressed emotional strain.

'Have you tried to get another doctor . . . the district surgeon?' I suggested.

'There is only the one, Mister. And he is a-way. He will not be back before to-morrow afternoon. There is no one else, Mister . . . please. I will pay . . .' His hand fumbled under the wet mackintosh and reappeared with a small yellow pouch from which he drew minted sovereigns — in those days not so rare as they are now — 'anything that Mister likes, if Mister will come to my wife. . . .'

'What is the matter with your wife?'

'It is' — he drawled his i's and e's in the manner customary to his race when it speaks English — 'the baby. The pains came on early this morning and there is something . . .'

'Have you no midwife . . . no nurse?' I asked, regretting that my own nurse was not with me. Such an emergency would have appealed to Sister Hassall. It did not in the least appeal to me. My last confinement — the last time I had 'delivered' a woman, had been when I had acted as a locum at New Cross for a friend who was in general practice. A straightforward business, such as all child-bearing should be, would not indeed give me much trouble, but the man had hinted that there was 'something'. I had no obstetric instruments with me. I would have to improvise. I did not like the prospect at all.

'The old woman is there, Mister. It is she that wants the doctor. She says it is urguent'—he persisted in making three syllables of the word as if to stress its primary importance.

'My car is at the garage . . .' I began, but he interrupted quickly.

'I have a car for the doctor. I bring the doctor there and back, quickly. And I pay, too. . . .'

'It is not a question of payment. If you are sure that the midwife wants help, I shall have to come with you.'

I put up whatever I could scrape together as an emergency obstetrical bag, not forgetting a pair of domestic scissors. If it was really a matter of life and death, the scissors might be useful. I had no obstetric forceps, and if the child could not be born naturally or with the help of such mechanical aid as I could give, one might have to sacrifice it to save the mother's life. One does so by perforating the head with the scissors.

Outside, plainly visible in the flashing lightning, stood a dilapidated touring car, its hood already so drenched by the rain that trickles of water ran down the seats. The native waiter fetched a couple of blankets and I wrapped one of them round my greatcoat and spread the other on the wet cushion. The little Hindu climbed in, had some difficulty in starting the engine, clicked noisily in gear, and raced at full speed down the one street of the town. I noticed that both his headlights were not functioning, but the wet, untarred street surface was well lighted by the flashes, and the noise of the decrepit car was muffled by the thunder. It was a most unpleasant drive, for twice the car skidded violently in the slush, and it seemed hours to me before we arrived at the coolie shop. As a matter of fact the shop was only a couple of miles away from the hotel and we drove in what must have been record time.

It was the usual wayside coolie shop so common throughout the Province. A rudely constructed brick building, roofed with corrugated iron, with the shop in front and the dwelling opening from the shop — a kitchen and a couple of rooms. Behind, a small zinc sentry-box for lavatory. We went through the shop, now dark except when the lightning played in through the open door and the crevices of the window shutters, and he motioned me into the adjoining room. 'If Mister will go in,' he said, ' . . . she is there. I go make Mister a cup of tea. . . .'

'That's just the thing. Make plenty. And get some light in here.' For a cup of hot tea is sometimes a great help to the woman in labour, and making it keeps a fussy husband occupied.

In the adjoining room a young woman was lying on a low bed, an older woman bending and crooning over her. The younger looked up timidly when I came in, and when she saw that it was a stranger pulled the sheet over her face. The midwife, as I judged the older woman to be, began garrulously to explain things. The pains had been coming strongly in the early morning, but had ceased in the afternoon; the woman was becoming exhausted, and there was something wrong. I examined the mother, but so far as I could make out there was nothing abnormal. The head of the child and the natural outlet showed nothing unusual, and the mother's pulse gave no indication of a weakening heart. The examination lifted a load from me, for I judged that labour would take its normal and natural course, and that the child would be born in the early hours of the following morning. It was a straightforward business, needing no intervention, mechanical or otherwise, similar to the forty-odd confinements I had attended in Peabody's Buildings and the other tenements that comprised my district when a student at Guy's. Indeed, there was much in the surroundings that recalled those early obstetrical experiences. They teach the young medical student more than he can learn in the wards, for they traverse the whole gamut of human emotions, these assistancies at the births of the poor. How often had I been the confidant of much-married women, who between the pains, when the inveterate urge to gossip overwhelmed the apprehension of the next bout, discoursed frankly on things of whose existence a missionary's child knew very little. One of the confidences that shocked me then was the lament of a hyper-generous lady whose husband was a sailor, periodically away from home. 'You can't imagine, Doctor,' she said, disparagingly, 'how unneighbourly Mrs. N—— is. Her's is a sailor too, and when he came home and she was unable, I obliged her, and now when mine's home, she won't oblige me.' To-day I can understand, even sympathize with her.

I reassured the women, and went into the shop. My Hindu had spread a little table with a clean white napkin, and on it had placed a saucer of ginger snaps, a pot of tea, milk and sugar. Everything was neat and clean. 'Get a cup for your wife,' I told him, and then, in answer to his piteous appealing look, 'It's all right. There is nothing wrong, and I expect your son will be born before many hours are past. You'd like it to be a son, wouldn't you?'

'It does not matter what it is, Doctor. It's my wife that I am frightened of.'

'There is no need to be frightened. Everything is going

on well. As a matter of fact I might just as well go back to the hotel. There's really nothing to do. . . .'

'But, please . . .'

'Oh yes, I'll stay until your child is born. I'll go in again presently. Take in the tea now, and tell the old woman to throw away the water I washed in. There's lysol in it, poison. And she must have some more hot water ready. I've told her, but see that she does it.'

He disappeared, and I sat down and drank my tea. The storm still raged outside, several inches of rain must have fallen but the thunder still rolled though with abating crescendos. Presently he came back, and stood diffidently in attendance.

'Don't worry,' I said. 'Get yourself a cup, and sit down here. There's plenty of tea. . . .'

The suggestion seemed to stagger him. It needed some persuasion to induce him to accept it, but finally he compromised. I poured out a cup of tea for him, and he sat down on a packing-case a yard or two away while we chatted. We chatted until the child was born, which happened sooner than I expected, for by four o'clock he had brought me back to the hotel. I learned much from that chat. Before that time I had thought very little about the coolie question. I had heard it sporadically discussed, chiefly in the towns and on the High- and Middle-veld; in the Bushveld it was rarely referred to. What I had heard had made me suppose that the Asiatics were all aliens, undesirable aliens, whose presence in a community already puzzled by the preponderance of natives could be regarded as a menace and a complication of the problem. The coolie, I was told, lived on the smell of an oil rag, undersold his competitors, cheated and intrigued, exploited the poor white, and was in every way a parasite insidiously poisoning the commonwealth by introducing impossible economic standards of living. Now I heard the other side of the case. In 1860 the first Indian immigrants entered Natal as labourers for the plantations. In six years 5000 such immigrants settled in that Province. Their number was greatly increased when in 1874 the sugar planters recruited their labour from India, so that in 1930 the total Indian population of Natal was estimated to be nearly 170,000. In the Cape Colony there were few of them; in the Orange Free State barely a hundred. They entered the Transvaal from Natal in 1881, chiefly as traders, but strong feeling against them was aroused and the Republican Government was urged to prohibit their entry. In view of the provisions of Article 64 of the London Convention of 1884, the Government could not forbid Indians from settling in the Republic, but it could, and did, hedge their settlement round with restrictions that were calculated to discourage their entry. They could not become burghers of the State, they could not own immovable property, except in streets, wards or locations specially set apart for them, they had to pay a registration fee of £25 and could only reside in locations assigned to them by the Government. There was some question as to whether the provisions of this restricting legislation, the Act of 1885, did not infringe the terms of the London Convention, but the British Government did not interfere and the Act was promulgated two years later. The registration fee was abolished in 1907, and various modifications of the restrictions have from time to time been gazetted, but to-day the disabilities of the 16,000-odd 'coolies' in the Transvaal are certainly not less than they were in republican days.

My little Hindu shopkeeper, once his confidence had been gained — and he found that he could talk to one who was at least not aggressively unfriendly — spoke with a pathetic eloquence about these disabilities. 'I am, like you, Doctor, a South African. I was born here; my parents were born here. Some of us go back to India, but I consider this my home, and I am as much a citizen of South Africa as you are. But I have no part in electing the Government, I have no vote, and I can never get it. I cannot buy land; this shop I can only lease, and I can be turned out at any time. I cannot go from one Province to another without a permit. If I go away to India, or anywhere else I suppose, and remain away for three years, I can never again enter South Africa, although I am a South African. I have no share in the benefits for which I pay as an ordinary tax-payer. I must pay for the education of my children myself, just as my parents had to pay for mine. It is vairy hard, Doctor. It is not fair.'

'My father told me, Doctor — he was an old man when he died, Doctor, and as much a South African as I am — he told me how he had once called on the old President. My father said he was vairy kind, vairy friendly. "You Indians," the old President said, "are as much my children as my burghers, but you must wait. You must grow up first." I can understand that, Doctor. But now you have slammed the door and bolted it, and that is not fair, Doctor. Shall I make some more tea for you?' I drank more tea. 'Most of you are still children, in the sense the old President meant,' I said. 'And anyway you are better off here than you would be in India.'

'Not those like I am, Doctor. I have made good. I am worth quite a lot, but there are some of us who have much more. And we are South Africans. This is our home, Doctor. Why should we be regarded as less than the Kafirs and called coolies?'

Why indeed? The next morning at the hotel I met a member of one of my school committees, an intelligent man, liberal in his outlook, born under the old Republic. I repeated some of the arguments of my Hindu.

'Sad cases make bad law,' he quoted, admonishingly. 'I know the fellow. He's one of the better class Indians, and I have no objection to him. But the coolies are a damned danger, Doc, and the sooner they are expelled the better all of us will be pleased. If something isn't done, there'll be no white trader left in the Transvaal when my children grow up. They grab everything, and we can't compete with them.'

I discussed the question with a Jewish friend. He was equally vehement in his denunciation of the Indians. 'It is a shame how they exploit the poor people,' he declared. 'If it weren't for the Gold Law, they'd be as much a nuisance on the diggings as they are in the small towns. As for them being good South Africans, that is all twaddle. They are Indians, pure and simple, and they will never be assimilated here.'

I did not have the heart to tell him that those were almost the same words that I had heard spoken when his own co-religionists were discussed by some of my non-Jewish acquaintances. Personal feelings alter our sense of values, both ethical and material. The Indian is execrated because he is thrifty, hard working, and capable of acquiring a prosperity which to the poor white seems unattainable. The Jew is hated for the same reason. Anti-Semitism and anti-Asiatic feeling are the products of an intolerance that is based on economic conditions, an intolerance that is in itself an expression of fear, the fear of being unable to withstand competition. No civilization buttressed by class legislation that is the result of such fear can defeat the attritive influence of time and culture, neither of which makes any allowance for inferiority that must be continually strengthened by artificial supports. It is a pity that those sections of the community in South Africa that are to-day benefited by such class legislation do not realize that it is a double-edged weapon that sooner or later will be turned against them.

CHAPTER XV

DOCTORING

The Bushveld is a district of wide spaces, with bad roads and scattered farms. It is badly served so far as medical aid is concerned. When I made acquaintance with it, the few doctors in the towns were pitifully inadequate in numbers to give it proper medical service, and when most of them volunteered for active service, the few who remained found it quite impossible to cope with the work.

A Bushveld doctor may be called out to attend to a patient who lives a hundred or two hundred miles away; the visit may entail a couple of days' absence from home, and a journey that is fatiguing and may even be dangerous when the state of the weather and the roads makes travelling a professional hazard. For the most part the community had to depend on home treatment and home remedies, except in cases where it was imperative that an assistance more skilled than what could be locally supplied should be summoned.

In consequence of this scarcity of doctors, I found myself frequently called upon to do work that I was unaccustomed to do. Every doctor on the register is supposed, especially in South Africa, to be able to do everything that a doctor may be called upon to do. In Europe, even in rural areas, it is already realized to some extent that medicine is too vast and variegated a field for one man's effort to work, and that its intricacies are too complicated for one man's brain to encompass them all. Specialization — which means simply concentration of skill upon one particular branch of medical art — is acknowledged and appreciated. In South Africa, specialization was unknown, except so far as it concerned men who were employed in public health activities as full time officials of the municipalities. It is true there were in the large towns, at Johannesburg, Pretoria, Durban, and Cape Town, men who specialized in diseases of the eye and who did nothing else, but even the sharp distinction between surgeons and physicians, although the profession was beginning to recognize it, was not yet appreciated by the general public. Men who devoted themselves almost exclusively to surgery did general practice, while every doctor in general practice was called upon to do work which in Europe would have been looked upon as highly specialized work, such as major surgery. The public demanded from the family doctor expert all-round competence, and every doctor on the register was supposed to possess such catholic competency and to display it when called upon to do so. The result was that most of my colleagues were men who had, through practice and experience, attained a skill and proficiency in the practical art of medicine that were astonishing. No less surprising were the excellent results obtained, in general, though on occasion one saw the other side of the picture which was not so good to look upon.

My own speciality, the one branch in which I had, so far as it was possible for me to do so, perfected myself by study and practice, was school medical work. With the exception of a few weeks that I had spent in a busy London waterside practice, doing locum tenens work for a friend, I had had no experience of general practice. My experience had been gained solely in large hospitals where I had first worked as an aspirant for surgical posts on the staff and consequently directed my efforts to purely surgical work, with a special bent towards orthopaedics — the surgery of deformities — and later on switched away towards paediatrics, which is the study of diseases of children. I was thus a specialist in a very definite branch of medicine, more limited, in one sense, than any of my colleagues because my practice consisted not in treating sick children but in ascertaining what children among the school-going population of the Province were defective. When I had separated the well children — those able to profit by class instruction — from the defective children — those who, because they suffered from some defect that fatigued them and interfered with their receptive powers, were unable effectively to profit by such instruction — my work was done. The treatment of the defects discovered at examination was the care of the general practitioner, and no provision had been made, or could then be made, for their adequate treatment by the State. We all recognized that this was an anomalous state of things. Medical inspection of schools should, as a necessary corollary, be followed up by the free treatment, at State expense, of defective children whose parents could not afford to pay for treatment. In my London work, treatment and inspection were co-ordinated. The defective child was sent to hospital or to a treatment centre and the necessary treatment was given as a matter of course. Here there was no provision for such treatment. When I started the work, I was under the impression that the facilities for treatment in the Transvaal were adequate to deal with the comparatively small number of defectives that would be listed by one inspector working on his own. Even at high pressure, such a single-handed inspector could not deal with more than four to five thousand children a year, and on an estimate of a defective percentage between 20 and 30, the number of children needing treatment would not be too great to be dealt with by the local practitioners. Experience showed, however, that the percentage of defective children in the schools was nearer 60 than 30. In the Bushveld, especially, the percentage was very high; in some schools all the children were defective. After a few visits I saw that it was farcical to continue inspections without making some provision for treatment, and my Administration fully agreed with me. In the towns it was not difficult to make arrangements for such treatment, and my professional colleagues lent me all their support, willingly and generously, to establish local treatment centres or to provide for the free treatment of necessitous children privately. But in the Bushveld, where medical services were quite inadequate, treatment was often a matter of the greatest difficulty.

In time I carried with me whatever was necessary for emergency treatment and for the correction of what are classed as minor ailments of school children. Wherever possible the children were referred to their own medical attendant, and I assumed that if there was only one practitioner in the nearest town, all the surrounding country was his territory, and that I had no business to interfere, even to the extent of giving advice, with his practice. I rigidly adhered to that policy, but there were many occasions when it could not be followed, simply because no other medical aid than what I myself was able to give was available. In such circumstances I acted for the local doctor, reported what I had done to him, and regarded myself as his substitute for the time being who gave emergency treatment and handed over the case at the first convenient opportunity.

To the Bushveld community such a policy was strange and inexplicable. I was a Government doctor, and the obvious and only duty of a doctor was to treat the sick. Medical inspection of schools was an innovation whose object and scope were not grasped, not even by the schools boards and committees. These latter took up the logical position that it was absurd to tell parents that their children were defective and to leave it at that. What was the Government doctor for? Why was he paid out of revenue to which all taxpayers contributed, if he did not do as a doctor should and give the children medicine? For to the Bushveld, treatment means medicine. It is essentially a bottle-loving community, and directions on a label are regarded as being as powerful as the written charms of a real Turkish *hakim*.

When the school doctor arrived at a Bushveld school, the parents turned up with exemplary celerity. But they did not come merely to witness the inspection of their children or to listen to the talk with which it was sometimes prefaced. They came, primarily, to get advice and treatment for their own complaints, imaginary or actual. It was utterly useless to say that I did not practise. What was the doctor for but to treat illness, give advice and medicine, particularly medicine?

They came with all sorts of difficulties, some of which were easily dealt with, others again that it was impossible to overcome with lack of the means — time, facilities, help of skilled nurses or assistants — at my disposal. In the first category fell matters that could be improved by advice founded on a little knowledge of physiology aided by the application of some common sense. I gained far more kudos than was deserved in such cases. There was, for instance, the plethoric old gentleman who had, as he pathetically stated, consulted 'really first-class doctors' — a left-handed compliment, for it implied that as a last resort he came to me — for dizziness, black spots that obscured his vision — what we doctors call 'moving flies' — and increasing shortness of breath. He had been told that all his trouble was caused by high blood pressure, a fashionable diagnosis that means nothing. I noticed that a roll of flesh overlapped his tight neck-band and suggested that he should go collarless for a week; there is much evil in constricting the veins of the neck by wearing collars that are a size and a half too tight. As a placebo, he was given plain water coloured with burnt sugar solution. His speedy restoration to health was ascribed to the medicine, but he had the good sense to wear loose collars afterwards, and I had the satisfaction of knowing that I had gained a convert to the simple faith of common-sense hygiene.

Not all who came to me, or to whom I was called, could be bettered so simply or so effectively. When travelling from an inspected school one day, my car was stopped by some natives, who pleaded that I should help one of them who had been severely mauled by a bush buck. The patient was a young man, who lay outside the hut on the grass and was engaged in washing his wounds with water from a dirty pot. Part of his intestines protruded from the wound, for the horn of the bush buck had ripped open the lower portion of his abdomen, and although he had not bled much, the wound was contaminated by mud and filth. There seemed no possibility that he would escape a septic peritonitis, and the obvious thing was to take him to the nearest hospital, a hundred miles away, and do what surgery could attempt. Even that seemed hopeless, for by this time the wound was infected. But the suggestion that he should be moved was obstinately rejected, and in the circumstances all that could be done was to sponge the escaped bit of gut, that fortunately did not seem damaged, return it into the abdomen, and suture up the wound, leaving a small bit of gauze to act as a drain. He smiled when this was done, and seemed none the worse for the double mauling that he had undergone, but I left him convinced in my own mind that there would be complications which could only end fatally. There were no complications. The patient made an uninterrupted recovery, and a month later went about showing his scars to his admiring contemporaries. When I told a local colleague about the case he was not at all impressed. 'I know a small boy', he said, 'who was gored in the same way, only more so. His intestine was ripped open, but his father pinned it together with thorns, and brought the child to me a week later, and there was nothing for me to do. The wound was healing up nicely and I left it alone, though the child has a rupture now. One couldn't very well expect anything else, but if it had been you or I septic peritonitis would have ended the story.' An even more wonderful example of primitive surgery was narrated by a colleague who told of a native who had succoured his son, similarly gored. In this case, also, the gut was actually ripped open. The father took a reed from the river bed, whittled it down to a convenient size, inserted it into the open gut, and sutured up the wound with home-made sutures. Here, too, the boy made an uninterrupted recovery.

My native driver, who claimed to be my brother by baptism because my grandfather had 'thrown water on his head' years before I was born, asked me to see a friend. 'It's a great chief, *Baas*,' he said, 'and he can afford to pay

Baas well. He'll give *Baas* a cow and two heifers if *Baas* will see him.'

'Why doesn't he see the district surgeon or some other doctor, *Outa*? I don't practise. I look at the children. . . .'

'Ach, *Baas*, he has seen so many doctors. They can do nothing for him. But I told him I am driving the new Government doctor around, who makes *paljas* (magic) out of plants that he gathers by the roadside. . . .'

'That is very wrong of you, *Outa*. You know, I told you that I cannot make magic. You must go to the *isanusi* for that.'

'He has, *Baas*, he has. The *isanusis* have got many heifers from him. But *Baas* can but see him . . . to please me, *Baas*. After all, the old *Baas*, who was *Baas*'s own grandfather and a kindly hearted man, would not have refused to see him. . . .'

The native chief came to see me at the village hotel where I was temporarily domiciled. He drove up in an immodestly opulent spider, drawn by four sleek mules, and was assisted by two of his headmen who carried him into the little summerhouse in the garden that served as a consulting room. I could do nothing. His left thigh was immensely swollen by a growth of the bone, the sort of growth that expands so that the bony shell becomes brittle and when one presses on it makes the sound that surgeons call 'egg-shell crackling' — a sign that is of ominous significance. He had a sarcoma, a malignant growth of the thigh bone, and there were indications that the disease had progressed too far for operation to hold out any hope of cure. All I could do was to advise him to go to one of the larger hospitals and have expert advice and a thorough examination under the X-rays. My native driver did not appear to be much concerned about the prognosis. He seemed more interested in the fee, and when I told him that I had charged nothing, he looked shocked and remarked that any advice was worth paying for if the patient happened to be as rich as that chief was.

Doctors' fees, indeed, were a frequent subject of discussion. Owing to the isolation and the long distances that had to be travelled, mileage was bound to be an item that figured largely in the doctors' accounts, but the public resentment against what it called 'overcharging' did not appear to me to be justified when the circumstances were taken into consideration. Yet so strong was the feeling on the point that when the Medical Bill of 1928 was under discussion in parliament, the Minister in charge of the Bill was forced to insert a clause in it by which every doctor is bound, when his charge is in excess of what is customary in his district or area, to inform the patient beforehand what the cost of treatment is likely to be. The charges ordinarily made are not what might be called excessive, and as a matter of fact, though I was frequently troubled with complaints about overcharging by people who considered that they had to pay too dearly for treatment received from their medical attendants, there were very few cases in which such a complaint was justified. One rich farmer — not in the Bushveld, for there are no rich farmers there — inveighed against his doctor who had sent him an account for sixty pounds — not guineas. The doctor had come fifty miles by car, on a road that was one continuous marsh of mud, to attend a member of the family for what was locally known as 'a knot in the gut'. The knot proved to be appendicitis, and the doctor operated on the patient, who made an excellent recovery. A specialist would have charged fifty to a hundred guineas for the operation alone, and probably as much for coming such a distance under such inclement circumstances. I reminded the complainant that in some parts of the world it was customary to charge one-twelfth of the patient's annual income for a life-saving operation. He was incredulous; no law, he argued, would allow such iniquity. Yet he had cheerfully paid his attorney double the doctor's fee for saving something that was much less valuable to him than his daughter's life. The community in South Africa, urban as well as rural, has not yet learned to value medical service.

It was pleasant, at times, to meet with men who appreciated what my colleagues had done for them. One patient caused me much embarrassment by asking me to see his doctor and expostulate with him. 'You see, Doctor,' he said, 'Dr. E—— knows I am fairly well off. I am not a poor *bywoner*. I can afford to pay. But it is not right to send me such a bill.'

I made a gesture of dissent. 'I don't know the circumstances,' I said. 'You must excuse me, but I can't interfere between you and your doctor. If you think the bill is not what it should be, why don't you go and tell him so? Every doctor will . . .'

'But I tell you, Doctor, it is not right. I broke my leg — here, at the thigh, high up. I fell off a rick, and I couldn't get up, and they carried me into the house and we sent for the doctor. He came and he said I had broken my leg, and he took me in his cart to his own house, and put my leg in an iron contraption, and I stayed with him for a couple of months. I asked him for his account, repeatedly, but he never sent it. Then at last I wrote him, saying that he must send me his bill, and he sends me this. Now I ask you, Doctor, is it right to treat me like this? After all, I am not a child, Doctor.'

'Then why not go and see him and explain. . . .'

'Ach, Doctor, you don't know Dr. E——. He flies into a rage, and I don't want him to think ill of me. Now if you could see him . . .'

'It is a matter between you and him. If you really can't pay . . .'

'Can't pay . . . who says I can't pay? It is not that, Doctor. It is the account I object to. If Doctor will glance at it . . .'

He held it out to me, and I glanced at it, to please him. I had no intention to act as intermediary. But the account was certainly surprising. It stated: 'To medical attendance and medicine — 10s. 6d.'

'It's a mistake,' I said. 'You've got somebody else's account.'

'That's what I think, too, Doctor. But if you will explain to Dr. E——. I should like to pay what I owe, or as much of it as I can, for I can't repay all that he did for me. I expected he would charge me a hundred pounds, or fifty at least. And to get this. . . .'

His doctor was well known in the district, an admirable but somewhat violent-tempered practitioner, whom I had not met before. The patient introduced me to him the same morning when we met him strolling across the village square, and, fortified by my moral support, handed the bill over with the remark, 'I fancy you've made a mistake, Doctor.'

'Do you think so?' my colleague said, in a voice that a schoolmaster bitterly annoyed might have used in speaking to his annoyance, 'Very well, then, we'll cross off the sixpence. And you can pay me now.'

My colleague took my arm and led me apart. 'You know

I made a hash of that fellow's leg,' he said, confidentially. 'He has almost an inch shortening, and I am ashamed of such work. I couldn't very well charge him anything, but as he importuned me, I sent him a nominal account. And now he'll think I overcharged him.'

I assured him that his patient had no such thought in mind. 'We both thought you had made a mistake, but if it is that way you should at least charge him some nominal sum . . .'

'That's what I did,' he asserted, and turned the conversation. I saw the patient again that night, and in my turn explained the position. Three-quarters of an inch shortening with some eversion of the foot one could really not consider, in those days, as a bad result in a case of extra-capsular fracture of the thigh, and the patient himself was quite satisfied with it. But this was one of the few cases known to me in which a patient had complained of under-charging and had considered the smallness of the doctor's bill derogatory to his own dignity. One other patient, seen in consultation by a famous specialist, I had known to reject the great man's advice because the consultation fee was much lower than he had anticipated. 'He can't be such a smart fellow if he charges so little,' he told me afterwards. 'I want the best man, and I can pay for it.' A week later he paid four times the great man's fee to a quack whose advice was much more to his liking.

Malaria and redwater should be the most dreaded diseases of the Bushveld. Because of their ubiquitous prevalence they are looked upon with the indifference that familiarity breeds. In striking contrast to the apathy with which they are regarded is the universal fear and horror of cancer and blindness. Both are common in the Bushveld, because both are concomitants of old age, but they are not more common there or anywhere in Africa than they are in Europe or America. Yet nowhere has the cancer quack so rich and lucrative a field for exploitation. At that time there was a notorious example of the breed, a woman who 'healed cancer' by 'drawing it out by the roots'. So high was her reputation that in one district men and women who would have scorned the suggestion that they were ignorant, came in a body to the magistrate to demand that she should be permitted to carry on her good work without interference from the police. A few years before equally ignorant and misguided citizens had petitioned the old Cape parliament to allow another cancer curer to carry on in defiance of the law. Parliament appointed a select committee that examined all the available evidence. The cancer curer showed patients who had been cured of 'inoperable cancer after having been given up by many doctors'. Dozens of patients testified to the value and super-excellence of her plasters. A few patients whom she had treated spoke disparagingly of her and her work, but that was not to be wondered at (said her supporters) for success creates jealousy. The select committee reported that it found her 'cure' to be a well-known escharotic (caustic) plaster, without the slightest remedial effect on cancer, that among her 'cured' patients it had not discovered one who had ever suffered from cancer, while the cancer patients whom she had treated had without exception suffered great pain and distress and had derived no benefit whatever from her plasters. Although much publicity was given to the report, that cancer curer went on with her work, and her dupes believed in her in spite of the overwhelmingly strong evidence of the utter uselessness and harmfulness of her method of cure. In the

Bushveld a similar naive credulity existed. There were several 'curers' the least objectionable of whom was a lady who claimed that she had relieved the distress of the disease by making the sufferers drink a decoction of a native root — a mixture of tannin and a vegetable bitter that could, at least, have no ill effects however impotent it was to cure cancer. Her colleagues in quackery all used 'absorbent plasters' impregnated with mixtures of zinc chloride, quicklime, arsenical paste, or combinations of these powerful caustics. They could not charge for treatment, so they sent in accounts for 'board and lodging' insisting always that the patients should spend some weeks under their immediate care. As they did not diagnose disease, nor do anything else 'pertaining to the practice of medicine' in the strictly legal sense of that vague term, they could not be charged with illicit practice. One would have thought that their want of success would have discouraged both them and their dupes, but that was by no means the case, and they had a wide clientele and were spoken of as women who were doing good work, hampered by the restrictions imposed by a godless and arrogant government that permitted the doctors on the register to exercise a monopoly of healing.

I saw many examples of the evils of cancer quackery. In some cases the harm was negative rather than positive. The patient, who suffered from a non-malignant swelling, a fatty tumour or a sebaceous cyst, which could have been quickly and painlessly removed by excision under a local anaesthetic, was treated by caustic plasters that removed the swelling, with much surrounding tissue, in a most lingeringly painful manner; the cavity that was left had to heal up by granulation, a process that took time and caused more pain. The removed piece of flesh was proudly exhibited as a proof of the efficacy of treatment, and the serrations of muscle, corroded by the caustic, were demonstrated as the 'roots of the cancer'. The majority of cases that went to the curers were cases of such non-malignant tumours, and they went because the patients stood in too great awe of the surgeon's knife, and preferred the more exquisite torture of removal by a slow caustic to the clean, quick excision under an anaesthetic. The main harm that was done, apart from the misery unnecessarily suffered by the patient, was the credit gained by the quack for relief that might have been obtained by much simpler and far less painful methods of treatment.

Positive harm was done in cases of real cancer that were tackled by these quacks in their early stages, when the disease was still operable and the patient had a fair chance of cure by proper surgical means. On my first visit to a Bushveld school one of the parents showed me a small abraded wart on his lower lip. It was a tiny epithelioma, a skin cancer, as yet localized to a small portion of the lip. I told him what I thought it was, and urged him strongly to have it removed, patiently explaining how it could be painlessly taken away, and how, if it were left or irritated, it would infect neighbouring glands and lead to death. Some months later I saw that patient again in a town hospital. He had been treated by a cancer curer, and had a large, festering sore on his cheek, while the cancer had eroded his lip, encroached on the gum, and attacked the glands in his neck so that nothing could be done for him. Nowadays he might have had a chance with radium treatment, but at that time radium was unknown. I saw women with small, easily removable cancers of the breast, who under treatment by plasters were made pitiable wrecks of humanity, ceaselessly gnawed by pain from the open sores caused by corrosion, and weakened by sepsis and suffering. It was useless to cite the select committee's report and to tell these people of the futility of the cancer curers. The fear of cancer was traditionally too strong, or perhaps the ingrained detestation of the surgeon's knife, which in the old days had been almost equally impotent to stay the advance of the disease, was too great to counteract the belief that the curers possessed some means, of which the doctors were ignorant, by which the cancer could be removed.

Almost as viciously futile were the ministrations of the itinerant quacks who pretended to cure defective eyesight. One, an ignorant but plausible and exceedingly business-like man, whose real profession had been to prospect for gold, travelled with a stock of cheap, steel-rimmed spectacles, and I came across many of his victims who had paid more for utterly unsuitable glasses than they would have had to pay for really useful treatment given by an opthalmologist or competent optician. Another charlatan vended an oil, guaranteed to cure all defects of the eye. It was cheap cylinder oil, variously coloured, and he charged half a sovereign the ounce. Incidentally the oil was a cure for appendicitis, leprosy, and falling sickness — a panacea, indeed, that paid very handsomly for the periodical trips he made into the rural areas.

In my talks to parents I touched upon the evils of quackery, and possibly did some good. Where one sows broadcast, a few seeds may alight upon fertile soil and sprout. But superstition is nowhere so strong, so deeply ingrained, so obstinately perverse as in matters of health in a primitive community. That is not to be wondered at.

DOCTORING

For generations these people had to shift for themselves, to cure their illnesses without help from the faculty. They had come to rely on home remedies, on shifts and expedients that in the past had been found efficacious in the treatment of disease. Their therapy was essentially empirical, but they lacked the ability to apply the 'trial and error' method that is the test of empiricism. Most of the futilities that they employed had the sanction of custom and tradition. Among these were examples of organotherapy such as our ancestors believed in — the dung of goats, the ground-up bones of a lizard, nail shavings, and powdered dried earthworms. The last interested me much, for it is mentioned in practically all old official pharmacopoeias. A kindly old woman showed me how it was administered. The earthworms were washed in salt water, dipped in strong peach brandy, and threaded on a string; then they were dried in the sun, and when thoroughly dried they were powdered, mixed with cinnamon and coriander, and administered in warm tea. Then they were said to be excellent for whooping-cough.

CHAPTER XVI

THE RIGHT TO DIE

'THEY would like you to call and see the widow L——,
Doctor,' said the Teacher when I had finished inspection
one morning at a school. 'They have been waiting all the
morning.'

I detest calling and seeing patients with whom I have
nothing to do. It is not my business. My obligation is to
look after children at school. Not to attend patients of my
colleagues, whose condition I am not acquainted with and
for whom I can invariably do very little. But when the
attending physician is sixty and more miles away, and when
the matter may be one of urgency, one cannot always insist
on professional etiquette.

'What is the matter? Hasn't she got her own doctor?'
I asked, to procrastinate.

'She has cancer, Doctor. The District Surgeon sees her
occasionally. But they say she is in much pain, and if you
could see your way clear . . .'

Put like that one can only acquiesce. They had a donkey
cart, but I preferred my car, and the grandson went with me
to show the way. He was not communicative.

'Grandma has had it for a long time, Doctor. She has
been to a cancer doctor but he did not do her much good.
We've put her in a rondavel, outside as . . . but Doctor will
see for himself.'

The clouds were gathering when we reached grand-
mother's place. My return journey, I knew, would be made
with the rain beating on my windscreen, obscuring the way,

and the lightning playing pyrotechnics along the wire fence when I had to halt and open the gates. Not a pleasant prospect, but one takes these things philosophically in the Bushveld.

The rondavel was a thing of beauty, against that background of argilaceous thunder-cloud. A gigantic bougainvillea, more red than magenta, wreathed over the grass thatch; a clump of gorgeous cannas, crimson and spotted gold, grew beside it; an umbrageous foxberry tree flung big branches over it.

A woman came to meet us when we drove up, anxious faced, solemn, very serious.

'She is in such pain, Doctor! If you could only do something ... But it is so difficult for us. Not that we want her ... but it is dreadful to see her like that, Doctor.'

I went into the rondavel. Outside the air had been pleasantly humid, with a tang of budding branches and the fresh scent of veld flowers still open under the afternoon sun. Inside it was sodden with an odour of decay and the sour smell of putrescent flesh almost unbearable to one not inured to such dismalness.

She lay on a low couch, propped up by pillows and a bolster. A woman of near sixty, showing in feature and complexion the omens that even a lay augur could easily read. Her one breast was a mass of septic cancer, so swollen and fissured with foul smelling sinuses that it reminded one of the rare recorded cases of mammary sarcoma, and it was evident that she was suffering much from the pain of pressure of secondary deposits on nerves. Her forehead was budded with sweat, and her dry tongue flickered about her cracked lips, in and out, to get such relief it could obtain from the humid air.

271

'It's the Government doctor, Ma,' said the woman who brought me in. 'He who looks after the school children, Ma.'

'Oh, then perhaps . . .' the sick woman's voice was very thin. Obviously it cost her an effort to speak. But she was a strong character, typical of such women in the Bushveld; women who endure hardship and suffering with stolid patience, who are hard on themselves and on others because they have been trained in a school that exacts much from the individual.

'I should like to talk to him under four eyes' — the vernacular request for privacy — she said. 'Do you go outside, Martha, until we call you, and see that the doctor gets some coffee.'

I sat down by the couch side. The smell from those festering openings in her breast was almost unbearable. A cursory examination made it plain that the disease was so far advanced that any hope of alleviation was illusory. Her lungs were affected; her liver was riddled; there were secondary deposits, the aftermath that the disease sows in all tissues that its maddened cells can reach, all over her.

'Doctor,' she said, and reached her yellow hand to claw mine, 'the pain is dreadful, and I am only a misery to my folk. The District Surgeon has been, and he told me that two-three months would see me out. But this is now the fourth month since he has been, Doctor, and daily it becomes worse. Cannot Doctor put me out of my misery? You have drugs — things, ways, for doing that?'

I had none. I had not anticipated such a call, and in my bag I carried nothing that could be depended upon to give her that sure and certain relief for which she craved, a painless death. I had not even the means to still her pains. Aspirin and some cannabis indica were all I could offer her.

I might have gone back and returned with morphia. A nurse, too, would have eased her misery, made her more comfortable, helped her to bear what was left of life to her. As it was I could do little, beyond instructing her daughter how to deodorize those awful-smelling festering holes in her breast, and promising that I would ask the District Surgeon to call and visit her as soon as possible.

Her look when I left her was a reproach. 'You are just like him, Doctor,' she whispered. 'You can, but you won't give me the only thing that can help me and . . . others.'

I often bless 'whatever Gods there be' that I am not in private practice, and that such episodes as that of the woman in the bougainvillea enwreathed rondavel do not disturb my conscience. For I confess that the request of a sufferer, who anticipates from life nothing but abject misery and abundant pain, and who realizes that continued existence is a woe to him and a plenitude of anxiety and discomfort to those who attend him, for permanent relief such as can only come from death, is a demand that the doctor should face conscientiously. I discussed this case with the District Surgeon, who readily agreed that the woman had nothing to live for. She was sodden with cancer; every nerve-fibre of her responded hourly to pressure pain that sapped her strength and gave her torment more relentless than any that her ancestors endured at the hands of the atrocious Tittleman, reputed the most artistic of inquisitorial torturers in the days when Holland cursed what was done for the greater glory of God.

'I can't leave her enough morphia,' he said, apologetically, 'really to ease her. Two grains is nothing, and I daren't give her more. You don't expect me to kill her, do you?'

That attitude of mind is common enough in my profession. Our role is to relieve suffering, to assuage pain, to save life. We habitually shrink from taking life, and the thought of killing anyone, no matter how preferable death might be to life to anyone, is repugnant to our training and our tradition. We have often confessed to it. One of our greatest surgeons, Ambroise Paré, tells how he found soldiers so fearfully mutilated that no means that he could employ could ward death from them, and how monstrous he thought it that a charitable comrade cut their throats because otherwise they were bound to die in agony. The layman looks at the matter from another point of view. He waxes dithyrambic about his courage in shortening existences of whose destiny he knows nothing. We doctors feel different, for our experience, apart altogether from our training, has made us diffident in arrogating to ourselves the right to sentence to death even those to whom a painful death seems inevitable and inescapable.

I think that diffidence is largely due to the fact that we all know that what seems inevitable is sometimes mercifully diverted by forces which we left out of consideration in making our forecast. That happens rarely, but it does sometimes happen, and it cannot be altogether discounted. But there are cases, like that of the woman in the rondavel, where our logic and our humanity both seem at fault. We cannot help that. Public opinion, made effective by a realization of the facts, may in time help us to clarify our disturbed professional consciences, and assign to us the right, under certain well-defined conditions and with equally well-expressed precautions, to act as merciful executioners in cases where the infliction of a painless death becomes an obligation upon us and a boon to the sufferer.

When I was a ward clerk, a junior medical student in a large London hospital, I found one morning in one of the beds a man who had been sent in to undergo a trivial operation. My patient was a yeoman who had been invalided from South Africa, where he had typhoid fever. He had married and settled down on a small chicken farm. A birthmark on his breast had worried him; his braces had irritated it, and he had gone to his doctor who advised him to have it removed. My duty as ward clerk was to take his history, examine him, and write a report for my chief. In examining him I had the help of the house surgeon, a newly qualified youngster, whose experience and knowledge though far greater than my own, were still not expert. Between us we agreed that the condition was that of an ordinary birth mark, technically called a pigmented mole, and that a small operation, an excision of the offending spot, was all that was required.

My chief, a well-known surgeon, came round that afternoon, followed by a class of senior and post-graduate students, for he was reputed one of the best teachers in London. He looked at my patient and frowned. I read my report, and he nodded.

'You say his liver is palpable. What exactly do you mean?' he asked.

'It is an inch below the costal margin, Sir.'

'Very well. Colonel D——,'—he gestured towards one of the post-graduate students—'would you mind examining the patient for us. We'll go over there.'

He led the way to the end of the ward, and talked about livers. After a few minutes Colonel D—— came back.

'Well?'—the chief's chin thrust forward aggressively. 'What did you find, Colonel?'

'Diffuse melanotic sarcomatosis, Sir. Primary focus in the breast, but with his lungs and liver in that state . . .' and the Colonel shrugged his shoulders.

The chief gave a lecture on sarcoma, melanotic sarcoma, the most insidious, the most despairing of all cancers. Then he took me by my arm. 'Come along with me,' he said, 'I've got to tell him.'

Very gently, very kindly he explained to the patient. The man did not follow the explanation; he only grasped that he could leave hospital the same afternoon if he liked.

'But aren't you going to operate on me, Doctor?' he asked. 'Aren't you going to take this little wart away? It worries me. . . .'

'My good fellow, I can take it away for you — nothing easier. I can take away your breast — your arm — half of you for that matter, but it won't do the slightest good. You must be brave, and look facts in the face. You have one of the worst forms of cancer, and I am afraid it is going to kill you. I'm sorry, but we can't do anything.'

That episode made a tremendous impression on my adolescent mind. Afterwards, when I became more intimate with the chief, I reverted to it when I dined with him and enjoyed his very excellent Montrachet. I hinted that he could have operated and at least helped the man to a painless death. There are ways of doing such things. 'I have never been able to convince myself that it is my duty,' he said sadly. 'Perhaps it is. You'll have to make up your mind about it when you go into practice, but don't, for God's sake, start from the assumption that it's your duty to set things right, except such things as you have the power and the means to correct. And if you once give up your hope that science will ultimately give you the means to right what

Nature wrongs, you might as well leave medicine, my boy. You don't think that is the first or only case where I had to tell the patient that we could do nothing for him, do you?'

'No, Sir. But it made a terrific impression on me. When he asked you—"How long do you give me, Doctor?" and you did not reply . . . you remember how his voice rose when he exclaimed "Two years, Doctor?" and you shook your head . . . "A year, Doctor?" and you still shook your head. . . .'

'My recollection is that I was very frank with him. I told him, it's not a matter of years, perhaps not even of months. It was an advanced case, so far as I remember. But when I was a medical student, my lad, I saw much worse, and to-day those cases which were then hopeless — take peritonitis; we couldn't save one case in those days, and now you know its mortality is not so very high — to-day we can do much for them. I remember a chap who came in with hydrophobia — you've never seen them in their convulsions; they are worse than cases of strychnine poisoning. If there ever was a case in which one was justified in putting an end to the patient's sufferings by a whiff of chloroform, that was the sort of case. Yet to-day, hydrophobia is a preventable disease. Cancer isn't yet, but if you think it never will be, go back to journalism, my boy, and don't pretend to be a doctor.'

The proof of the pudding is in the eating, is a proverbial saying that has no gastrosophic justification but expresses tritely a conception of values that one can apply in practice. Among my colleagues I have found very few who preferred to do 'what Cato did and Addison approved' when they knew that they had to face death by disease, with pain and suffering before the natural end came. My uncle, a medical man, who initiated me into the mysteries of anatomy when I was a small boy, suffered from cancer of the larynx, at that time a type of cancer that much interested the lay public, for Morell Mackenzie had just published his *Frederick the Noble* in which the course and symptoms of the disease were graphically described. My uncle was tracheotomized by Butlin, and came home, as he was perfectly well aware, to die from suffocation caused by the perichondritis that would at the end block his air passages. I remember visiting him in his bedroom, redolent with camphor and benzoin fumes, and how he pointed to a bottle of chloral and a hypodermic syringe on the little table beside his bed. 'There I have the means to cheat death,' he whispered, 'but I want to see it out. I am keeping notes of what it feels like, and so long as' — he mentioned his wife — 'does not mind, I'll go on.'

We all look at death differently. Probably no man's thoughts about it correspond to those of his fellow-man. The child, happily, does not think about it at all; death, to him, is as incomprehensible as is old age. The adolescent toys with it, particularly when he is introspective, because whatever is dramatic, whatever places him in the centre of an imaginative picture, appeals. At that age suicide is not uncommon, but it is almost never a reaction to escape physical suffering or bodily pain. It is invariably the result of psychical, emotional strain begotten of maladjustment to environmental factors that can and should be counteracted by proper and sympathetic treatment. Middle-aged suicides, too, fall in the same class, although among them there are instances of men and women who choose death in preference to possible suffering from disease. After middle life, however, self-destruction to escape pain, to make an end, quickly and surely, to possibly long protracted bodily suffering, is not uncommon. The victim feels that he has had from life as much as he can obtain, and death is contemplated as a relief from pangs that he has endured and from greater misery yet to come. Pain is something about which we know little. Its close cousinship to pleasure has been unwarrantably stressed, for the two are in reality not akin, although superficially they may appear to be so. Pain is a very definite sensation, evoked by reactions in particular pain-nerves, and not merely the result, as we formerly supposed, of alterations in the nerves of feeling, the sensory nerves of the body. Modern research makes us tend to believe that pain is the result of some chemical substance, manufactured by the tissues themselves, quite independent of any outside stimulus. Whatever may be the explanation of pain, its influence upon the mind of the sufferer transcends that of any other bodily stimulus, especially when the victim is old and experienced enough to be aware of its futility as a warning of approaching danger or as a corrective of some internal disturbance. The patient plagued in an advanced stage of cancer by pain knows perfectly well that he is being plagued in vain; his increasing torment does not in the least benefit him. It merely exhausts his vital powers, depletes his energy and saps his moral strength. In the initial stage of the disease pain might have had some meaning, but when cancer starts it is usually painless, it gives no warning through pain of its dreadful vindictiveness. Only when no human aid can avail does it add pain to the triad of weariness, poisoning, and starvation that are its significant features, and when that time comes who shall presume to judge between the sick man and a convention so often disregarded in practice? The sick man begs, clamours for, relief from pain so acute, inevitable, and, so far as we can see, purposeless that its presence seems even to the most believing an arrogant denial of the divine goodness, a constant reminder of the suzerainty of evil whose similars mankind sees in distress and suffering. When drugs no longer can assuage, the patient gradually or quickly, according to his sense of life's values, begins to balance the benefits of euthanasia against the certainty of enduring more constant and increasingly severe pain. In such circumstances, where the end is inevitable but may be prolonged beyond the capacity of nerves to bear or a mind to contemplate, is it morally, ethically wrong for the doctor to lend his professional aid to expedite the patient into a death that is a painless end to such suffering?

That is the question that every doctor, at some time or other, has to consider. Most of us shirk our duty to answer it, shoving it aside as something in the nature of a hypothetical postulate whose discussion trenches on philosophy. Some of us bluntly declare that in no circumstances whatsoever can a doctor be justified in taking life — a premise that is invalidated by our practice to kill the child in order to save the pregnant mother's life. Others, more logical, deem it an issue that must be argued not by them but by the public which is as much concerned and interested in it. They are shackled to the tradition that teaches 'above everything thou shalt do no hurt' — a tradition that dates from the days when palliation and symptomatic treatment were all that the doctor could apply. Surgery has shaken it, for often the surgeon has to risk death for his patient to save that patient's life. There are surgeons who on occasions shrink from taking even that risk; there are many who courageously face it, with the attendant obloquy that an ignorant public attaches to a 'death under an anaesthetic' — which means, in reality, a death as the result of surgical intervention that promised the only hope of life to the patient — and sometimes succeed in the attempt to snatch the patient away from death. It is a matter for individual consideration, for no one can prescribe the limits of responsibility where the circumstances are so diverse and where probability and possibility are so closely allied that experience and intuition alone can decide between them.

There are a few of my colleagues who, more logical still, act as their conscience directs them, making no parade of their conclusions in particular cases, but abiding by the conviction that they are true to the spirit of their calling by helping a fellow human being who craved from them what was in their power to give. There are times when life, this life to which we are all inclined to attach a value far higher than what Nature assesses it at, becomes an offence to him who has it, a sheer parody of joy and beauty, a caricature of its ideal loveliness so grotesque as to swamp all emotion except pity. When that stage is reached and the victim is conscious that his sole consolation lies in the effective translation of that emotion of pitying charity into action, and is eagerly wishful that it should be so translated, who shall say that it constitutes a moral offence on the part of the doctor to become a party to such action? When I remember the woman in the rondavel, I ask myself that question, and I can find only one answer to it, and that is 'None!'

CHAPTER XVII

IN CAMP

THREE circular native-made huts, of veld grass thatched over thorn tree poles, in a clearing under an immense old wild fig tree, a giant of its kind whose branches harbour an aviary, a family of squirrels, scores of brilliantly tufted beetles, and a ceaselessly droning orchestra of cicadas. Farther away, on the left, partly hidden by bush, the *skerms* or rough shelters of the native attendants. Round everything, the circumvallation of a thorn-wood stockade, beyond which lies the scrub, a densely wooded expanse of country, criss-crossed by game paths.

That is the 'out-lie' place or camp site on one of the many untenanted farms of the Bushveld. These are privately owned farms, not obtained under Government grant, and not used for farming at all, but merely as game preserves. Once a year the owner comes, generally in winter time when there is less danger of fever, and lives in the huts for whatever period he can take leave of his town business. If he has no huts, he brings tents and a marquee. He brings his car, and his friends bring their cars. They bring ample provisions and stores, and plenty of ammunition. For the chief object is to spend a few weeks away from the cares of civilization, to return to Nature, and to enjoy the delights of the Bushveld.

Land values are preposterously high throughout the Union. In the Bushveld they are perhaps higher, in proportion to the benefits that may be obtained from land owning, than anywhere else. Privately owned land that still holds game and some water, can hardly be bought for less than a pound an acre; its real value, apart from the game, is probably a shilling an acre, and even at that price it would not pay to farm on it. Government land can be purchased much more cheaply, but the grant is conditioned by so many vexatious restrictions that the poor white settler alone can benefit. One of the most lamentable derelictions of the government of the country since Union has been its inability to initiate a practical policy of land settlement and to modify the absurd land legislation that at present prevents the exploitation of unoccupied areas. Instead of enabling the small wage earner — the civil servant, town clerk or artisan, who may cherish hopes of ultimately owning a small farm of his own — to buy government land and to improve it gradually until he is in a position to live on it, the Government insists on effective occupation by the proprietor himself — a condition that in nine cases out of ten makes it impossible for the best type of small pensioner to buy such land, while at the same time it places a premium upon its occupation by poor whites whose capital is quite inadequate properly to maintain occupation. A policy of small-holdings, on the lines so successfully adopted in Canada and Australia, would be immeasurably more beneficial to the country than the present antiquated system that is based on conditions that no longer obtain.

I can speak feelingly on the subject. These restrictions prevented me from obtaining what Horace valued the most, a 'parva rura', amid the Bushveld scrub. I was a civil servant, drawing a good salary, and able to put aside yearly a couple of hundred pounds. Two brother civil servants, equally fortunate, but, like myself, equally much bound by service and therefore unable, personally to 'occupy' a farm, agreed to join with me in purchasing a few hundred morgen of Government land in a tract that was splendidly wooded but pestilentially malarious. Our intention was to build on it, to cultivate it bit by bit, as our means allowed, and in time to make it a healthy settlement. We proposed to install as our representative a paid occupier, and to visit the place whenever there was an opportunity to do so. The land was valued at four shillings per morgen, but we offered five, half a crown per acre, which was far beyond its value as an agricultural proposition. Our proposals were turned down. The Department of Lands, though sympathetic, regretted that it had no power to waive the occupation clause. If we wanted the land, we must be prepared to reside on it for at least six months during the year — a condition manifestly impossible to comply with. Years later that tract of land was surveyed and parcelled out among poor whites whose settlement was not a success.

Some of my pleasantest vacations have been spent in these Bushveld camps. In July, when the schools were closed, the inspectors had a breathing spell, and I invariably took mine in country that was already familiar to me but in an environment that was different from that in which I had carried on most of my work. In the December vacation there were seaside camps, and my time was fairly occupied, but in the winter vacation it was far more pleasant to languish in the mild climate of the hibernating Bushveld than to shiver in the Highveld cold. One woke at daybreak, when the glorious dawn of a Bushveld day coloured the east — a dawn that always reminded me of Multatuli's description of what Saidjah saw when he was mourning his lost Adinda. 'The sun had not yet risen. *Mata hari* (the eye of day) had

284

not yet looked upon the valleys. But the stars were paling overhead as if they were ashamed of the coming victory of light stronger than theirs. Strange tints flitted above the tree tops that seemed so much darker against the lightening background of sky. A glow flew over the clouds in the east, arrows of gold and fire, shot at random, that fell back into the impenetrable darkness still hiding the day from his eyes ... On all sides it grew gradually clearer. He could see the landscape ... the little grove of palm trees at Badoer ... there lay the village ... there Adinda was sleeping! Now it lightened more and more. There came a streak of blueish red that seemed to clutch at the clouds, whose edges became gleaming, luminous, iridescent. Once more those fiery arrows shot across the sky, no longer falling into impenetrable darkness, but sinking to the ground, uniting, casting radiating streams of light over the scrub. They coalesced, crossed, wreathed, turned, sank, expanded into immense bundles of fire and gold against a screen of silver and purple and azure ... everywhere ... everywhere.' That describes a Bushveld sunrise.

The natives brought coffee and biscuits, which one consumed in the light of the camp-fire, dimly glowing after its exuberance of flame. A camp-fire is a matter of some meticulousness, in preparation as well as in keeping up. I learned how to make it early in my career as a Bushveld *hakim*. I had halted at a suitable camping site, and built up what I thought was a suitable camp-fire, brushwood and briars that crackled encouragingly and gave out plenty of exhilarating heat. Another car came along, and selected the same site, a vindication of my own perspicuity that cheered me much. The occupants were Sir Thomas Cullinan, the discoverer of the Cullinan diamond, a great pioneer and a charming camp mate, and a Rhodesian friend; they were on their way to Buluwayo.

'You've a sorry fire,' said Sir Thomas, disparagingly. 'I see I'll have to show you how to make a proper camp-fire.'

He took a hatchet and disappeared into the scrub, and presently we heard the sound of chopping. He came back dragging with him a large trunk of a dead tree which he put transversely across the fire. 'It'll burn in the middle, and all you have to do is to push the two ends together. That'll last you to the middle of next day,' he said.

And that is the Bushveld camp-fire — an immense log laid astride the mother-fire. It burns through its centre, and you merely push the two ends together; when you wake in the early dawn, there are the two stumps, smouldering lively, from which you may gain as much warmth and comfort as you have a right to expect.

After the early morning coffee, you may please yourself what you will do in camp. The hunters trudge off after kudu or whatever may interest them, with the natives straggling in retinue behind. I sometimes accompanied them, although I have no taste for shooting and no desire to collect trophies. Of all vagaries of the collecting instinct, the strangest and most childish, apart from stamps, has always seemed to me to be the collection of heads and horns, but I readily confess that it is all a matter of individual taste and that my own predilection for plants and fossils may seem as incomprehensible and as illogical to those of my friends who prefer these shielded and abbreviated remnants of animals that they have shot. More often I wandered away by myself with field glasses and a shot gun, to lie in some glade near the river and watch the blue monkeys playing in the thorn trees.

At midday came luncheon, and after that a further spell of

indolence, spent as individual choice dictated. Towards sunset, when the game came out of their shelter from the midday heat, there was plenty to observe for anyone who took an interest in what Nature so prodigally displayed around him.

And there is abundance of interest in the Bushveld on a fine winter afternoon. It is true, the veld is not then at its best. It lacks the green and the freshness of summer. Its general appearance is russet, variegated by contrasting reds and crimsons, due mainly to the splendour of the different species of aloes. The aloe is a lily, or cousin to the lilies, and some three hundred varieties of it are known. It is essentially an African plant; outside the continent of Africa only a few species exist. It is a polymorphous plant, ranging from one so small that it seems to be a dwarfed hyacinth (*Aloe minima:* a cream-flowered species that grows on the high tablelands of Barberton) to the forty feet tall *A. bainsii* of the eastern Cape Province. Its spike of shortly petiolated flowers varies in colour from a brilliant carmine to a chrome yellow or cream, but its peculiarity is that it is nearly always locally massed and makes a splash amidst the dull grey and dun of the winter starved grass. Colour on the Bushveld in winter is nearly always supplied by aloes, though the albizzia, the barbacenia — those curious raggle-taggle loofah-like trunks that blossom into a beautiful blue — and the flowering mimosa add odd pigments that complement, though they can hardly rival, its contrast. The deciduous trees have shed their leaves, and the landscape in winter is thus more open, less mysterious and sombre than in summer. There is less animal life about; the migratory birds have left, and the game, that is always there, seems less active, though more alert. Even the blue monkeys are subdued, and one hardly ever meets a snake. For the field naturalist, winter is not the ideal time to visit the Bushveld.

But the real enjoyment of a winter's camp in the Bushveld is at night, around the camp-fire. 'Men', wrote Erasmus to his friend, 'reveal themselves more fully when they are at their ease, carefree and composed.' It may not be strictly true, that dictum of a man who was himself very learned but sadly deficient in his knowledge of human nature. But it is certainly applicable to camp life in the Bushveld. Round the camp-fire one shares experience; one discusses things in a spirit more charitable than in the sharp, actinic light of the day, that seems to inhibit rather than to encourage confidences. The camp-fire exhilarates. It damps that dull fatalism that is so characteristic of the Bushveld — a fatalism that is founded on life's experiences. Hundreds of years ago Terence knew it when he made old Demipho say: 'Omnes, quom secundae res sunt maxume, tum, mexume, meditari secum oportet, quo pacto advorsam aerumnam ferant — pericla, damna, exilia. Peregre rediens semper cogitet aut fili peccatum aut uxoris mortem aut morbum filiae, communia esse haec, nequid horum unquam accidat animo novom. Quidquid praeter spem eveniat, omne id deputare esse in lucro.'

We sat round the camp-fire one night — the Mining Engineer, the Advocate, the Political Secretary of a Powerful Party, an Irish South African who was an official of the Land Bank, and myself, and we talked, like the Walrus, of many things.

We talked of Johannesburg.

Everywhere in the Union of South Africa, when men come together and the conversation ranges from the weather to sport and from sport to other subjects, somewhere in the gamut Johannesburg crops up. For it is the inevitable background against which all other interests are silhouetted, that big, complacent, uncomfortable, endlessly aching, everlastingly turbulent mining centre that strives, hitherto unsuccessfully, to be a city and is as yet only a settlement.

There is romance in its history. The romance of failure and achievement, of prodigous wealth suddenly gained by chance or patiently waited and worked for, of industry and political intrigue precariously balanced against one another for a quarter of a century; of great names and lurid personalities jostling lesser lights in the struggle for existence; of great undertakings grandly conceived and grandly carried out, and of some ideals tragically shattered. Much of it is known, being part of the story that is familiar, more or less, to every citizen on the Rand. Some of it has never been written, and probably will never be chronicled, being bound up with that secret history of South Africa of which most of us are afraid to write.

The Mining Engineer touched one aspect.

'Did I ever tell you fellows of Malherbe's deal?' he asked, filling his corroded pipe with Magaliesberg out of a green bag. We assured him that he had not.

'It's a remarkable yarn,' he went on, settling himself comfortably against the trunk of the fig tree. 'Malherbe was the President's treasurer in the old days, and he was always looking for ways and means to replenish the treasure chest. The Transvaal was very hard up, as you know, and direct taxation was anathema. But there was Government land, and some were willing to buy. A farmer who coveted some land adjoining his farm was willing to pay for it, but at his own figure, which was exactly twenty pounds. Malherbe refused to sell at that price. But President Machado came unexpectedly to Pretoria, and Malherbe went to see Oom Paul. He found the old chap on the stoep, smoking his morning pipe.

'"Sit down, man," said the President, who wasn't so old then. "Sit you down and drink a cup of coffee."

'"Thankful, President," said the Treasurer, and took the *riempie*-seated chair on the old man's right. They puffed their pipes in silence, looking across the street towards the west where the morning glow was still lingering on the hills, for both were early risers.

'"President," said the Treasurer. "The Portuguese governor came last night."

'"I know," said the President. "I shall have to call on him, but I suppose that can wait until he calls on me. Isn't that the custom?"

'"I believe so, President. The visitor calls first. But, President, we shall have to show him some kind of honour. That, too, is the custom."

'The President spat on the stoep.

'"How much money have you got for that?" he inquired, bluntly.

'"Very little, President," answered the Treasurer, sadly. "But we shall have to do the best we can."

'"What do you propose?"

'"I thought of a luncheon, President. At the hotel. Then he and you can make speeches. It need only last an hour or so, and we need not invite so many folk. I could do it for, say, twenty pounds."

'"And where are we to get twenty pounds from, nephew?"

'"I shall have to scrape it together from somewhere, President. If I have your permission, I could make a plan. There is hardly time to call an Executive Council meeting, is there?"

'"You don't need an Executive Council meeting. Make a plan, do. Provided it is not more than twenty pounds, you may give the Portuguese gentleman his luncheon. I should not like him to go away and think that we were inhospitable."

'The Treasurer left the presence and strolled down Church Street, thinking out a plan. On the square he chanced upon the farmer who had offered twenty pounds for the land adjoining his own. It was barren land, rocky land, scarcely good enough for grazing. Nobody else had offered to buy it, and the farmer's offer dated back eighteen months. But the Treasurer had an inspiration.

'He called out to the farmer, "Here, Prinsloo, I want a word with you," and when they had shaken hands and inquired, as custom decreed, after their respective healths and the well-being of their respective households, he asked, "Do you still want that bit of land?"

'"I don't *want* it exactly," replied the farmer, cautiously emphasizing the verb. "But I can do with it as an annexe to my own farm, and if you wish to sell my offer's still open."

'"Let me see, you offered fifty pounds, didn't you?"

'"I certainly never did. Twenty pounds was my limit."

'"Well, well! Is that so? But the land is worth more. There are others after it. I daresay, however, we can let you have it for forty."

'"That's just double of what I will pay. But another five won't break me, so let us say twenty-five."

'"Make it thirty-five, Prinsloo. Do, man. It's for Government use; we need the money badly just now. Look you, we are in a bit of a hole. Here's the Portuguese governor come from Delagoa Bay on a visit — a state visit, if you please — and we must entertain the fellow. And the treasury is empty, so to speak. I was just talking to the President about it, and we must make a plan. Thirty-five won't break you, man."

'Prinsloo pondered the offer.

'"Look here," he said, "I have just sold some oxen to Becketts. I owe them some money, and I don't know what my balance is. Likely it is more than thirty-five pounds, likely it is less. But I doubt if it is less than thirty. Well, here is what I propose. Let's go down to Becketts and find out. If my credit balance is more than thirty pounds, you take it and I take the farm. If it is less, I make it up to thirty pounds and you sell the farm to me for that price. Understood?"

'"Top," said the Treasurer, which is colloquial Afrikaans for "It's a bet".

'They interviewed Becketts' accountant. Prinsloo's credit with the firm exceeded thirty pounds by a couple of pounds, and Prinsloo became owner of a bit of land which he sold, some eighteen months later, when the excitement over the gold discoveries raged high, for forty thousand. To-day that farm is conservatively estimated as being worth four hundred million.'

'I know,' said the Advocate, nodding his head. 'I've heard that story before. It was the Modder farm, of course.'

'Yes,' said the Mining Engineer. 'And afterwards Prinsloo bought another farm, in the Pretoria district, and again struck it lucky. He sold a portion of it to the Premier Diamond Mining Company, and it yielded the Cullinan diamond. I wonder if you can cap that experience in the history of mining.'

'I don't know enough about mining to try,' said the Advocate, dryly. 'But I don't fancy that money so lightly gained does much good to the gainer. Nor, I should think, to the country as a whole.'

'Don't drivel,' said the Mining Engineer, fiercely. 'The mining industry is the biggest asset to this country — its only asset, if you ask me. What else is the damn place good for? Agriculture? You make me laugh! South Africa is not an agricultural country, and never will be one. With the exception of patches along the coast belt, and little bits here and there — here in the Bushveld, for instance, along the river — the soil is not deep and fertile enough to give any farmer more than two per cent return on his capital, not counting his own labour. Ranching, I grant you — ranching in the Lebombo valley or in the Waterberg. But that needs capital and organization. It's not a one man's job. No, farming is a bastard industry in this country, take my word for it, and we have too many such already.'

'What about your mines, then?' — the Advocate was mildly sarcastic. 'Half of them are dud propositions, carried on the shoulders of the others. And they exploit wealth that should remain in the country. . . .'

'And does remain,' retorted the Mining Engineer, sharply. 'Seventy-five per cent of what accrues from the mining industry stays here and benefits us. What more do you want?'

'I should prefer 100 per cent to stay,' said the Advocate mildly. 'Between you and me and that maroela tree, which is the nearest approach to a doorpost that we have, I should like to see the mines nationalized. When I was a youngster, working on a Cape Town paper, I once had a talk with Rhodes and I heard him say that that was the ultimate solution. . . .'

'Nonsense. Rhodes was a business man, not a visionary

man. No industry or trade ever prospers when it has been nationalized. Nationalization simply means ruin. Look at our railways. . . .'

'I won't,' said the Advocate, with decision. 'They are an eyesore. I told the General Manager some time back that I could give him fifty immediate suggestions for improving them, but he was far too much interested in one of his detective yarns.'

'What strikes me,' said the Political Secretary, who had been pensively silent during the argument, engaged in polishing his mouth organ which he had not been allowed to play upon, 'is that Johannesburg does nothing but live on its prosperity.'

'That's exactly what I have always complained of,' agreed the Advocate. 'It is the most selfish city on God's earth. It affects the airs of a new-rich nobody, and screams with excitement when it doesn't get what it wants. . . .'

'It generally manages to get what it wants,' interjected the Irish South African, dryly.

'That's because it rules the country. Haven't you got that clear yet, fathead?' said the Advocate. 'Look at the Press. Half of it is owned by Johannesburg, and the other half influenced by it. Some day Johannesburg will wake up and realize that it can do pretty much what it likes with the rest of us.'

'Yes, that is so,' remarked the Political Secretary, thoughtfully. 'A Reef Party, all out for its own interests, will be a mighty strong one, and if it is well led it will dominate all the others. But that is because we are so much divided on political-personal questions.'

'Don't for heaven's sake talk politics,' pleaded the Mining Engineer. 'I disagree *in toto* with your premisses. I maintain that Johannesburg sets the pace for the rest of the country. It realizes its responsibilities and lives up to them.'

'Indeed' — the Advocate was again sarcastic. 'You might point out to the meeting where it has so happily led us? I suppose you mean in culture — in art — in science — in achievement that counts, eh? Honestly, now, I can't say that I am convinced. I have been through the slums, you know. I went through the strike, too.'

'Just look at the amounts it has spent on these things,' said the Mining Engineer appealingly. 'Look at what it has done for education, for instance. And in my own science — in engineering, in metallurgy, in . . . in everything.'

'I admit that it has spent money' — the Advocate knocked the dottel out of his pipe, and surreptitiously replenished it from the Irish South African's pouch — 'but I don't for a moment admit that it has given a fair share of its wealth for anything that really counts in the shaping of a nation.'

'What's a nation?' queried the Land Bank official. 'When I was a nipper I was told that there was only one that counted — the Irish. My grandfather was a Fenian, and, as you know, I was brought up to curse England and everything that was English. Did I ever tell you what happened to me in our war?'

'Carry on,' said the Political Secretary. 'Doc here doesn't know.'

'I was commandeered,' began the Irish South African, 'and as I was a youngster and all in favour of shooting the adjectival English, I went ahead with my bandolier and *biltong* — plenty of *biltong*, for you never know what might happen — but before I went to join up I saw Father D——. "Father," I said, "is it wrong to shoot the English?" "Son," he replied, "it is not a question of English or Dutch; it's a question of your duty as a citizen." "That's all right, Father," I said, and I started off, quite happy. At Tugela, as you know, we shot them. I fired my Mauser till its barrel became too hot, and was quite disappointed when the general came along and said we had to cross the river and take their surrender. I was first across and rushed up to them. Mind you, I had been shooting at the English, and I expected them to be English. You can imagine what my feelings were when one of the youngsters — about my own age, he was, I remember — stepped forward and said, "We're the Dublin Fusiliers".'

'Nation's a matter of language,' said the Advocate, dogmatically, as if he were enunciating a proposition in Roman-Dutch law — on which he is an authority. 'We're two nations here, English and Afrikaans, and we'll never get together until we settle the language difficulty.'

'That,' said the Political Secretary, 'is tommy-rot. We're talking English, and we all of us speak Afrikaans as well as, or better than, we do English.'

I joined in the conversation, to which I had so far listened with interest. 'I know a dear old Catholic priest, Father Kelly, who ministers to a congregation on the Cape Flats. His home language is Gaelic, although, having been educated at Rome, he talks both Italian and Latin quite fluently. He preaches in English to a congregation of Germans whose home language is Afrikaans.'

We talked of 'our war' — *ons oorlog* — in which they had all taken part. The Mining Engineer and the Political Secretary had been on General Botha's staff, and the Irish South African had been in his commando. They told stories of their experiences, exciting experiences, of dark nights when they had groped to find their way through the barbed wire fencing stringed with condensed milk tins to give a ringing warning when it was cut — of scurrying rushes to escape from encircling drives — of temporary success in capturing a convoy — of wanderings, inexorably pursued by lumbering columns, through the same Bushveld in which we were now camping. They spoke of it all objectively, laughing over their misfortunes, bearing no grudge, hardly with any feeling at all in voice or gesture, except when they touched upon something that had left its mark even after fifteen years.

The Mining Engineer contributed such a touch. He told of his dog, a wire-haired fox terrier that he had rescued from a band of bullying boys on one of the dumps of the old Robinson mine. Because of that, he had called the dog 'Dump'. When the war came, the Mining Engineer, then a mere apprentice, went on commando, faithfully followed by an old Hottentot retainer who acted as his orderly, and the dog went with them. In laager the dog was trained to bark whenever he saw khaki or anyone dressed in that colour. When the Boers were forced back from Natal, the Mining Engineer went with his commando into the eastern Transvaal and was made a dispatch rider. On one occasion he was sent by General Botha to warn a commando, far away in the Bushveld, of an encircling movement, and as usual, although his old native retainer warned him against it, he took the dog with him. They travelled by night, lying concealed during the daytime, for they had to dodge columns and blockhouse lines, and were fortunate in reaching within fifty miles of where the commando which they had to warn was lying. But that evening they were seen by a couple of scouts, and the Mining Engineer lay down behind an ant heap and fired his Mauser, killing one of the scouts. He went forward, the other mounted man having galloped away, but found that he had shot the man through the head and could do nothing for him. Strapped to the saddle was a sword, which the old Hottentot annexed. 'It is a sharp knife, *Baas*,' he told the Mining Engineer, 'and it'll do grandly to cut our way through the bush if we have to walk.'

'We went on,' said the Mining Engineer, 'but found that the scout must have given warning, for it was not very long before we saw two converging columns on the sky-line. Our only hope was to hide in the bush, and we made for it, turning our horses loose, and scrambling on foot through the thicket. The *Outa* (old native) led me to a big hollow wild fig, and we climbed up and dropped down into the hollow trunk, where we lay safe and snug. I carried Dump with me, and we reckoned we'd wait until midnight, when the columns had given up the search, and make our way through the bush to our horses and ride on to warn the commando. But one column came right into the clearing where our fig tree stood, and camped there. I could hear the men talking, quite close to our tree, but none of them suspected it was hollow, and we were safe enough. When their camp was quiet, I told the *Outa* that we must get a move on, but he shook his head. "We can't get out, *Baas*," he said, "not with the dog with us. You see, *Baas*, the dog will bark as soon as he sees or smells the khakis, and then we can't escape. We must wait till they go." But we couldn't do that, you know, for I knew this was probably the detachment that had been told off to attack that commando, and it was imperative that we should get off and warn our men. I suggested that I should muffle Dump's head in my coat, but the old native pointed out that that would not prevent him from barking. "We must kill him, *Baas*," he said. "If *Baas* wants to warn the commandant and get away hide-whole, Baas must kill the

dog. It's the only way. . . ." Well . . . I wasted an hour in
arguing with him, but he was right . . . and there was nothing
else to do. I held out a bit of *biltong* and Dump stretched
out his neck and the *Outa* swung the scout's sword . . . We
buried the dog in the tree, and climbed out. Oh, we made
our escape all right . . . but when I think of the little chap
coming forward to nose the *biltong* . . .'

The Political Secretary struck another note, tactfully, to
obliterate the sense of tragedy. 'When we took that convoy,'
he said, turning to the Irish South African who had been
party to the exploit, 'you remember how jealously each man
guarded his wagon. There were twenty wagons, and a couple
took possession of each and regarded it as their own special
perquisite. As there were ample supplies for all of us, and
much more than we could use, we soon shared our possessions, but one old burgher, who had annexed a wagon all to
himself, obstinately refused to let anyone approach his
capture. "It's mine," he declared, "and I'm going to eat
what's in it myself without anyone's help." We left him at
it, and sat round the fire, gorging on biscuits, sardines and
tinned stuff — most of the wagons contained tinned stuff.
At last the old man ventured from his wagon and came
forward, holding a tin in his hand. "Is there anyone," he
asked in an appealing voice, "who will exchange a tin of little
birds' gizzards for a tin of jam?" He had opened every case
in his wagon, and found nothing but tinned oysters, which
he had sampled and did not at all like.'

They told of the inroads into Natal and the Cape Colony,
of the first flush of success in the early December of 1899,
and of the dismal two years of flight and guerrilla warfare
that followed. And then they talked of other things, switch-
ing away from the subject that was after all the most

interesting because it represented their lives' greatest adventure at an age when adolescence is most impressionable, a soft clay for Fate to work, make or mar.

In the crisp Bushveld night, so translucently green before the moon has set that objects are easily distinguished in the dusk, one could lie and listen to the single or combined sounds that voice the activities of veld animals that play under the stars. They range, these sounds, in descending order from the roar of the lion prowling along the banks of the dry bed of the river to the twittering stridulation of the tiny brown beetles whose faint luminescence radiates from their hidy-holes. Like the songs of birds, no one has yet explained the meaning of most of these sounds. Why does the lion roar? No hunter knows why, although most hunters have their own pet theory on the subject. Or the zebra bark or the hartebeest make those cooing noises that remind one of a dog with distemper? To the stranger most of these night sounds are totally unfamiliar, and their causation matter of much perplexity until experience and observation bring conviction. Most strange and incomprehensible is the short, staccato yelp of the zebra, an animal that one would normally expect to bray. Yet I have only once heard them bray, and my Bushveld friends assure me that I was lucky to have had that experience.

CHAPTER XVIII

SEX AND SENTIMENT

WHERE children grow up in an environment that offers them ample opportunity to become acquainted, at a comparatively early age, with the ordinary and normal forms of sex expression, they rarely show the inhibitions and aberrancies of character and conduct that are indirectly the result of ignorance of the meaning and scope of the sexual instinct. It is the young adolescent who has been screened from all contact with the manifold forms of sex expression who develops those peculiar, to teachers and parents alike incomprehensible and annoying, traits that are usually taken to be signs of 'pubertal psychosis'. Suppressed curiosity and repressed emotion play the very devil with the introvert child who is permitted to reach, and progress beyond, puberty, without an explanation that will enlighten him or her as to the function and purpose of bodily organs that suddenly, and with startling regularity, are thrown into an activity for which juvenile experience can find no precedent. It is with such ignorance that the experienced parent, teacher or school doctor has sometimes to deal. There would be no necessity to deal with it if children were allowed to learn what their bodily organs have to do and in what way their physiological activity is manifested.

My Bushveld children were for the most part in that happy position that they did not need instruction on this subject. Around them they saw daily the normal body displayed in its pristine nakedness, in the shape of juvenile and adolescent natives of both sexes who go about with the flimsiest of covering or with no covering at all. They lived on farms where there is abundant opportunity to observe the manner in which life comes into existence. The boys helped when the cow calved, and the girls knew quite as well as did their parents when the old sow would have her next litter. On the open veld they saw almost as much, for in springtime, the season of pairing and copulating, they could not stroll far from the homestead without meeting two animals, mostly insects or reptiles, engaged in that intimate embrace of fertilization. They learned equally much from the conversations that they overheard, for although the Bushveld folk are not lewd, nor except on occasion coarse in their talk, they are forthright and see no reason to use euphuisms where the simple truth serves just as well. Their relations with the natives, too, made enlightenment more easy. They nearly all spoke a native dialect, and could easily understand and follow what was said in the *kraals* or round the huts, and there, too, sex matters were discussed, if not freely then at least with less reticence than would have been expected in a more sophisticated community.

I never experienced in the Bushveld schools anything that tended to show that such early initiation in what are absurdly called 'the mysteries of sex' produced reactions that found expression in a-social conduct. All the Bushveld schools are — or were at that time — mixed schools, and co-education was the rule to which there was not a single exception. Moreover, in nearly all schools the pupils were widely diversified in age. There were young children, of six and seven years of age, in the same room and in the same playground with boys and girls who to all intents and purposes were already young men and women. Such a situation creates problems and difficulties of which every teacher who has had experience of them can tell, but here it was a rarity when anything occurred that needed more than a timely word or tactful interference for its readjustment with the normal. The children, as it appeared to me, took little or no interest, beyond that aroused by mere curiosity when they were faced with something outside their experience, in sex matters. In the town schools, where the relations between the sexes were less intimate openly, the situation was altogether different. There one saw a good deal of the sly, furtive approach that is so characteristic of the partly enlightened juvenile — the obscenities scribbled on privy walls, the secretive notes passed, through the intermediary of juniors, between girls and boys, the covert expression of adolescent emotion in familiarities on the playground, that sometimes developed serious complications. But not in the Bushveld.

I confess that this surprised me. In such circumstances, with such children, in such a community, one would have expected to find more evidence of a disregard of convention simply because there was, or appeared to be, immeasurably more temptation. In this sub-tropical climate children grow up very quickly; they reach puberty, apparently, at an earlier age than do urban children, although on this point, again, one has no certain and definite data. My woman assistant, Dr. Cleaver, investigated the matter so far as the girls were concerned and so far as it was possible to investigate it, but her untimely death prevented her from completing the task. Her tentative conclusions, which she confided to me, were that the onset of the menstrual period in Bushveld girls was not appreciably sooner than in Highveld girls, when age alone was taken into consideration. For the Transvaal as a whole, the average age of onset agreed very closely with that determined by investigation in Australia. Deductions from age are however fallacious. One has to take development into consideration, and my own experience goes to show that on the average the Bushveld girl seems to develop, glandularly, more rapidly than the Highveld girl, so far, at least, as normal, healthy girls are concerned. The prevalent malnutrition and chronic malaria stunt growth and retard development of girth and height, but, curiously enough, appear to act as endocrine stimulants and to hasten the onset of puberty.

It is of course much more difficult to determine the onset of puberty in boys. Its climax is the production of developed sperm, and not merely the development of the secondary sexual characters. In examinations of centrifugalized urine of boys of fourteen, to find bilharzia ova, it was not uncommon to light upon spermatozoa. Taking all points into consideration, I came to the conclusion that twelve to thirteen years for boys and eleven to twelve for girls could be fairly assumed to be the averages of onset of puberty in the two sexes. Yet, notwithstanding this comparatively early puberty, I do not remember having met with a single case of the effects of sexual precocity in the Bushveld, though I have notes of several such cases elsewhere in the Transvaal. One of my colleagues told me that he had delivered a girl of twelve. I found one of fourteen who was in her sixth month of pregnancy, and another of fifteen and a half, also advanced in pregnancy. In the latter case the child was attending school, and her condition was discovered at the routine examination. I feel sure that in the Bushveld it would not have been left for the school doctor to have made the diagnosis of pregnancy. There a parent, who had, quite rightly, kept her girl out of school, asked me to come to the farm to examine the child. 'Although it is unbelievable, Doctor,' she said, 'I am afraid that there is a child coming. Yet she denies it, and I have always found Hessie a truthful daughter.' The girl had an ovarian cyst, or at any rate a freely movable pelvic tumour that could not be mistaken for pregnancy. She was sent to hospital, operated upon, and made a good recovery.

From the Bushveld point of view there is nothing derogatory in these early pregnancies, provided that the girl is married. Every year there are many marriages between quite young girls and boys. The statistics of such juvenile unions are published yearly by the Census Department, and those who are interested in them can find them in the departmental reports. Early marriage in such a community is a communal safeguard, even though it has a profoundly demoralizing effect in the long run. Illegitimate intercourse is frowned upon, and in a community that is so intimately solid it cannot be kept secret. The parents recognize that repressive continence in such an environment is bound to defeat its object, and prefer that the children, who have conceived a mutual liking (*sinnigheid*) should marry. The children know this quite well, and arrange matters accordingly. The result is, on the one hand, a healthy, sane outlook upon sex, so far as the relations between boy and girl are concerned, and on the other hand, a far too early and inexperienced adventure into matrimony that may afterwards lead to disaster. While there is a praiseworthy avoidance of that cautious, temporizing courting, that is content with the surrogate for true marital intercourse, so often seen in urban areas, there is at the same time often an impetuous and irresponsible rashness in contracting marriage at an age and in circumstances when neither party can fully realize what marriage means.

A housefather in one of the poor white institutions told me a story that well illustrates this characteristic. 'One of my seventeen-year-old boys, a quiet, steady, well-behaved youngster, came to me one day, and asked if he might be allowed to leave the institution. I asked him why he wanted to go. "Well, Uncle," he replied, "my Auntie has died and left me a legacy, so I need no longer remain here." "I am very glad to hear it, my boy. And what do you intend to do now?" "Well, Uncle, I have thought of getting married and settling down." "Getting married? But to whom?" "Well, Uncle, there's a girl on the farm who will say the yes-word if I ask her." When he left, I remembered that I had not asked him what his legacy consisted of, so I repaired the omission. "Well, Uncle," he said, "it's not very much. About eight pounds or so." Six months later I met the boy again. He was trudging the streets to find work. I called him to me and inquired how he was getting on. "Well, Uncle, to tell you the truth, not so well. If I had known what it was like to be married I would have spent Auntie's legacy in buying a bicycle. It's hard work trudging on foot."'

That boy's case can be paralleled by others. Among the poor whites, early marriage, irresponsible marriage, is the rule rather than the exception. On the farms, where there is always the charity that doles from its own meagre store, sacrificing itself to help a fellow-being in greater need, the children from such marriages are not too badly off; for, although desperately poor, the parents can always feed and clothe them with the help of the kindly neighbours. But when the couple migrate to the town, in the vain search for work, the lot of the whole family becomes ten times worse, and the children are exposed to influences that are woefully deteriorating, while the parents find a melancholy solace in getting more children. The most saddening stories are those one hears at the Mothers' Clinics in the large towns, where these women come for relief, for the lactogen to feed their recurrent babies, and the free meals that the municipality provides. A woman of twenty-six, with nine children, four alive; one of twenty-one with three children and carrying a fourth; one of thirty-two who had endured twelve pregnancies — these are among the supplicants seen recently at one of the Clinics. There is a movement, fostered by the women themselves, to introduce birth control, but the Church frowns at it, just as it discourages cremation, and the mere suggestion that it should be applied is as yet regarded as an affront and an insult. Quite recently the first book on the subject has been published in Afrikaans — a courageous experiment on the part of author and publisher alike — but there is no evidence that there is any real desire to introduce birth limitation and, by means of vigorous propaganda, to stop these early, irresponsible marriages or to lessen the burden that these early married women have to bear. Nor can one blame the youths who contract these juvenile marriages. There is nothing for them to do on the farm, except to watch the vicissitudes of the weather and dream of the wealth that their more fortunate fellows are squandering in the towns. Marriage is at least action, the assertion of an independence that, however limited and confined, satisfies the urge towards self-realization.

In a primitive community, imbued with the stern principles of Calvinistic tradition to which it tenaciously clung, it was reasonable to suppose that conventions in regard to sex expression should have been regulated by repressive laws, as was the case in the early settlements in New England. Indeed, the Trekker community in the Transvaal in its early days might have been likened to the colony of Massachusetts at the time when Mistress Prynne was condemned 'for the remainder of her natural life, to wear a mark of shame upon her bosom'. As is well known, the repressive Massachusetts legislation, that had for its object the suppression of illicit sexual intercourse, not only failed to achieve its intention but actually increased the practices against which it was enacted. May, in his interesting study *Social Control of Sex Expression*, states that 'the strict precautions taken by the Puritans against social intercourse between the unattached of the opposite sexes led to two foreseeable consequences. The one was an exaggerated amount of homosexual expression ... The other and more recognized result of the Puritan attitude towards sexual expression was bundling. Bundling consisted in two persons of opposite sex, generally completely dressed, occupying the same bed. It was of two sorts; between strangers and between lovers. The first sort was a simple domestic makeshift arising from the necessities of a new country. Where a married couple boasted but one bed, it was a mark of hospitality for the host to allow the visitor, male or female, to use his half of the bed while the host himself slept on the floor. This form of bundling was by no means peculiar to America. The other expression of bundling, between lovers, was engaged in upon the mutual understanding that innocent endearments should not be exceeded. This form, too, developed originally from limitations of wealth and convenience. To utilize the bed-covering was to save firewood and candle-light. Bundling was dangerous not to the extent to which it was practised but to the extent to which it was exceeded.'

In the Bushveld neither of these results has happened. Bundling in its first form is at present unknown, though there is evidence that it formerly existed in exceptional cases. In its second form, it is replaced by the old custom, now dying out, of 'sitting up'. The young man and his maid come together in the dining-room, and sit together on the sofa, with the lighted candle on the little table beside them, and the elders leave them discreetly alone. There is an implied, and scrupulously observed, understanding that the bounds of conventional courting should in no circumstances be exceeded. If, after some hours of such isolated companionship the parties agree that they are sufficiently in love to marry, the parents are called in and the formal consent to the marriage is obtained, a consent which is a foregone conclusion, for no father or mother would have allowed such 'up-sitting' unless they had already decided that the suitor was an eligible son-in-law. The betrothal is announced, the banns are called thrice, and the wedding follows as soon after as is convenient for all concerned. That custom has fallen into disuse. Courting is quicker, but it is almost never surreptitious, and although there are exceptions, in general Bushveld parents have no reason to complain of the sex relations of their children. These matters are treated as ordinary, everyday affairs; no halo of mysterious innuendo surrounds them, and the children learn, from an early age, to regard them in a sober, common-sense way as things that may legitimately be suffused with some sentiment but that need not be slobbered with affectation or disguised by transparent subterfuge.

The question of homosexuality falls into another, and altogether different category. The Bushveld community is as homosexual and as bisexual as any other community living under similar conditions, but the manifestations of homo- and bi-sexual traits in it are less obvious than they are elsewhere. It is lamentable that homosexuality is still regarded, even by some medical men, as a sex perversion, and that its discussion has been overloaded by the jargon of pseudo-scientific inanities. There would be less difficulty in understanding it, and in dealing with its manifestations sanely, if we were to rid ourselves of the traditional concept, enshrined in the law of practically all Protestant countries, that it is an anti-social abnormality. In South Africa it is still, I believe, a capital crime for two male citizens to practise it, although the last recorded case in which sentence of death was pronounced (but not carried out) was in 1861 and since then the accused have been proceeded against for *crimen injuria* and not, as the old indictments have it, for 'a venereal affair with one of his own sex', with a correspondingly lower sentence. The law against homosexuality, applicable only to males, is a remnant of Canon law, which again is a relic of Mosaic law, grounded, as Westermarck has shown, not on utilitarian considerations, as modern exponents of Roman Dutch law allege, but on a purely religious basis. In every primitive community there exists a tendency tacitly to evade laws that are not self-evidently necessary for preserving the integrity of the community, and from the earliest times that tendency has operated in South Africa. The statistics of homosexuality, as recorded in the convictions by courts of law, are no evidence of its incidence; they are merely a faint index of anti-social acts committed by persons who may or may not be homosexual, just as the statistics for rape and assaults upon women are an index of similarly anti-social acts by persons who may or may not be heterosexual. From the point of view of the teacher and the school doctor, homosexuality is of no greater importance or significance than heterosexuality. Both may give rise to difficulties and problems that should be dealt with by a study of the personality of the child, with a view to teaching him to learn what every citizen should know, how to control himself. Among the natives homosexuality is well known, and looked upon in this sane, common-sense way, for the average native is logical in his view of sex and strictly utilitarian in applying his traditional conventions that express it. He knows quite well that homosexuality is everywhere about — he has only to look at the game to see numerous instances of it — and he has never experienced that its manifestations are any more injurious to his communal integrity than are the manifestations of heterosexuality. Indeed, were he asked his opinion he would probably say that heterosexual loss of control is of far greater baneful significance to his tribe than homosexuality; the former spoils his property, the latter causes him no material loss.

Practically all native tribes in the Transvaal had their tribal 'pubertal schools' in which adolescents received their initiation and training in tribal matters. In such schools the sexes, that had hitherto lived under a system of co-education in the *kraal*, were rigidly separated for the time necessary to inculcate in the pupils the conventions sanctioned by custom and experience. It is popularly supposed that these 'initiation schools' are primarily concerned with sex conventions, but that is by no means the case, although it is quite true that the relation of the tribe to sex is emphasized. Such practices as circumcision, flagellation, incising the skin over the face, and filing the front teeth, have as much a totemistic as a sexual significance. The fact that for a certain limited period the male pupils of such schools are permitted a licence far in excess of what the grown-up tribesmen allow themselves, and are even encouraged to transgress taboos in speech and gestures, leads one to suppose that their elders are perfectly well aware that purely repressive measures cannot permanently eradicate the tendency for uncontrolled passion to vent itself in a-social conduct, and prefer to let the youngsters learn through experience how necessary it is, in the interests of all concerned, that certain emotions should be manifested within conventional limits. It is very difficult for a European to get admission to these initiation schools, and the accounts given of what goes on in them by the natives who have matriculated and are 'full tribesmen' are necessarily coloured and therefore to some extent untrustworthy. In my capacity as doctor, I attempted to obtain permission from my native, unregistered colleagues who supervised the ritual circumcisions at these schools, to witness some of the ceremonies, but the two gatherings that I attended were obviously arranged for my benefit and could not be considered models of what such things are. Dr. Werner Eiselen, who has had many opportunities to become acquainted with these schools, and whose knowledge of native languages enables him to converse fluently with both the novices and the initiated, has given an interesting description of the ritual in his thesis *Stamskole* (Tribal Schools) published in 1929. According to him the curriculum consists in a traditional code whose intention is to inculcate tribal solidarity. The boys are taught to endure pain and discomfort by hardening processes that culminate in the final trial of mutilation, to honour the elders and headmen of their tribe, to know the various folk songs and tribal cries, and to become acquainted with the tribal conventions regarding sex. Apparently all parts of this quadruple

312

programme are thought to be of equal importance; if possible the first is considered to be the main object of the school. In any case, such gatherings of youths at an age when they stand most in need of clarifying their impressions of sex, provide the wise men of the tribe with an excellent opportunity to readjust youngsters who have slipped out of conventional alignment and to do so with the least difficulty and with an authority that has behind it the whole weight of tribal and traditional sanction. The natives with whom I talked on this subject told me that the supervisors held not only 'regimental talks' or lectures to the congregation of boys, but took each boy apart and subjected him to an examination that has much in common with what is known as 'psycho-analysis'. That these interviews were of practical utility to the boys seems evident from the fact that notwithstanding the opposition of missionaries and some officials to the holding of such tribal schools, the custom of initiating young adolescents in this manner is still strong among the natives. Some missionaries are broad-minded enough to recognize that the schools serve a useful purpose, and I know of one who did not hesitate to address the initiated when they came back from a month's sojourn in the wilds, and to tell them that, now that they had learned to behave themselves like men, they should live up to what they had learned. But he was a very understanding man, and the natives called him 'The Knowing One'. The majority of his colleagues, I am afraid, regard the schools as an excuse for unbridled debauchery, and do not hesitate to condemn them as such.

I was glad to find, among my more experienced teachers, an understanding of and a sympathy with the difficulties of adolescence that enabled them to deal with these problems of maladjustment in a sensible way. As I have already said, few of such problems cropped up in the co-educational Bushveld schools. One saw, of course, the usual surges of adolescent and pubertal emotion; small girls who had a lively attachment to older girls; boys who had equally passionate friendships among themselves. Sometimes these were continued long after school, but they could not by any stretch of imagination be called demoralizing. Sometimes, too, parents consulted me about sex matters in connection with their children's behaviour, but the problems that they brought for solution were never very puzzling, and in every case there was no difficulty in bringing about a satisfactory readjustment.

There was a certain amount of ignorance, or rather of perverted knowledge, that on occasion accounted for the parents' own inability to effect such readjustment without an appeal to an outsider. Once a couple, already well past middle age, brought their youngest son to me, a boy of ten, naturally intelligent and lively but depressed and fatigued by the chronic malaria from which he suffered. I pointed this out, outlined his enlarged spleen with the indelible pencil so that the parents could see for themselves how big it was, and suggested that he should be treated. Neither of them was satisfied. You have not examined him below, Doctor', said his father. Ordinarily it is not necessary, at a routine school examination, to strip the child completely, and where possible I avoided doing so; an experienced examiner can usually tell if there is any necessity to proceed further, and in this case I had not considered it necessary. As I had possibly overlooked a rupture, of which the parents might be aware, I examined the boy further, and found him quite normal. When he had left the room, the father leaned forward and said impressively, 'Now, Doctor, speaking quite frankly, can he ever have a child?' I am not sure if I was alert enough not to show my surprise, but I managed to reply that there was no anatomical reason why the youngster should not have a child when he grew old enough to marry. 'Why do you ask me such a question?' I added.

'You see, Doctor,' said the mother impressively, 'Dirkie (little Richard) is a twin; his little twin sister unfortunately died of the dysentery when she was quite small. And Dirkie has been so strange. . . .'

'That is probably because he is malarious. I have told you. . . .'

'But doctor knows that the fever does not make one not able to breed, and that one of twins when he marries does not get a child. . . .'

It flashed across my mind that I had somewhere heard of this superstition. It is, I believe, essentially an agricultural one, held by some cattle breeders who hold that twins are 'freemartins' and unable to breed. All I could do was to assure them that I knew of no scientific evidence to warrant such a supposition, but I do not think that I quite convinced them. There were many farmers who believed implicitly in telegony — that the first mating influenced all the subsequent progeny from that mother. I strove hard to convince General Botha that there is no proof of this theory, but he brushed all my arguments aside. 'If you cross an Afrikaner cow with a Friesland bull, you will never get pure red calves from her,' he said. In the southern American states I was told that the belief in telegony was one of the factors that predisposed the community to countenance lynchings. I once had an opportunity to chat with a farmer whose daughter had been raped by a negro. The negro had been riddled with bullets, and his body was floating in the harbour when I landed. The father of the girl discussed the matter quite placidly. 'My daughter has been ruined for life,' he said, simply. 'Her children will always have that —— blood in them.' That is the popular conception of telegony.

I met with no other quaint superstitions of a similar kind in the Bushveld, although I met with them among Bushveld people who had migrated to the towns, and had absorbed the prejudices of their new environment. In the towns, indeed, the solid common sense of the Bushveld community seemed to be unable to withstand the insidious attrition of a laxer attitude towards sex, and things were by no means so satisfactory as they were in rural areas. In the Bushveld community people spoke frankly and freely; when there was anything that demanded attention, the school committee met and investigated the matter. At one school I was asked to examine both the teacher and the children, because the committee had received an anonymous letter hinting that things were not quite as they should be. I pointed out that I had no authority to examine the teacher, and that such anonymous hints should be treated with the contempt they deserved, but both teacher and parents insisted that it was a serious accusation and that something should be done. A careful examination showed that there was nothing wrong. This was the one solitary case in which I encountered base innuendo and anonymous accusation in the Bushveld. In the towns such anonymous letters were not infrequently received by the Department. They usually hinted that there was leprosy or venereal disease among the children, but in the majority of cases the suspicions were quite unfounded.

Every medical inspector of schools meets with cases of aberration of conduct on occasion, and is sometimes able to use his special knowledge to correct wrong impressions and be of some assistance to teachers and pupils alike. On one occasion I could fortunately obviate what might easily have developed into a serious accusation against a teacher. I was asked by a magistrate to give an opinion on the severity with which a boy had been caned. The Bushveld has no objection to corporal punishment at school; on the contrary, it believes in it. But there are exceptions to every rule, and in this particular case the mother of the boy had complained that her son had been so severely thrashed that 'something had to be done'. The sergeant of police brought the boy to me at the hotel where I was staying with a brother Inspector whom I asked to be present at the examination. The boy, a cheery-faced youngster of fourteen, protested against the fuss that was being made; he did not mind a hiding, and he admitted that he had been naughty. But his mother took a different view. 'Look at his bottom, Doctor,' she cried, and the sergeant supported her. 'I really think, Doctor,' he said, 'that it's a little too much.' We looked at the boy's buttocks. They were a variegated field of blue and green, presenting what appeared to be a succession of bruises. My brother Inspector held up his hands in horror. 'The fellow must have thrashed him very severely,' he said, primly. 'I shall have to look into this.' 'Wait a minute,' I said, and told the boy to strip off his shirt. I drew my finger across his back, criss-cross wise, and immediately heavy red weals appeared in the skin. I took a ruler and drew its edge across the boy's thigh; similar but more bruised-looking marks appeared. 'How many cuts did you get, sonny?' 'Three, sir.' 'Did you feel them overmuch?' 'No, sir, but ma will make a fuss.' 'That's all right, then. Sergeant, just show the magistrate what kind of boy he is . . . I'll write a note.' And I explained to my little audience that some people, curiously enough those who appear to be least sensible to painful stimuli, show this rapid skin reaction, known as dermographia, on the slightest blow or pressure. In this case it was surprising that neither the mother nor the boy himself was aware of his peculiarity.

CHAPTER XIX

THE NATIVE

No one in the Bushveld seems so happy, so carefree, so thoroughly appreciative of life as the Native. I met him tilling his mealie lands, his little patches of sweet potatoes and *marankas*, his more productive and profitable millet fields, and he always had an appealing smile, even when he looked half-starved and when I knew that he dragged about with him a spleen that was four times its normal size. I met his women-folk, models of muscular deportment, most gracefully balancing heavy loads on their heads and trudging, upright and taut, with that easy swing of the hips that denotes perfect balance, through the high grass without the slightest regard for whatever dangers lurked in it. In a lion country, where it was not unusual to meet the animals strolling quietly near the road, such disinterestedness was surprising, to say the least. I met his children, dozens of them, scores of them, near every hut or group of huts: children of all ages and sizes, the small ones so incredibly alike that one could not tell their sex if one did not know that the little girls wore fringed loin coverings and the little boys used these things without fringes. I could never tell his tribe. There are so many tribes that it is a matter of expert knowledge to distinguish between them, and as I never learned — to my shame be it said — to talk his language sufficiently well to speak three consecutive words in it, I was debarred from inquiring directly from him to which branch of the Bantu family he belonged. 'Bantu' simply means 'people', but it is a generic name for practically all South African natives, except those who are of Hottentot or Bushman descent.

In the Transvaal there are many sub-divisions of the Bantu. I gathered that they all were cousins, though perhaps not very germane, of the Zulu race, though most of them did not show the fine physical build of the typical Zulu. In the Bushveld there had been Zulus, the *impi* of Mosile-katsi, the Silkaats of the Boers, Chaka's great captain, who, getting too popular for his chief's peace of mind, had feared assassination and forestalled it by fleeing with his legion as far from Natal as he could conveniently go. With his *impi* he had occupied the Middleveld, assimilated into his own group such natives as he found there, after having first showed them, very drastically, that he was not a fellow to stand any nonsense, and founded his own realm, which he had ruled with much wisdom. When the emigrant Boers came into conflict with him, he had at first fought them, but finding that his *impis* could not prevail against them, he had trekked north, across the river, into the territory now known as Rhodesia, where he had founded another kingdom, that of the Matabele. Here he had reigned in peace until his death, when he was succeeded by his ill-fated and much less wise son, Lobengula, who was dispossessed by the Chartered Company. Silkaats, from all accounts, was a clever, broadminded man. He welcomed the Boer hunters who came to shoot in his kingdom, and treated them with courtesy and kindness. The Lichtenburg party, the first white men, presumably, who explored the Zambezi Falls, took charge of the king's son to initiate him into the way in which white men shot big game and to teach him how to ride a white man's horse. In return, the King granted them many privileges and showed them much honour.

It is doubtful if to-day the majority of the Bushveld natives know much about these tales of the past. Perhaps in the big native locations in the north-eastern part of the Transvaal, tribal tradition is kept green, and it may be that round the fire at night the old men narrate the history of the Bantu from the days when they wandered down from the lake country and settled beyond the Drakensbergen. But in the western Bushveld there is little tribal solidarity. There are scattered groups too widely dispersed to have common interests, united merely by a common language that is locally so differentiated that there are many dialects. They retain their generic peculiarities, and have more or less the same conventions and customs throughout the Union, but there is a looseness and an instability that prevent one from looking at them as one looks at the large native tribes elsewhere in the Province. Here and there one finds them congregated together into small tribes, ruled by head-men appointed, according to ancient custom indeed, but really by grace of the Department of Native Affairs that gazettes these appointments just as the appointments of justices of the peace and commissioners of oaths are gazetted. Now and then the existence of such conglomerations of natives is brought to public notice by the proclamations declaring such and such a location to be under curfew rules, or others stating that chief so-and-so has leave to levy a special tax to pay for a farm that the tribe wishes to buy.

The Native suffers from so many restrictions, or what we civilized and democratized Europeans would account restrictions, that it is surprising to find him so invariably cheerful, so constitutionally extrovert. Forced labour is legal in the Transvaal. A farmer on whose farm there are native tenants has the right to exact from them manual labour for a certain period of the year. No one — no one, at least, of the European community, sees anything derogatory to the prestige or the dignity of the white man in such legislation, although it is in no way inferior in its denial of individual liberty than was the 'culture system' of Governor van den Bosch in Java. When it is remembered that Wallace and Money, both kind-hearted and conscientious men, vigorously defended the 'culture system', the evils of which Dekker sketched in his forgotten romance *Max Havelaar*, one need not be surprised that in South Africa there are many men, equally kind-hearted and conscientious, who are wholeheartedly in favour of the Transvaal Act that legalizes forced native labour. But it is somewhat astonishing that the arguments used up to 1910, when the last indentured Chinaman left the Transvaal, to rid the then Crown Colony of the incubus of slave labour, have so speedily been forgotten that their repetition in the debate on this Act, when it was yet a Bill, evoked sneers instead of sympathy.

The Native has few privileges and many obligations. He has to pay an individual tax, although he is indirectly taxed heavily for the European dress he is forced to wear when he goes outside his native areas. He has to carry an identification pass — which, in itself, is not anything to grumble at provided it is not, as now, meant to imply a discrimination between black and white. After all, a passport of identity is required in every civilized country, and if every citizen of the Union were called upon to carry one, much of the agitation against passes that is now evident among urban natives would cease. But the Bushveld, like the rest of the Union that holds the 'northern view', will not see that point. To hint that every citizen should have a pass

322

is to hint at something that the white community feels is derogatory to its dignity, because it has always held the pass to be something that applies to the native alone, and the suggestion that a white man should also have a pass is resented. I sometimes told my Bushveld friends of my own experience when I was once pass-less in a European country, but my well-meant effort to show the necessity for identification papers for every citizen was never taken in good part, even though I laid stress on the point that the country that exacted such guarantees of respectability was Holland.

I had gone over from London, at the instance of a London newspaper, to interview President Kruger who was then living at Utrecht. There were rumours of peace negotiations pending. The Queen of Holland had interested herself in the matter; wires were being pulled; it was natural that the public was curious to know what the Republican exiles in Holland thought about the possibilities of peace. I was a South African journalist, acting as a free lance, and was approached. I had just come to London from Cape Town, and had not travelled in Holland, although I had been on the Continent before. I visited the Foreign and the Colonial Office, neither of which had any objections, and I started off, with credentials and letters of introduction to certain highly placed gentlemen and with a personal note to the President written by a gentleman whose daughter happened to be Paul Kruger's godchild. I was assured that a passport was entirely unnecessary for Holland; it was then one of those Continental countries that demanded no passports from English tourists. When I arrived at Utrecht, I entered the usual particulars in the hotel visitors' book, and went to bed after supper. I was awakened at daylight by a 'police agent', who demanded to see my papers. I told him that I had no papers, for I saw no necessity to show him any of the introductory letters I had with me; my visiting card was surely sufficient. 'Then the gentleman must come with me,' he said firmly. I was allowed to put on my slippers and dressing-gown, and I managed to stow my letters in the breast pocket of the latter before I accompanied the mild-looking but obviously very official policeman to the bureau. 'This gentleman's belongings are to be kept until the police notifies you,' he told the office waiter, who in the presence of authority was cringingly deferential.

We walked through the silent and frosty morning, and on the way, being young and curious and having in my journalistic career had much to do with policedom, I tried to get my guardian to talk. I asked him questions about his beat, about the liquor laws, about licences — I spoke about anything that I thought might evoke his interest, but he was monosyllabic in his replies. We arrived at the 'bureau' and I was ushered into a long corridor and told to take a seat on a stone bench which already held two occupants.

One was an anxious old woman, who was only too glad to impart her troubles to a sympathetic listener. I understood that she had failed to pay her licence for a new dog that drew her little vegetable cart; there would be a fine, and in those pre-war days — this was in the winter of 1902 — a fine was a matter of great importance to one who was not earning a guilder a day. My left-hand neighbour was a student who had spent the night very unwisely, but was fortunately quite unaware of his present position and was snoring very audibly. Through an open door at the end of the corridor shone a light, and from it came a very pleasant warmth. Where I sat it was cold and by no means comfortable. The constable, who, the old woman told me, was properly speaking a sergeant, paced up and down, walking the whole length of the stone-flagged alley to keep himself warm. When I asked him, somewhat petulantly I am afraid, how long I was to be kept waiting, he shrugged his shoulders. *'Mynheer* will be called in *mynheer's* turn, when the Commissioner so decides.'

When my guardian was at the far end of the corridor, I got up and walked towards the door at the other end from where the light shone. I knocked and a sharp voice from inside called out 'Enter'. The sergeant rushed up and clutched my arm, but I had already pushed open the door. Inside the room, which was the Commissioner's office, were two officials, one, obviously the great man himself, frock-coated with the little narrow ribbon in his buttonhole, a fat man with a monocle that would not stay in his orbit however much he screwed up his face to fix it, and a minor official, as obviously his chief clerk, to whom he was dictating. 'Who', said the Commissioner, trying to fix me with his monocle that kept slipping down and needed constant readjustment, 'who is this obstreperous individual, Sergeant?' 'This', said the sergeant breathlessly, 'is the young gentleman from the hotel whom I was ordered to apprehend.' 'Then', barked the Commissioner, 'you will please take *mynheer* outside until I am ready for the interrogation.' The sergeant edged closer, with a 'come-along-young-feller-me-lad' look in his eye, but I did not relish a further period of waiting on a cold stone bench, however interesting had been the old lady's description of the way in which she had cured her new dog of his distemper. 'Pardon me, Mr. Commissioner, but may I ask if I am under arrest?' I asked. The chief clerk nudged the Commissioner, very deferentially, and the two whispered together, after the Commissioner's hand, holding the monocle, had made a peremptory gesture in the direction of the sergeant. 'There is no question of . . . ah . . . an arrest,' said the Commissioner, again screwing the glass into his orbit, '*Mynheer* is simply held for interrogation. . . .' 'But may I ask for what, Mr. Commissioner?' 'I am told, *mynheer*' — the monocle fell down, despite the efforts of the facial muscles to retain its grip — 'that *mynheer* has no papers. . . .' 'If you mean a passport, sir, I was assured that no passport was necessary to travel in Holland. . . .' 'And pray who assured you of this preposterous . . . ah . . . supposition?' asked the Commissioner very scornfully. 'As I understand *mynheer* is a student, *mynheer* must be perfectly well aware that papers of identification are necessary in every civilized country.' 'I showed my card to the sergeant. I am a British subject, a journalist. . . .' 'Anyone can have a card printed' — the monocle was again requisitioned — 'a card lends itself easily to any . . .' — the chief clerk gave another deferential nudge — 'Ah, the presumption is . . . it is necessary that *mynheer* should give some proof of identity. . . .' 'I have such proofs here, sir, but they are in the shape of letters. . . .' 'Letters . . . anyone may have letters . . . yes, yes . . .' — the chief clerk was again interfering, and the two whispered together, while the sergeant stood patiently waiting. 'Ah . . . er . . . perhaps, if the gentleman were to produce the letters we might be able to waive the interrogation. . . .' 'Certainly, Mr. Commissioner.' I produced a sheaf of envelopes from my dressing-coat pocket. 'You will be able to see, sir, that I am vouched for by . . .' But the chief clerk, who had taken the letters had already read the superscriptions, and drew the Commissioner's attention to them. An immediate improvement of relations set in. With his monocle firmly screwed into his eye, the Commissioner held up one envelope, addressed to His Excellency Dr. Kuyper, then Prime Minister. '*Mynheer* permits?' he asked, almost apologetically. 'Certainly. Or any of the others, sir.' He drew the letter from the open envelope, and glanced at the signature, the chief clerk peering over his shoulder. The monocle dropped from its resting-place as he barked out 'Sergeant!' 'Sir'—the sergeant stood stiff at attention. 'Sergeant, coffee and cigars for the gentleman.' The sergeant saluted and wheeled left with military precision. The chief clerk pulled forward a chair. 'If the gentleman will please be seated . . . a misunderstanding. It will be explained.' It was. 'You see, sir,' said the Commissioner, confidentially, 'we get a telegram. A minor, a young University student, has eloped with a young lady; we are informed that they make for Utrecht. We are on the look-out. *Mynheer* can imagine what the parents feel. We know, of course, who enters this town and who leaves it; this is a civilized country, sir, and these are ordinary police precautions necessary to safeguard the community. We find that a minor has registered at the hotel. . . .' 'But, sir, I am not a minor. I am over twenty-one years of age.' 'Pardon me, sir, but majority age is twenty-three' (it was then, though the law has, I believe, been changed since) 'and as you entered your age as twenty-one, the sergeant was sent to bring you for interrogation. It is an unfortunate mistake, but if I may venture to advise you, sir, you should not travel without a passport. Mr. Cherry, the consul, will supply you with one, and it will give me great satisfaction to be of any assistance in the matter. The sergeant will now fetch a fiacre, and take you back to your hotel.' The sergeant fetched the fiacre. The Commissioner and the chief clerk escorted me to the vehicle, the little old woman rising and standing at attention when we passed her in the corridor on our way out. When I bade them good-bye, the Commissioner leaned into the cab and made prodigious play with his monocle. '*Mynheer* will, I presume, see Dr. Kuyper?' he asked, in a whisper. 'Certainly, if I can.' 'May I ask, *mynheer* . . .' 'Oh, certainly, Mr. Commissioner. I will not tell him about our meeting.' It flashed through my mind that now was the time to put in a word for the little old lady and her dog, but the door was already shut and the opportunity was lost. But two nights later the chief clerk came with an invitation to witness Schiller's *Räuber* that a travelling company was playing at the local theatre. Unfortunately, I had no time to renew my acquaintance with the Commissioner.

When I told this story to my Bushveld friends, they smiled but were entirely unconvinced. Such things cannot happen here to white men.

There are other disabilities under which the Native labours. He has no part in the administration of the country; although he pays taxes, he is voteless. He may even employ white men to work for him, but he is always in an inferior position, and I have heard him call his white *bywoner*, who works for him on his farm, 'Master' (*Baas*). The dice are loaded against him in all industries, although without his assistance no industry in South Africa can exist. There is a growing tendency that he should not be allowed to drive a motor car, although his sharp eyesight and his high motor efficiency make him an admirable driver. He does not always get justice in the courts of law. Yet he smiles and is apparently happy. He is, says the Boer, a child, with a child's easy resilience, a child's forgetfulness and a child's waywardness.

Sometimes the Native Commissioners gave me educated natives to act as guides — a native constable or interpreter. I spent days with these men, travelling by strange routes, camping on the veld, visiting native as well as European schools. They could always speak Afrikaans; some spoke quite good English. I tried to get their view of the matter, but I do not think they ever gave me their full confidence, for the native is cautious. I never even learned what my native nickname was. That I had one I knew perfectly well, for every official has his appropriate nickname; but although I was very curious to find out what mine was, I never discovered it.

I visited what is perhaps the best managed and most picturesque mission school in the Province, the fine *Grace Dieu* settlement to the west of Pietersburg, belonging to the Church of the Province. Here is a simple, beautiful school building, in which some hundreds of natives are educated, trained to be teachers, and taught to be artisans. I visited Elim, a French mission in the eastern Bushveld, which has an excellent hospital in which at that time the late Dr. Borle did much interesting research work on the varieties of plasmodia in malaria. Wherever possible I visited native schools and mission stations, for I was eager to obtain statistics and data about native invalidity, and to compare and contrast native children with white children. These investigations removed many preconceptions from my mind. I found that dental caries, for example, was quite as frequent among native children as among white children; malaria and bilharziasis were even more prevalent; malnutrition was lamentably common, and deficiency disease was widespread. No one, doing the work that I did, could fail to be struck by the incidence of native ill health and by its reaction upon the white community. I came to the conclusion, after a couple of years' work in the Bushveld, that it was hopeless to try and prevent white degeneration unless some attempt was made to give the natives an adequate medical service and to deal with native ill health in an organized and systematized manner.

When I started my work in the Bushveld there was practically no medical service for the natives, although the district surgeons gave such help as was urgently required. They vaccinated against the small-pox, or its local representative, *amaas*, and they treated venereal disease which was said to be very prevalent. As a matter of fact I found that venereal disease, in its congenital form at least as exemplified among school children, was less common than I had been led to believe. There was some yaws, which is a disease caused by a different spirochaete from that which causes syphilis, but there was little blindness that could be ascribed to gonorrhoea, and in the native schools one did not see many children who presented evidence of congenital syphilis, nor any who showed signs of rickets. The prevalent defects were defects caused by malnutrition of the mother that had reacted badly upon the unborn child, and defects caused by the two most common Bushveld maladies, redwater and malaria. The mission hospitals did good work, but as a medical man I have always held the view that mission hospitals are, or should be, redundant in a country where health is a matter for the State to attend to. Public health and education are national necessities; they should be a charge upon the population as a whole and should not be dependent upon sectarian charity. Nothing can be more demoralizing than proselytizing with the aid of calico bandages and doses of quinine, and I have always felt that medical missionaries, even when they do not use their medical science to further their sectarian propaganda, should not be tolerated in a community that realizes its responsibilities towards the natives. In a recent report of one missionary doctor one learns that he was 'called upon to perform a very severe operation upon a native woman' with whom he 'talked earnestly before she underwent the trial'. We are not told the nature of the operation; if it was really severe, demanding the greatest mental calm in all concerned, no words can be sufficiently hard to characterize the inhumanity of the surgeon who had the temerity to discuss with the patient questions likely to disturb her mind before he mercifully anaesthetized her. Yet this incident was narrated not with regret but with unctuous complacency, and ever since I read it I have felt unkindly towards medical missionaries.

There were some of my brother Inspectors who hoped much from what they called 'the civilizing influence of Christianity'. Unfortunately, although I am a missionary's child, I have never been able to convince myself that that influence is at all formative or permanent. Sir William Hoy, then General Manager of the South African Railways, told me that there were in the Transvaal more than two hundred Christian sects, all clamouring for concession privileges. The bulk of them one finds on the Reef, which is abnormally impressionable, as every cosmopolitan and neurotic community is. But among the natives, too, Christianity has dehisced into a multitude of sects, and although the large mass of the natives is supposed to be nominally Christian, the percentage of understanding Christians among them must be very small. Nor is this to be wondered at, any more than one need wonder at the multiplicity of Christian sects among the natives themselves. Christianity is something that the Bantu mind does not readily assimilate, however much it might give the impression of doing so. In comparison with a simple creed, like Mohammedanism, it is a complicated business, of which even the educated native can give no concatenated explanation. I have talked with many 'Christian natives' but never yet found one who was able to give a succinct, clear account of what he believed; he invariably explained his creed in terms of his native fetishism, and he had no conception of the difficulties that his explanation raised, and, needless to say, no means of comparison with other religions, of which he knew nothing. In sharp contrast to such 'Christianized natives' are the South African Mohammedans, the Cape Malays, who for centuries have held their ancestral religion in all its purity, and have given proof, time and again, that they are willing to make sacrifices for it and to live up to it. As a community they are the most law abiding and harmonious in the country, notwithstanding that they live in urban surroundings that are thoroughly demoralizing. Carlyle's torrent of sentences when asked for his opinion about proselytizing work among Mohammedans recurs to one's mind when one looks at this community and compares it with the Christianized natives. 'Benthamic utility, virtue by profit and loss, reducing this God's world to a dead brute steam engine, the infinite celestial soul of man to a kind of hay balance for weighing thistles on, pleasures and pains on — if you ask me which gives, Mohammed or they, the falser view, the beggarlier

view of man and his destinies in this universe, I will answer
that it is not Mohammed.' The simplicity of the Moham-
medan creed is its strongest appeal to heathenism and
fetishism. It is enunciated in the dictum of the Khalif
Omar in the well-known sentence: 'Islam is that thou
bearest witness that there is no God but God, Eternal,
begetting not nor begotten, and naught like unto Him;
that thou be steadfast in prayer, charitable, fasting at the
appointed time, and make the pilgrimage to the Ka'aba if it
be in thy power to do so.' An intensely practical creed,
especially suitable for a tropical climate, since it inculcates
meditation, moderation, cleanliness and charity, and leaves
points of eschatology severely alone. At present it is a
religion that is absolutely unknown to the South African
native, but in time it will appeal to him with much greater
force and insistence than Christianity does. Moreover, it
will not provide him, as Christianity does, with that incomprehensible paradox that the practice of the religion he is
invited to embrace differs when its adherents happen to be
white from that which they are supposed to follow when
they happen to be black.

That indeed, altogether apart from the intricacies of
Christian eschatology, must be the ever-puzzling question
that the logical native asks himself — why must the precepts
of these good teachers of mine, these guardians to whom I
am merely a ward, differ so furiously and sometimes so
frantically from their invariable practice? Junghuhn, in his
thoughtful book, *Light and Shadows*, that purports to
describe real conversations between what we call savages
and enterprising missionaries, tells how the missionary is
asked, by an intelligent savage, to explain why his 'religion
begins with a miracle and ends with an absurdity'. The

average Bantu does not generally ask such a question; he has far too much respect for the white man, and perhaps for himself, to take the story that the missionary tells him at its face value; he presumes it to be as symbolic as the stories that his own witch-doctors tell him, though, like the natives who in Stevenson's fable told the missionary about the eddy, he realizes that there is something sometimes in all these stories. But he does question the honesty with which these highfalutin principles of Christianity are carried out; he is beginning to question them more and more every day, and I am told — unfortunately my ignorance of his language prevents me from testing the statement — that in his growing literature (at present the only way in which he can air his views without danger to himself) he is expressing his doubts with some sarcasm and a great deal of eloquence. There are already several 'novels' that have been published in Zulu and Xosa, and my brother Inspectors who can read these languages assure me that some of them are very forcible expressions of perplexity at the way the white 'guardian' deals with his native ward.

Of that perplexity I noticed several indications. Once, driving with a native policeman, I had pointed out to me a thorn bush on which my companion and a white policeman on patrol had found flaps and tatters of human flesh, the remains of a piccaninny sacrificed to make *muti* (rain charms). The bush was gaudily in blossom, its particoloured flowers of chrome yellow and mauve falling over it like a double tinted veil, for it was a 'sickle thorn' which when in bloom is a lovely sight. I stopped the car, and my guide showed me where the fillets had been spiked on the thorns. He and the other policeman had removed them all, and some of them had been exhibited at the trial. 'Oh yes, the murderers had been hanged all right. But ...', and my policeman grew apologetically reminiscent, 'there had been a good rainfall that season.' A piccaninny's life did not count so much where the welfare of the whole community was concerned, and it was obviously silly to make such a fuss about it.

Later I asked my official companion why folk killed their twins. I remembered the firkins that the missionary's wife had shown me in her garden, and was very curious to hear something more about the matter. 'They don't do it so often now, *Baas*,' said the policeman. 'If they are caught doing it, we take them to jail.' 'But why do it at all?' 'Well, *Baas*, they are not proper children, not according to what we think. They are a sin and a vexation when they grow up, that is what we think. But it is against the law to do it now.' I could not judge from his tone whether he thought the law wrong or the custom. My scientific curiosity urged me to ask a wholly improper question. 'Was it because you thought — because there is some idea among you that twins mean something . . . something that shouldn't have occurred?' 'I don't really know, *Baas*. The old men say that sometimes twins have different fathers. . . .' 'Dear me, your old men must be very clever to have found that out' — I knew that, scientifically, one or two instances are known where such a supposition might have been argued from the facts, but I was totally unprepared to hear it enunciated by a native, even though he wore leggings and a slouch hat and had S A P on his shoulder-straps. 'What do your old men say now, when the law allows the twins to grow up?' 'They say no good will come of it, *Baas*. There are two in the location I come from, *Baas*. They're no good. Already they are nuisances, and before very long they'll be in jail.' Incidentally I may add that I never heard anything that gave support to the now generally accepted view of anthropologists — insisted upon by Basile Tanghe in his monograph on the Congo natives — that twins are feared because they are supposed to typify the divine bi-sexuality. There was a general agreement that twins were 'difficult' when they grew up, and that such difficult children might, and most often did, develop anti-social characteristics that made them undesirable members of their tribe.

He told me of the ritual murders that, some years before, had excited a mild interest when the circuit court tried the headmen of a native tribe who shouldered the responsibility of eliminating an undesirable. I could see that he was puzzled in his mind about the justice that had been done in that case. The murdered person was a menace to the tribe — an abnormal, anti-social misfit who in the old days would have been quietly but expeditiously got rid of by a process of 'smelling out', but who had to be made innocuous by what the law called a conspiracy. Like our religion, our law is strange and illogical to the native mind. In other countries, where white men are responsible for native 'wards', some attention is paid to the conventions and tribal sanctions of these wards. An experienced mistress in charge of a kindergarten school would be a fool if she did not make allowances for the manner in which her charges reasoned. We seem to imagine that everything in South Africa can be brought within the limits of the code of Justinian, framed to suit conventions that existed two thousand years ago. It is true there is a native code, but it applies to native areas alone, and in mixed areas justice is meted out to the native on the same principles that apply to Europeans. That seems to me not only utterly wrong but a danger to white civilization in the future.

My native constable told me of a peculiar case, in which he was personally interested, for the individual concerned happened to be a blood relation. This native, it appeared, masqueraded as a woman, and was well known to the police. He had been repeatedly sentenced, and on his last appearance before a magistrate had been punished with solitary confinement and a spare diet. It was easy to identify him as a 'travestite', a peculiar form of fetishism that needs treatment and not punishment. In the tribe such abnormalities — or perversions as we call them, forgetting that the sexual impulse may express itself in many ways that are bizarre and strange — were not unknown. The native constable was quite frank about these matters. He said that the 'old men' had told him, when he was in the 'puberty school', that some men had a woman's feelings and some women were capable of being 'ringed', i.e. regarded as men. There was nothing abnormal or incomprehensible about it; it was an ordinary, accepted phenomenon, that led to no a-social conduct provided the 'young men' were properly instructed. I assured him that that was the way educated white men looked at these phenomena; but he inquired, why then were so many natives prosecuted for practices that the native mind did not look upon as anti-social. I confess I had no ready reply.

An intelligent, Afrikaans-speaking native, a Shangaan, showed me through the caves of Makepaan, north of Pietersburg, where, years ago, the Boers had besieged a native tribe. There is little of interest to be seen there to-day, for the limestone deposits have been worked for the cement factories, and few relics are to be gleaned. We did discover one skull, and one thigh bone, together with some fragments of native pottery. 'They were bad folk, these, *Baas*,' said my guide, quite impersonally. 'They shouldn't have done it.' I was not certain whether he referred to the Boers or to the natives, but his subsequent words made it clear what he had in mind. 'It is not that they were badly treated, *Baas*, but they were much too uppish. Me, I have always found that it doesn't pay to be too uppish with the white folk.'

That is the prevailing sentiment among the natives of the Bushveld. They live in an environment that is on the whole kindly and companionate. Now and then one hears of brutality to natives, but when all the circumstances are taken into consideration — the isolation of these farms, the feudal power of the farmers, the traditional belief that where natives are concerned might is equivalent to right — one wonders not at what they suffer but at what they lose. That is because the Bushveld community is at heart imbued with the same sentiments towards the natives as its fore-fathers, who were slave owners, cherished. The native is a chattel, to be treated as such. After all Aristotle defined a slave as such — an animate tool. A bad master, a craftsman indifferent to his own interests, would neglect and blunt his tools. So cruelty — except in those few and far between instances where innate sadistic tendencies would have bred cruelty in any case — was unknown, but the tradition that the native, like the child, should learn discipline and authority, was observed, and the laws that the community made expressed that tradition. It is the northern tradition, that differs from the southern tradition which is still held in some repute in the Cape Province, in that it has been coloured by fear and by the intolerance bred of fear; but it is an understandable tradition and in the circumstances it must be reckoned with. It is a tradition, moreover, that is not limited to the Afrikaans-speaking community; it is one equally honoured by English-speaking settlers who have felt that apprehension of the numerical superiority of the native.

I have sometimes thought that if native affairs were removed entirely beyond the interference of politicians — if one were to succeed in getting a department of native affairs that was, like our railways, a separate, extraordinary administrative department, responsible in the first instance to the highest judicial tribunal of the land instead of to the legislative body elected by voters who are largely obsessed by this 'northern' view — there might be a chance to solve our native problem. I no longer hold that view. The present tendency is to imagine that our native problem can be solved by what is known as segregation: which in practice means that the native should nowhere compete with the white man but that the white man should, where convenient, make use of the native. Theoretically segregation is the solution of the problem. Van Goens and van Riebeeck knew it to be a solution when they advocated that their embryonic white settlement should be cut off from all contagion with native influences by cutting a canal across the Cape peninsula. In those days such a policy might have been feasible. To-day it is merely farcical. The native is an integral part of the community of South Africa and it is scientifically absurd to contemplate the development of the white community without contemplating at the same time the development of the preponderant native population, and frankly to face the inevitable consequences of such development.

339

CHAPTER XX

AFTERTHOUGHTS

Ten years of work in the Bushveld among a community so primitive and in many ways so lovable, have yielded an experience from which it may be permissible to draw certain conclusions. I frankly admit that there is a vast difference between the ability to describe experience and the capacity to draw valid conclusions from it. The former implies memory, the recollection of events that took place and of the circumstances in which they occurred, together with some semblance of arrangement and poise in telling of them. The latter purports to be much more, a competence to compare, to judge impartially, to weigh accurately, to value according to fair standards of worth, to take into consideration trivialities that may influence the account for better or worse, and, in short, to draw deductions that may be, after all, wholly fallacious and unjustified. One who attempts to do that may well say, as Newman said in his *Apologia*, 'I have done various bold things in my life; this is the boldest.'

My excuse for embarking on it must be the sense of responsibility that any South African, who is fully aware of the conditions in these backveld districts and is honestly desirous of helping his people, must be conscious of when he contemplates the past and has the temerity to picture what might happen in the future. Public opinion in the Union is to-day less organized and less knowledgeable than it was before Union took place. The reasons for that are mainly that since 1913 it has centred not around problems of national importance, but around party dissensions that owe their existence to personal animosities artificially crystallized into what appeared to be principles and obscured by political ideologies that originate from prejudice and cultural dissimilarities rather than from a broad-based, creative patriotism, able and willing to take from the past that which is formative and good and to throw on the rubbish heap whatever is outworn and productive of strife and dissent. Since the death of General Botha our politicians have been like Gratiano, 'speaking an infinite deal of nothing, their reasoning like two grains of wheat hid in two bushels of chaff, for which you shall seek all day ere you find them and when you have them they are not worth the search'. The present allocation of the most essential functions of civilizing government to ignorant and incapable Provincial Councils acts as a constant drag upon genuine and germane progress, and until it is abolished and these vital and important functions of administrative government are centrally organized, there is no hope of bettering the conditions that are gradually sapping the integrity of the rural population. As if by a cruel jest of Fate, the administrative capital of the Union is at a spot which is totally unsuited to develop energy in those who have to live there; its climate is soporific, depressing and demoralizing. Pretoria is in spirit and essence merely a magnified village, intensely sensitive to criticism, with the sensitiveness of a patriarch out of touch with youth and innovation. It owes whatever stimulates it to its juxtaposition to Johannesburg, that throbbing nerve centre of industry and activity whose unlimited and easily earned wealth are colossal factors in shaping the destinies of South

Africa. Whatever improvement or progress is to be anticipated in the future is unlikely to emanate from the capital, simply because the complacency that is bred there reacts disastrously upon all reform that attempts to go to the root of the evils from which the country to-day suffers.

Of these evils the chief is the steady dispersal of a potentially strong and healthy peasant community from the land, which is its sanctuary and stay, into the industrialized centres where unemployment is already a powerful deteriorating factor. A second evil is the degeneration that is observable in the rural community itself, as the result of preventable disease like malaria and redwater, and of the lack of a balanced diet. You must not tell it in Gath nor whisper it in Askelon, so be it you speak or whisper in understandable Afrikaans, that there is such degeneration, for to do so is accounted rank, unadulterated 'racialism' more virulent and venomous than hinting that South Africa is as yet quite unable to defend herself from foreign aggression. Thirdly (which, as Mrs. Shandy remarked on a memorable occasion when she ventured on an observation of her own, is merely a compound of whatever precedes) there is the demoralizing effect of this drift to the towns and this ever-present rural invalidity among both whites and natives, upon the rising generation of Europeans, an effect that is not yet realized but that is nevertheless apparent to all who have worked in the schools. When the public is told that more than half of the school-going population is physically defective, there is an immediate stir of feeling, but unhappily the stimulus is evanescent, and nothing results from it. I have often felt it a pity that Nature is not more dramatic, so dramatic as to bring home to all of us a realization of the truth that interference with her activities spells ruin in succeeding generations. If malaria were a disease as deadly as tetanus or small-pox, we would to-day have none of it in the Bushveld. It is racially and economically many times worse than lockjaw or cholera. But because it does not kill, outright and quickly, it is regarded as a companionable scourge. A nation really earnest about the welfare of its future citizens would at any cost have abolished malaria from its territory within a couple of decades.

While politicians are talking about white civilization in Africa, and constructing cotton-wool incubators for our worn-out poor whites, they are assuming that the problem of European civilization is merely an economic one. So it is in a sense, for at bottom all questions that concern the stability of a community are, strictly speaking, economic questions. But we do not, generally, regard them in the light of pure economics, for there are many subsidiary factors to be considered. The problem that confronts the white people in South Africa is how to raise future white generations that are sound, healthy, an asset instead of a liability to the State. To solve that problem needs investigation, co-operation, and by no means least of all, experiment. Investigation must be made to tell us how these deadly factors that are now productive of degeneration can best be counteracted. We know already how seriously the neglect of consideration for our native population, its health and its progress towards civilization, militates against the development of the white community. Native ill health reacts upon European health and well-being. The limitation of competitive effort through the exclusion of the native from practically all industries, except in the field of unskilled and almost slave labour, reacts upon the morale of the whites. Class

class legislation of any kind inevitably produces inferiority among the protected classes by eliminating the fricative stimulus of rivalry and emulation, and substituting for it an artificial security subversive of effort and endeavour. But there are many things we do not yet know. We have to collect facts, obtain data, try experiment, proceed in fact by trial-and-error methods, before we are in a position to formulate schemes that will be both practical and beneficial. On two points, especially, we need information. These are the influence of environment, humidity, light, altitude, electrical atmospheric change, on the temperament and psyche of our South African children, and the importance of certain food factors in their diet. Much of the degeneration that is to be seen in all schools, but that is more extensively prevalent among poor white children, is caused by bad feeding, by underfeeding, rather than by actual deficiency of food. Such underfeeding is met with in secondary schools, among a class of children that cannot be counted poor; it is invariably the result of a badly balanced diet, though in some cases it is to be ascribed to wrong methods of preparing food and to an insistence on dietetic conventions that are outworn.

A year ago, the Medical Association, gathered in Congress at Grahamstown, discussed for two days this question of the deterioration of the white population. In the absence of positive data, it was manifestly impossible to arrive at any valid conclusions on the subject, but the consensus of opinion was that the situation is disquieting. Dr. Laidler, the Medical Officer of Health for a large urban centre, who has had extensive experience as a country practitioner in one of the most backward of all rural districts, in a thoughtful and enlightening paper, laid stress on the disturbing features of the picture that our white population presents to-day. He said:

'South Africa is in an unhappy position. The presence of a strong race causes a region to be more civilized than would be expected on the basis of climatic energy. We have numerous races and intermediates. There are each year between a hundred and two hundred mixed marriages, apart from the unknown amount of unsanctioned germ plasm that is let loose upon the land. The South African population has brought itself to a highly artificial position, and it is now necessary for it to rectify its position. The number of recessive unit characters embedded in it increases with each generation, and the probability of reversion, after a temporary overshadowing by dominant characteristics, increases equally ... It is useless to look for compensatory Utopias of honest co-operation and scientific socialism before there has been a peaceful penetration of commercial brains by a new ethical standard, assisted by government effort through legislation ... There is need for a reconditioning of that public opinion to which all governments are supposed to defer. Public opinion is too slow in its uptake to acknowledge facts of life because it is too open to propaganda.'

Another contributor to the debate was a Transvaal medical man who has had similarly extensive experience of conditions in the Bushveld, Dr. A. Jurriaanse. He said:

'I remember my surprise at the manners, speech and good-breeding of the Boers on my arrival thirty-five years ago. Their word was their bond, their debts were paid, their views were broad. The children owed their culture and their ability to read and write to their mothers. To-day subdivision of farms and years of schooling have shrunk the circle of interest and the quickness of understanding of the children ... They could only live by the work of their hands, but cannot compete against the native ... The expensive golden calf of education has been futile, over-worshipped in this country. Not extension of education, but early removal after the saturation point is reached, to an industrial or farm school, is necessary ... One thing to me is certain ... we cannot afford to pretend to be a Democracy.'

The Medical Inspectors of Schools, who took part in the debate, furnished such statistics as they could gather. They came to the conclusion that these statistics suggested that 'the various factors affecting the physical and mental development of the children ... are not of a permanently deleterious nature, and can be modified by altering the environment'. That, too, is the comforting conclusion of the Carnegie Commission that investigated the conditions under which some selected few thousands of poor whites live. It is a conclusion we would all like to endorse. Our national pride makes us all too ready to endorse it without considering the difficulties that present themselves to an impartial observer.

My experience of Bushveld schools, supported by what I have seen of school children in both rural and urban areas in all the four Provinces, does not enable me to subscribe glibly to that conclusion. Undoubtedly our present unfortunate position is the direct result of a wrong and obsolete system of administration. When that has been altered, we may contemplate modification of the various factors adversely affecting our younger generation by changing the environment. The uneconomic and useless systems of education that we now support are the legacies of that antiquated administrative policy, a policy that persists because our politicians have been far too busy with non-essentials that are of so much importance to party solidarity to give any attention to new methods of administration and cultural development that are in course of trial in other countries. For twenty-five years we have had this policy of stagnation. If we charitably exclude the four years of the Great War, in which expansion and experiment could not be thought of, we may place the period of systematic neglect at twenty years. In that time, however, the dice against the younger generation have been loaded by legislation that is in no way constructive but contains the elements of future failure and friction. With Dr. Laidler, one can only say 'South Africa is in an unhappy position'.

That she should continue to remain in it, I cannot and will not believe when I reflect on what her white population has achieved in the past. That accomplishment is encouragement for the future, even though the present prospect is darkened by so many inauspicious omens that one may well despair of realizing hopes that appear to be visionary and Utopian. Even among her poor whites there is splendid material, in muscles and in brain, that will well repay careful nursing, training, co-ordination and cultivation. To take the Bushveld community as an example, one finds among its members examples of high-grade intelligence, super-normal motor efficiency, and natural aptitude for art and craft that are eminently suitable for development with State assistance. At present these nuggets are crushed

347

together with the low-grade, indifferent or altogether worth-less ore, in the old-fashioned education mill that turns out disappointingly low averages. A system of selection and clas-sification is urgently needed, as a preliminary to any measure of improvement that may be tried. Above all it is imperative that a part of the money now squandered on education that is a travesty of the reality should be diverted to benefit the health of the community by providing for the upkeep of medical services for both natives and Europeans. In comparison with the amount spent on education, the allowance for hospitalization — which in practice benefits the urban areas far more than it does the rural communities — is miserably inadequate, while there is practically no provision for the medical and health needs of the native population. The white community will have to learn that health is the first consideration of any community, and that education is of secondary importance. It will further have to comprehend that it cannot safeguard its own health, nor that of its children, if it systematically neglects to safe-guard the health of the native population that environs it.

To one who, not being a South African and therefore not personally interested in the matter, looks at the position to-day, as revealed in the statistics and estimates of expendi-ture that may be taken to indicate the value that the community attaches to different administrative functions, it may seem that the Union is proceeding along lines that are frankly farcical. It spends much annually on its misfits, which are the care of the central Government. The expendi-ture on asylums, reformatories and prisons has steadily risen since Union. Even before Union crime was a matter that was always readily paid for. The late Mr. Merriman remarked that the first thing a new township wanted was

348

money to build an expensive jail. Yet true reformative, reclamatory methods are still not applied. There is as yet no modern juvenile court, though in all large towns there are so-called children's courts which are merely the ordinary police courts held more or less *in camera*. There is still an amount of 'statutory crime' that breeds juvenile delinquency and is of no great social importance. The liquor laws, that should be regarded as antiquated in a country that is wine-producing and where viticulture is one of the few self-supporting industries, are regarded as sacrosanct, and are annually responsible for the demoralization of many white citizens. For the equipment of the large new hospital recently built at Cape Town, the public was appealed to by the Provincial administration that calmly stated that it had no money for this object, although it expends more than three million on education. What is more surprising, the public responded to the appeal, although it would indignantly have refused to equip a new boarding hostel or training college. The golden calf of education, of which Dr. Jurriaanse speaks, is adored only because its worship entails no self-help or sacrifice; it receives all its sustenance from the taxpayer. Health, that demands State supervision and should be a charge upon all citizens, is regarded as something that may be financed, on the model of the voluntary hospitals in Great Britain, by private philanthropy, aided by grants from the Provincial treasury. The mentality that acquiesces in such an arrangement may well be said to need reconditioning.

To effect improvement, such improvement as will secure the integrity of rural communities like those in the Bushveld, that are an asset to the State because they represent the sturdy primitiveness that is the bulwark of a nation, a radical reorganization of the administration of the country is necessary. The Provincial administrations serve no useful purpose. They multiply the number of voluble Gratianos, and constitute academies for the schooling of party politicians whose cumulative effect in the past has been lamentable. The important duties of supervising health services, communications, and education, both primary and secondary, should be functions of the central Government. Decentralization, under departmental heads who are altogether outside the turmoil of politics, should replace the present absurd system under which laymen, who have no experience in the administration of these services, act in an executive capacity. In two Provinces the unpopularity of the Provincial administrations has made the community favourable to such a radical modification of the compromise arrived at when Union was effected, but in the other two there is as yet no sign that the existing system is recognized as a failure. Nor is it at all likely that any change for the better will take place until the existing franchise, that makes every pauper the electoral equal of whoever doles out alms to him, provided that he is white, is modified to suit the conditions of the country and to preserve the cultural superiority of the civilized citizens.